The Technical Transformation of Agriculture in Communist China

Leslie T. C. Kuo

The Praeger Special Studies program—utilizing the most modern and efficient book production techniques and a selective worldwide distribution network—makes available to the academic, government, and business communities significant, timely research in U.S. and international economic, social, and political development.

The Technical Transformation of Agriculture in Communist China

Praeger Publishers   New York   Washington   London

PRAEGER SPECIAL STUDIES IN INTERNATIONAL ECONOMICS AND DEVELOPMENT

PRAEGER PUBLISHERS
111 Fourth Avenue, New York, N.Y. 10003, U.S.A.
5, Cromwell Place, London S.W.7, England

Published in the United States of America in 1972
by Praeger Publishers, Inc.

A country's agricultural productivity depends on a number of interrelated factors. Because of the diversity of political, economic, social, physical and other conditions, the factors involved vary greatly from country to country. In Communist China, a socialist system of ownership and management and a progressive program for technological improvement are considered as two essentials to increase agricultural productivity. These are generally referred to as the "socialist transformation" and the "technical transformation" of agriculture. Mao Tse-tung stated in 1955: "We are now carrying out a revolution not only in the social system, the change from private to public ownership, but also in technology, the change from handicraft to large-scale modern machine production, and the two revolutions are interconnected."

Although this principle is generally agreed upon among the Communist Chinese leaders, the programming of the two types of transformation has been a matter of dispute between Mao Tse-tung and Liu Shao-ch'i. Mao was of the opinion that early cooperativization would provide a more rational and efficient organization of labor and use of land and would make it easier for the state to collect agricultural products and speed up capital accumulation and industrialization--that only the large-scale farming through cooperativization could create suitable conditions for massive application of modern technology. For this reason, he argued, the socialist transformation of agriculture should play a more important role than the technical transformation during the First Five-Year Plan (1953-57) and the Second Five-Year Plan (1958-62), and the two should proceed at the same pace during the Third Five-Year Plan. Mao estimated that, although the socialist transformation would reach its final stage at the end of the Third Five-Year Plan, it would take four or five five-year plans, or from twenty to twenty-five years, to complete the technical transformation.*

---

*Mao Tse-tung, "On the Question of Agricultural Cooperativization," a report delivered at a meeting of the secretaries of the provincial, municipal and district committees of the Chinese Communist Party on July 31, 1955, in Jen-min Shou-ts'e [People's Handbook] (Peking, 1956), pp. 80-86.

Liu Shao-ch'i, on the other hand, advocated the postponement of cooperativization until industry was ready to carry out capital construction and to supply chemical fertilizers, agricultural machinery, and other necessities to the countryside. In his opinion, it was especially necessary to bring about mechanization first before carrying out cooperativization, because collective farms cannot be consolidated without mechanization, which, in turn, depends on industrialization.*

The socialist transformation has been carried out through several stages. At the outset of the regime, land ownership was redistributed according to a "land reform" program. Under a law promulgated in June 1950, some 700 million mou of land and large numbers of draft animals, farm tools, and other property were redistributed to farmers.** Later, farms were reorganized with an increasing degree of cooperativization through the establishment of first the mutual-aid teams, then the primary agricultural producers' cooperatives, and then the advanced agricultural producers' cooperatives. Finally, when the Leap Forward campaign was launched in 1958, farms in Communist China were placed under the management of the communes.

However, the progress of the socialist transformation of agriculture has not been altogether smooth sailing. The existence of the opposing views among the Chinese Communist Party leaders has resulted in a zigzag course of agricultural cooperativization. Attempts were made by Mao Tse-tung in the spring of 1953, in the fall of 1954, and again in the spring of 1955 to increase the tempo of cooperativization. As a result of strong opposition within the Party and resistance from peasants, on each occasion the attempt failed. During the fall of 1955 and the winter of 1955-56, cooperativization was intensified briefly, but the momentum was slowed down after the spring of 1956.

---

*"Hold High the Great Red Banner of Mao Tse-tung's Thought and Completely Knock Down China's Khrushchev," Nung-ts'un Ch'ing-nien [Rural Youth], Shanghai, Nos. 17-18, September 10, 1967, and September 25, 1967 (translated in Current Background, Hong Kong, No. 847, February 16, 1968), pp. 1-29.

**Liao Lu-yen, "A Great Victory in the Land Reform Movement During the Past Three Years," in Committee for the Promotion of China's Trade, ed., San-nien-lai Hsin-chung-kuo Ching-chi ti Ch'eng-chiu [New China's Economic Accomplishments in the Past Three Years] (Peking, 1952), pp. 111-18.

For more than two years, the pace of cooperativization continued to be moderate until the latter part of 1958, when the Leap Forward campaign was launched and the communes were established.

It was Mao Tse-tung's original intention to maintain, insofar as possible, the collective ownership of means of production and the unified distribution of income and products under the commune system. But it did not take long for many high officials to realize that such centralization of power would not help agricultural production, and that the original communalization plan and the major functions of the three levels of the commune (production team, production brigade, and commune) would have to be readjusted.

Disorganization of labor, caused by the sudden changeover in 1958 from the agricultural producers' cooperatives to the communes, resulted in a general breakdown of production and distribution systems. Shortage of skilled reapers in some rural areas delayed harvests. Payment to the peasants according to the amount of work was almost impossible, because of the centralized deployment of labor and the lack of an efficient accounting system. The neglect of financial management produced not only disorder in receipt and disbursement but also extravagance and waste. Agricultural production was badly affected, as were capital accumulation and distribution in the communes and the livelihood of commune members.

The agricultural situation deteriorated in 1959-61 as a result of natural calamities, particularly drought, floods, and pests. In order to permit the peasants to exercise more initiative, to suffer less interference, and to receive a larger share of income and output, the original organization of the communes was drastically modified. By the early part of 1963, with the exception of a few areas, the production team had become the basic unit for both accounting and production. The production team was accorded the right to keep its own accounts, to map out production plans, to prepare its own budget, and to distribute income to its members. The major functions of the production brigade were reduced to those of organizing cooperation among the production teams and running enterprises jointly owned by several production teams. The commune was assigned the responsibility for carrying out large agricultural projects and activities of a commune-wide or inter-commune nature. Moreover, the average size of most of the communes was reduced to approximately that of the former advanced agricultural producers' cooperatives, because large communes under the centralized management had proved inefficient in carrying out agricultural production.

The relaxation of centralized direction with better incentive for the peasants following the shift of certain functions from the commune and the production brigade to the production team apparently has continued to prevail. During the Cultural Revolution, 1966-69, bitter criticism was directed at measures formerly adopted by "a handful of persons in authority taking the capitalist road"; such measures included the extension of private plots and free markets and the fixing of output quotas based on the households. However, only in a few communes were peasants threatened with loss of these advantages, and even then no action was taken.

While adopting this more liberal policy, the government has from time to time called for the consolidation of the collective agricultural economy. Although there has been no open reversal of the policy of relaxation and decentralized control, it would seem that any substantial recovery of agricultural production might engender fear on the part of the authorities that the peasants, when better off, might resist the return to collectivism. The government has repeatedly made the point in its propaganda that communes, with their abundant capital, labor, and other resources, are more effective in fighting natural calamities and in carrying out large-scale projects than the former agricultural producers' cooperatives.

This, in brief, was the progress of the socialist transformation of agriculture during the first two decades of the Communist regime. Meanwhile, numerous measures were taken to innovate farming techniques as a means of improving agricultural production. Increasing attention has been given to such matters as scientific research, training of technical personnel, and popularization of improved farming methods. Mao Tse-tung has repeatedly urged the Chinese Communist Party to strive for attainment of the technical transformation of agriculture, although his primary priority is on cooperativization.

This study is primarily concerned with the technical aspect of agricultural development in Communist China. In the following chapters, the overall policies, guiding principles, programs, and methods for the technical transformation of agriculture adopted during the first two decades of the Communist regime will be examined. This examination will be followed by a discussion of the major technical measures for improving agricultural production. In discussing each of the technical measures, primary attention will be given to the planning and execution of the programs rather than to the details of agricultural technology. In each case, the situation before the Communist takeover, the highlights of the programs carried out by the new regime, and the major accomplishments and problems will be observed. On the basis of such a perspective, the progress of the technical transformation of agriculture will be evaluated, and an attempt will be made to determine, _inter alia_, the extent to which the technical innovation has helped agricultural productivity in Communist China and the prospects for the next few decades.

The evaluation of agricultural technology in Communist China is a complex undertaking. First, China is a large and varied country, extending across some 35 degrees of latitude and with extreme ranges in elevation, precipitation and soil. Consequently, many types of agriculture are practiced. Second, agricultural technology is itself not an entity but a complex of fields. Even the simplest approach involves an examination of a number of major topics. The present study is only a first step toward bringing into focus a general picture of technical innovations and their effects on agricultural production for the first two decades of the Chinese Communist regime. Additional studies of a specialized regional, or local nature will be needed for understanding the problem more thoroughly.

A further difficulty in making the present study is the lack of precise, dependable information. Most of the materials used in this study were compiled from Communist sources. In addition, the author has canvassed materials published in the United States as well as in Taiwan, Hong Kong, and Japan for the information not encountered in the Chinese Communist sources. Since under the Communist regime publishing is a state monopoly, a considerable portion of the information supplied by the authorities is undoubtedly for propaganda purposes. Although every caution has been taken in selecting and checking the materials, many facts and figures quoted in this study should be accepted with reservation. In particular, data on the progress of agricultural techniques, such as irrigated areas, tractor production, and chemical fertilizer production, for the Leap Forward period in 1958-59 suggested a level of progress that seemed highly unlikely. These data often suggested a sharp contrast between the time of the Leap Forward campaign and preceding periods. Therefore, many of the so-called "increases," "achievements," and other claims were statistical rather than actual. Statistics for the three consecutive years of crop failure (1959-61) and thereafter usually were released with a deliberate lack of clearness and more than occasional gaps. Like other statistical data, agricultural data usually are released in Communist China as isolated figures rather than in a meaningful series. Frequently, figures are given in percentages but not in actual amounts. Moreover, serious discrepancies can be found among the data supplied by different agencies or individuals.

Despite these and other limitations and deficiencies, some of the materials from the Communist sources do reveal or reflect in varying degrees Mainland China's agricultural situation and many of the problems and difficulties the present regime has encountered. In addition to numerous writings on various agricultural topics printed in Chinese books and periodicals, such materials as directives, public notices, complaints, invectives, "confessions," and self-criticisms frequently appear in the Communist press. From these materials it is at least possible to obtain a fairly clear idea of what actually took place in Chinese agriculture in the 1950's and 1960's. The present study is based on such a composite of data and views from many sources.

The compilation of the materials for the present study began in the early 1950's. A grant voted by the Joint Committee on Contemporary China, of the Social Science Research Council and the American Council of Learned Societies, enabled the author to take a leave of absence in 1963 and 1964 from his regular duties at the United States Department of Agriculture and to devote his full time to the completion of the first draft of the manuscript. Since then, the draft has been drastically revised and updated according to the latest data available to cover the first two decades of the Communist Chinese regime.

A major portion of the materials used in this study come from the National Agricultural Library of the United States Department of Agriculture, which maintains one of the largest collections of publications on Chinese agriculture. Of special importance to this study are some 1,000 monographs, 150 periodicals, and several leading Communist Chinese newspapers in the collection. Also frequently used are English materials on Mainland China, including Current Scene, China News Analysis, Far Eastern Economic Review, materials compiled by the American Consulate General in Hong Kong (Survey of China Mainland Press, Current Background, and Selections from China Mainland Magazines), Agricultural Information on Mainland China, compiled by the American Agricultural Attache in Hong Kong, translations by the Joint Publications Research Service in Washington, D. C., and releases of the New China News Agency and the China News Service in Peking. The author is most grateful to Foster E. Mohrhardt, former Director of the National Agricultural Library, and his successor, John Sherrod, for the facilities provided by the library, which expedited this study's progress enormously. He also wishes to express his appreciation to staff members of the Orientalia Division of the Library of Congress for their help in providing nonagricultural materials used in this study.

In addition to drawing upon many sources of materials, the author has consulted a number of specialists, including several in the U.S. Department of Agriculture. Special mention should be made of the assistance of J. Lossing Buck, for many years Head of the Department of Agricultural Economics at the University of Nanking, whose monumental Land Utilization in China and many other writings on Chinese agriculture are among the most important classics in this field. Mr. Buck painstakingly read the manuscript and made invaluable suggestions. The author also wished to thank Alexander Eckstein of the University of Michigan, who kindly reviewed the initial draft of the manuscript and suggested a number of important changes. For the technical terms used in this study, the Agricultural Research Service of the U.S. Department of Agriculture has given very helpful advice.

The completion of the present study would not have been possible without the unceasing inspiration and encouragement of my wife, Hsu-hua. As a chemist, she also has given very efficient assistance in checking the facts and figures, particularly those in the chapters on fertilization and plant protection.

Needless to say, the author is solely responsible for the views and interpretations presented and for the errors that inevitably will be found in this volume.

CONTENTS

LIST OF TABLES

LIST OF MAPS

LIST OF CHINESE
WEIGHTS AND MEASURES

Weight

1 tan (picul) = 0.055 short ton = 0.050 metric ton
1 chin (catty) = 1.102 pounds = 0.500 kilogram
1 liang (tael) = 1.102 ounces = 0.031 kilogram

Length

1 li = 0.311 mile = 0.500 kilometer
1 chang = 3.645 yards = 3.333 meters
1 ch'ih = 1.094 feet = 0.333 meter
1 ts'un = 1.312 inches = 0.333 decimeter

Area

1 ch'ing = 16.474 acres = 6.667 hectares
1 mou = 0.164 acre = 0.067 hectare

LIST OF ABBREVIATIONS

JMJP   Jen-min Jih-pao [People's Daily], Peking

JPRS   Joint Publications Research Service, Washington,
        D.C.

NCNA   New China News Agency, Peking

The Technical Transformation of Agriculture in Communist China

MAP 1 - China: Geographical Features

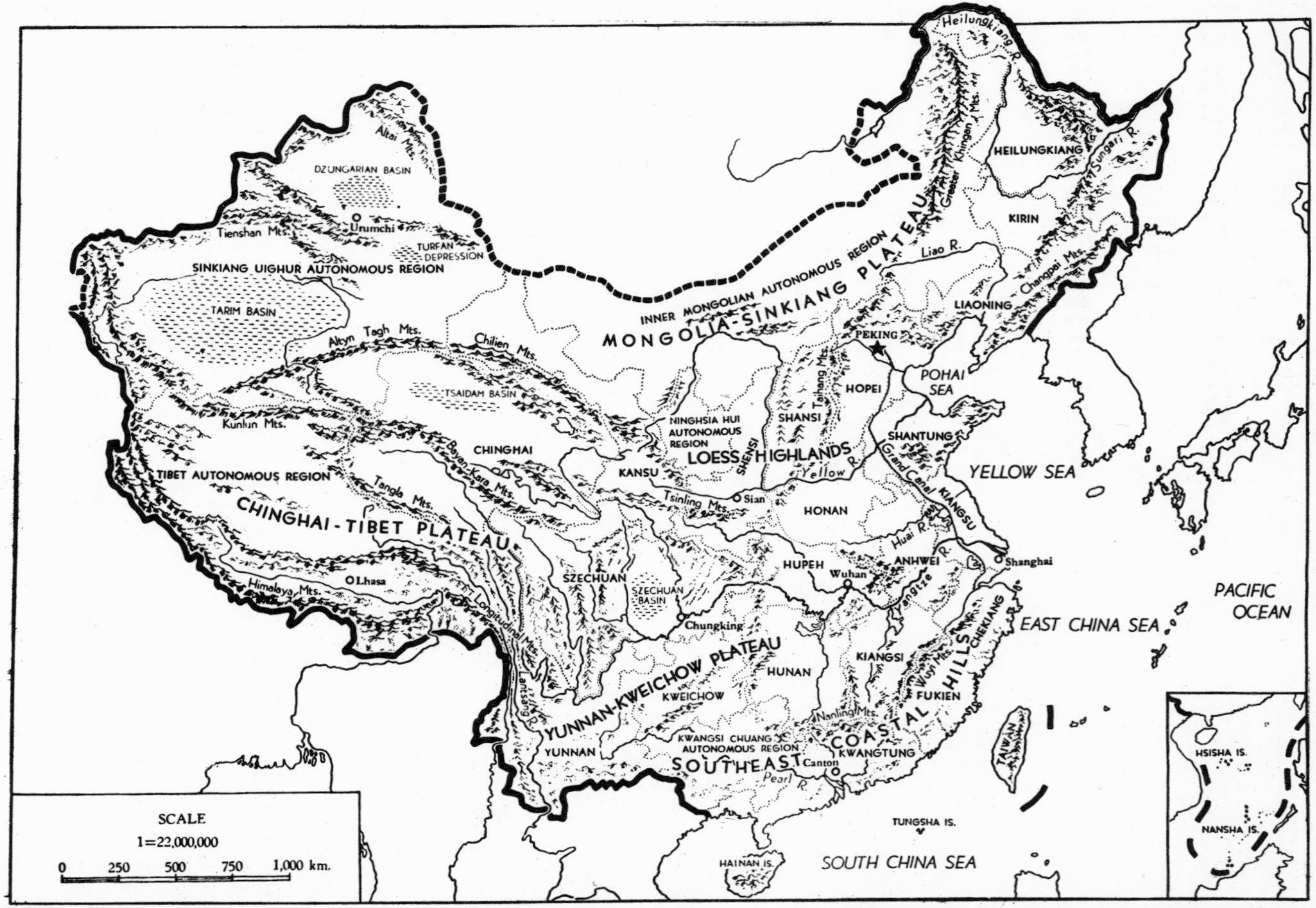

PACIFIC OCEAN

HSISHA IS.

NANSHA IS.

Liaotun Shan

Amur R.

HEILUNGKIANG

KIRIN

Greater Khingan Mts.

Heilungkiang R.

PLATEAU

LIAONING

EAST CHINA SEA

CHEKIANG

TAIWAN

COAST HILLS

FUKIEN

KIANGSI

TUNGSHA IS.

SOUTH CHINA SEA

HAINAN IS.

POHAI SEA

PEKING

HOPEI

SHANTUNG

YELLOW SEA

KIANGSU

Shanghai

Grand Canal

INNER MONGOLIAN AUTONOMOUS REGION

MONGOLIA-SINKIANG

SHANSI

SHENSI

LOESS HIGHLANDS

Taihang Mts.

Yellow R.

Sian

Tsinling Mts.

HONAN

ANHWEI

HUPEH

Wuhan

Huai R.

KWANGTUNG

KWANGSI CHUANG AUTONOMOUS REGION

SOUTHEAST

Canton

Pearl

NINGHSIA HUI AUTONOMOUS REGION

KANSU

CHINGHAI

Chilien Mts.

TSAIDAM BASIN

SZECHUAN

SZECHUAN BASIN

Chungking

KWEICHOW PLATEAU

YUNNAN-KWEICHOW PLATEAU

HUNAN

YUNNAN

Nan Tzh Mts.

Bayankara Mts.

Tangla Mts.

Kunlun Mts.

CHINGHAI - TIBET PLATEAU

TIBET AUTONOMOUS REGION

Himalaya Mts.

Lhasa

Tsangpo

Salween

Mekong

ALba Mts.

DZUNGARIAN BASIN

Urumchi

TURFAN DEPRESSION

Tienshan Mts.

SINKIANG UIGHUR AUTONOMOUS REGION

TARIM BASIN

With regard to land utilization, a country's agricultural production depends upon the area under cultivation and the yields per unit of the existing cultivated land. Throughout much of the world's history, man has increased the supply of food and other agricultural products mainly by expanding the areas under cultivation, and yields have remained rather constant at low levels. Only over the past two centuries have average world yields begun to make consistent gains.

For the years since 1950 especially, the four geographic regions classified as developed--North America, Western Europe, Oceania, and the Soviet Bloc--have been largely or entirely dependent on yield increases for additional output of grain and other principal crops. Of the three less developed geographic regions, much of South America and Africa have continued to be more dependent on additions to the cultivated area than on higher yields. But during the 1960's the densely populated Asian countries, with their diminishing land expansion potentials, have become more and more dependent on raising yields for increasing agricultural production. It is generally believed that even in some countries in Africa and Latin America the greater relative dependence on addition of new land will not likely continue much longer, and raising yields may be the better means of increasing their agricultural output.[1]

Like other densely populated, less developed countries, China has nearly exhausted the supply of new land that can readily be brought under cultivation. China therefore must look to raising yields for most of the additions to the supply of food and other agricultural products. In fact, for centuries intensive farming has been practiced in most agricultural regions of the country. Extensive use of water,

3

control of soil erosion, fertility maintenance, crop rotation, and control of weeds have largely accounted for the high yields of many crops.
In more recent decades, other measures, including plant breeding,
control of insects and diseases, and more extensive use of chemical
fertilizers, have been adopted to further raise yields. As a result of
these efforts, agricultural production in general during the 1920's
and 1930's improved rather steadily although not sufficiently to meet
the increasing needs. In 1936, China had its largest agricultural production in many years and this was attributed to the general agricultural improvement measures as well as to the effect of political
stability and favorable weather.

However, the improvement was abruptly interrupted by the
Sino-Japanese War (1937-45) and the civil strife that followed. Military
operations affected large sections of population and hindered normal
cultivation of the land in many areas. More than 70 million mou (11.7
million acres) of farmland were torn by the war, and some 17.5 million
farmers suffered directly or indirectly. Another 14 million mou (2.3
million acres) of farmland were devastated by the flood of the Yellow
River in Honan Province, affecting more than 3 million persons. (The
flood developed when the dike on the right bank of the river near
Chengchou was broken intentionally in 1938 by the National government
in order to slow down the advance of the Japanese armies.) Irrigation
systems for more than 10 million mou (1.7 million acres) of farmland
were destroyed or laid waste. Transportation and communication
facilities in many sections of the country were damaged. Not only
did agricultural production again decline to a low level but industries
closely related to agriculture--such as cotton spinning, flour milling,
and silk reeling--also suffered heavily. Agricultural trade was sharply
reduced, and a number of agricultural research and experiment projects
were discontinued.

During the Sino-Japanese War, most of the Chinese government's
activities were wartime emergency measures. Following the cessation
of the hostilities, important steps were taken to reconstruct agriculture
with the assistance of the United Nations Relief and Rehabilitation
Administration and a survey of problems relating to the development
of China's agriculture was made in 1946-47 by a mission composed
of American and Chinese specialists appointed by the two governments. Some progress was made but, on account of the immensity of
the problems as well as the depleted resources and insufficient personnel, much remained to be done. Moreover, the conflict between
the National government and the Communists deepened, and agricultural rehabilitation was badly affected by the civil strife.[2]

Thus, when the Communist regime took over Mainland China in 1949 it did not inherit a bountiful agriculture. There were numerous problems to be solved. Some of them were urgent and others of long-range nature. The task required large amounts of materials and services. And yet the new government's first objective in economic planning was industrialization, and agriculture was not given as much attention as it should have received. During the "Economic Recovery Period" (1949-52), programs and measures adopted for the improvement of agricultural production were mostly piecemeal and of regional or local nature. Agriculture as a major sector of the national economy was included in the First Five-Year Plan (1953-57) and the Second Five-Year Plan (1958-62), but its significance was much overshadowed by the emphasis on industrial development.

It was not until 1960, the second of three consecutive years of bad harvest, that the policy of "developing agriculture as the foundation of the national economy and industry as the leading factor" was adopted. Since then, the order of priority among the major sectors of the national economy has been agriculture, light industry, and heavy industry. One of the principal measures to implement the new emphasis on agriculture was for industry to provide as much aid as possible to agriculture. In fact, aid to agriculture was to be the most important way in which industry would fulfill its leading role in the national economy. Industrial development was to be primarily the development of machinery, equipment, and materials that would improve agricultural production.[3] More specifically, the most important objective of industrial aid to agriculture was to speed up the technical transformation of agriculture, for which goals and measures were provided in the National Program for Agricultural Development, 1956-67. The purposes, contents, and implementation of the Program will be discussed in the following chapters.

NOTES

1. Food and Agriculture Organization of the United Nations, The State of Food and Agriculture, 1968 (Rome, 1968), p. 76.

2. Government of the Republic of China, Annual Progress and Program Report on Food and Agriculture for China, 1947, submitted to the Conference of the Food and Agriculture Organization of the United Nations, Washington, D. C., August 1947. (Mimeographed.)

3. Leslie T. C. Kuo, "Industrial Aid to Agriculture in Communist China," International Development Review, Washington, D. C., Vol. IX, No. 2 (1967), pp. 6-10, 29.

The National Program for Agricultural Development, 1956-67, was described in its preamble as "a program of endeavor to develop agricultural production in our country and to raise the living standard of the peasants and the people as a whole during the period from the First Five-Year Plan to the Third." (See Appendix for a complete English translation of the Program.) The core of the Program consisted of the goals and measures to expand the area under cultivation and to raise yields per unit of existing cultivated land. In the twelve years beginning in 1956, the area cultivated by state farms was to be increased from the 1955 figure of more than 13 million mou to about 100 million mou (Article 16). The average annual yields of grain crops in the three principal grain-growing regions were to be raised from 150 to 400 chin per mou, from 208 to 500 chin per mou, and from 400 to 800 chin per mou, respectively, and the average annual yield of ginned cotton was to be raised from the 1955 figure of 35 chin per mou (the national average) to 40, 60, 80, or 100 chin per mou, depending on local conditions (Article 2).

The most important measures for attaining these goals, as prescribed in the Program, included the following:

1. Construction of water conservation projects

2. Expansion of the fertilizer supply

3. Improvement of old-style farm tools and popularization of modern farm tools

4. Extension of the use of the best and most suitable plant varieties.

5. Expansion of multiple cropping areas

6. Planting of more high-yielding crops

7. Adoption of the best farming methods

8. Improvement of the soil

9. Conservation of soil and water

10. Protection and breeding of draft animals

11. Extermination of insects, pests, and plant diseases

12. Reclamation of wasteland.

For some of these measures, the Program also set goals to be fulfilled by the end of 1967, including the expansion of paddy fields and irrigated land from 390 million _mou_ in 1955 to 900 million _mou_ in 1967; the raising of the capacity of the irrigation facilities to control droughts to between 30 and 50 days and, in places suitable for double-crop paddy fields, to between 50 to 70 days; the annual production of 5 to 7 million tons of chemical fertilizers by 1962, and 15 million tons by 1967; and the elimination of the most harmful insect pests and plant diseases within the twelve years 1956-68.

Although the 40-article program was primarily a blueprint for agricultural development in Communist China, it also covered such problems as general welfare, public health, education, transportation, communications, commerce, finance, household management, the eradication of rats, flies, mosquitoes, and bedbugs, and the encouragement of birth control. The preamble pointed out that these and many other tasks required the participation of both rural and urban people, and that they could only be effectively carried out with the coordinated efforts of the towns and the countryside.

The contents and goals of the Program have been a matter of dispute among Party leaders. The Program was first proposed by Mao Tse-tung in 1955 during the period of "High Tide of Rural Socialism." It was submitted in draft form by the Political Bureau of the Central Committee of the Chinese Communist Party to the Supreme State Conference, which adopted it on January 25, 1956. But, in the second half of 1956 and the beginning of 1957, there was strong opposition to the Program, which many Communist leaders considered to be overzealous and unrealistic. Thus, the Eighth

National Congress of the Chinese Communist Party, held in September 1956, did not approve the Program. However, following the Congress Mao Tse-tung relied on the support of the provincial secretaries of the Party to overcome his opponents and make the goals of the Program even more ambitious. As a result, the draft was first amended at the Third Plenary Session of the Eighth Central Committee of the Chinese Communist Party on October 9, 1957, and again at the Second Session of the Eighth National Congress of the Chinese Communist Party on May 23, 1958.[1]

Despite the revisions, Mao Tse-tung and his followers did not consider the goals prescribed in the Program high enough. During the Leap Forward campaign, the Program was actually sidelined. In the "Decision on the Question Concerning the Establishment of Rural Communes," adopted by the Central Committee of the Chinese Communist Party on August 29, 1958, the nation was urged to increase agricultural production by "two, several, ten and a dozen times."[2] When the Draft Program of the National Economy for 1959 was adopted by the Seventh Plenary Session of the Eighth Central Committee of the Chinese Communist Party on April 25, 1959, the grain production target for that year was set at 1,050,000 million chin (525 million metric tons), which was one-third more than the target for 1967 (720,000 million chin or 360 million metric tons), prescribed in the National Program for Agricultural Development.[3]

But the economic dislocation and agricultural crisis that was caused by the Leap Forward campaign and aggravated by the natural calamities in 1959 and 1960 made it necessary to bring the Program for up discussion again, after nearly two years of oblivion. Most of the production targets proposed by Mao Tse-tung and others had proved unattainable, and at the Second Session of the Second National People's Congress on April 10, 1960, the more conservative first revised draft of the Program was adopted with one insignificant change: Article 27 of the Program was amended so that bedbugs took the place of sparrows among the four pests to be exterminated, because it had been discovered that sparrows, unlovable as they are, are indispensable as the enemies of certain insects.[4] The first revised draft thus became the final version of the Program, superseding the second revised draft, which was never published.

NOTES

1. JMJP, October 10, 1957, p. 1; T'an Chen-lin, "Strive for the Fulfillment, Ahead of Schedule, of the National Program for Agricultural Development," JMJP, April 9, 1960, p. 1.

2. Hsin-hua Pan-yueh-k'an [New China Semimonthly], Peking, No. 18, 1958, pp. 1-2.

3. Hsin-hua Pan-yueh-k'an [New China Semimonthly], Peking, No. 8, 1959, p. 1.

4. JMJP, April 12, 1960, p. 1.

3

IMPLEMENTATION
OF
THE PROGRAM

Agricultural research, education, and extension are three of
the essential services that a government must provide for a country's
agricultural development. Research evolves new ideas and new techniques, education provides trained personnel, and extension assists
farmers in putting into practice the products of research. The three
services are complementary and mutually dependent. The effectiveness of the government's effort to improve agricultural production
depends on the organization and administration of these services. A
brief account of governmental organization and functions for agricultural development, as well as overall policies and guiding principles
of agricultural research, education, and extension, in Communist
China is given here as a background for discussing major aspects of
the technical transformation of agriculture.

Like other economic activities, agricultural development in
Communist China is completely controlled by the government and, in
turn, by the Communist Party. Under the State Council, the highest
executive body of the Communist Chinese government, are the Office
for Agriculture and Forestry and several ministries that perform
certain agricultural functions, including the ministries of agriculture,
forestry, food, marine products, state farms and land reclamation,
water conservation and electric power, agricultural machinery (renamed the "Eighth Ministry of Machine-Building Industry" in 1965),
and the Second Ministry of Machine-Building Industry, which is in
charge of semimechanized agricultural implements. In keeping with
the process of streamlining the central government structure after
the purges of the Cultural Revolution, the Ministry of Agriculture
and the Ministry of Forestry were merged in 1970 to form the Ministry of Agriculture and Forestry.[1] There are also several commissions,

bureaus, and special agencies under the State Council, each of which performs functions related to several fields, including agriculture; these include the State Economic Commission, the State Planning Commission, the State Capital Construction Commission, the State Statistical Bureau, the State Scientific and Technological Commission, the Agricultural Bank of China, and the Central Meteorological Bureau.

Above all these agencies is the Rural Work Department, which is directly under the Chinese Communist Party and makes paramount decisions on agriculture. For the supervision of work in communes, the Political Department of Agriculture and Forestry was created in August, 1965 under the Central Committee of the Chinese Communist Party.[2] Inevitably, there is much duplication and overlapping in the functions and operations of these organs under the weighty make-up of the central government. The structures of the provincial, hsien, commune, and other local government units are equally complicated.

Since the Cultural Revolution, all these central, provincial, and local government units have been run by the respective Revolutionary Committees, and in each committee the Party nucleus is the core of the leadership.[3] Obviously, all agricultural activities are under tight Party control.

AGRICULTURAL RESEARCH

Before the Communist takeover, agricultural research in China at the national level centered in (1) the National Bureau of Agricultural Research at Nanking, dealing mainly with crops; (2) the National Bureau of Animal Husbandry Research at Nanking; (3) the National Bureau of Forestry Research at Nanking; and (4) the National Bureau of Fisheries Research at Shanghai. A National Bureau of Agricultural Economics Research was planned shortly after the Sino-Japanese War. All of these bureaus were directly under the Ministry of Agriculture and Forestry, and each had experiment stations, field stations, and laboratories. In addition, a number of other agencies in the Ministry of Agriculture and Forestry conducted agricultural research to some degree. Some research also was done by the national colleges of agriculture.

At the provincial level, there was a great array of agricultural research institutes, agricultural experiment stations, seed- and animal-multiplication stations, demonstration farms, and other institutions for agricultural improvement. In general, these institutions were understaffed, poorly equipped, and inadequately financed. Most

of them conducted simple tests of fertilizers, pesticides, and plant
varieties. A few occasionally attempted more basic research, but
little of their work was systematically organized.[4]

During the early years of the Communist regime, agricultural
research in Mainland China was conducted for the most part by several
agencies under the Ministry of Agriculture and by a number of agricultural colleges. The Chinese Academy of Sciences, which was
entrusted with the task of promoting and coordinating scientific research
work generally, also conducted some research in certain agricultural
fields, including agronomy, entomology, plant pathology, forestry, and
water conservation.

The Chinese Academy of Agricultural Science was founded in
Peking on March 1, 1957, by the Ministry of Agriculture. Ting Ying,
a rice specialist, was elected its first president.[5] As the focal point
for the development of agricultural research, this academy, in addition
to carrying out its own program, coordinates the research work of
nearly 30 agricultural colleges and more than 200 other organizations
engaged in agricultural experimentation and research. The Chinese
Academy of Agricultural Science also cooperates with related institutes of the Chinese Academy of Sciences.

The Chinese Academy of Agricultural Science has established
more than twenty research institutes, each specializing in research
in a major field of agriculture, and a number of regional and provincial
research institutes. Many branch institutes and experiment stations
also have been set up in hsien (counties) and communes throughout
the country. Despite the fact that policy-making and the control of
agricultural research operations are highly centralized in the government, the research institutions are widely distributed throughout the
country. Although many of the research institutes under the Chinese
Academy of Agricultural Science are located in Peking, the national
capital, other institutes have been set up in areas where there is substantial production of the crop or animal in question. Among the institutes that have been established in Peking are those for plant breeding
and cultivation, soil and fertilizers, agricultural uses of atomic energy,
plant protection, vegetables, animal husbandry, apiculture, agricultural
mechanization, agricultural meteorology, agricultural economics, and
horticulture. Institutes located in other cities include those for seri-
culture (Chinkiang, Kiangsu Province), agricultural heritage (Nanking),
tea (Hangchou, Chekiang), pomology (Hsincheng, Liaoning), cotton
(Anyang, Honan), hemp (Yuanchiang, Hunan), potatoes (Shuchien,
Kiangsu), marsh gas (Fuyang, Anhwei), Chinese veterinary medicine
(Lanchou, Kansu), citrus (Chungking), and tobacco (Tsinan, Shantung).

Institutes for the following fields also have been mentioned, although
their precise locations are not known: veterinary science (Western),
horses, oxen, water buffaloes, hogs, sheep, hide and fur animals,
poultry, oil-bearing crops, oak silkworm culture, and farm irrigation.

In addition, there are six regional research institutes under the
Chinese Academy of Agricultural Science: for Northeast China, North-
west China, East China, South China, North China, and Central China.
There are also provincial research institutes in Chekiang, Hupeh,
Shensi, Shantung, Shansi, Anhwei, Kwangtung, Fukien, and Kiangsu.
Many hsien, municipalities, and communes also have established
institutes and other research and experimental facilities to further
extend the organizational network for agricultural research.

Among the host of slogans spawned by Mao Tse-tung, "walking
on two legs" has the peculiar merit of apparently fitting any situation
that confronts Communist China. Many interpretations have been poured
into this mold. At the beginning of the Leap Forward campaign in
1958, for example, the slogan stood for the simultaneous development
of backyard primitive furnaces and of modern metallurgy with Soviet
assistance. When the primitive furnaces petered out in early 1959,
the slogan was made to cover the parallel development of heavy and
medium metallurgy.

In the technical transformation of agriculture, "walking on two
legs" means numerous things. Modern mechanization of farming is
carried out simultaneously with the improvement and innovation of
native tools and implements. The technique of acupuncture and other
methods of native veterinarians are used together with the findings
of modern veterinary science. In improving the soil, the use of both
chemical and organic fertilizers is promoted. In plant protection,
chemical pesticides as well as "native agricultural drugs" are used.
In water conservation, large reservoirs and dams are constructed
side by side with small canals, ditches, and wells.

Scientists have gone to the villages to learn about the farmers'
ways, problems, and common beliefs. At the same time, farmers are
encouraged to participate in experimentation, the development of new
plant varieties, the designing of improved tools and implements, the
survey of soils, and other activities. Thus, the scientists and the
masses are brought close together. Communist leaders recognize
that it will take a long time to develop and apply modern agricultural
science on a broad basis in China, and they believe that agricultural
production can be increased at a higher speed by using the combined
methods of old and new, native and foreign, scientific and primitive.

At the same time, the emphasis on having research workers go to the countryside to work with the peasants appears to be aimed at providing a means for indoctrinating the scientists with Communist principles and practices and thus making it more certain that they remain an integral part of the Communist pattern.

In addition to conducting laboratory and field experiments, the Chinese Academy of Agricultural Science has another major function that it carries out simultaneously: "collecting the past experiences of the masses." During the latter half of 1958, a majority of the academy's technical staff members lived and worked with farmers in the villages from time to time in order to discuss the farmers' production experiences with them and at the same time to give the farmers any assistance they might need. In 1959, more than 360 centers were established for this purpose. On the basis of information collected from the farmers, publications dealing with rice, cotton, wheat, fruits, mulberries, animal diseases, plant protection, fertilizers, soil conservation, and other subjects have been prepared.[6]

A much-publicized example of "walking on two legs" was Ch'en Yung-k'ang, a farmer of Kiangsu Province, who in 1950 was selected as one of national model farmers and in 1958 was appointed to the research staff of the East China Agricultural Research Institute of the Chinese Academy of Agricultural Science. Ch'en has to his credit a high-yielding rice strain that he bred from a rice plant selected twenty years earlier in his rice fields. Based on his observation of the growth, shape, and subtle color changes of the leaves of the rice plants on a few mou of land, Ch'en maintains that the leaves of late rice change from dark green to lighter green and vice versa six times before the harvest. In his opinion, manure and water should be so applied as to make the change of color occur at the proper time, in order to lead to sturdy growth and high yield. This is what he calls the theory of "san huang san hei" (three yellow and three black).

Ch'en's skill of rice growing is said to have further improved in recent years while he was working in collaboration with scientists of the Chinese Academy of Agricultural Science. Working together, they have achieved yields of about 1,000 chin of rice per mou on their experimental plots, and the highest yield has reached 1,240 chin of upland rice per mou.[7]

Some supported Ch'en's theory; others maintained that the change in leaf color was a common phenomenon that had nothing to do with the growth of rice and that Ch'en's harvests were not sufficient basis for drawing scientific conclusions.[8] In any case, committees for popularizing Ch'en Yung-k'ang's rice-growing methods were set up in 1963 by all governments and communes in the Soochow District, Kiangsu Province. His methods were applied on experimental farms totaling more than 6,000 hectares in thousands of villages, all of which had better harvests in 1963 than in 1962, according to the People's Daily.[9]

Another example of "walking on two legs" is Pei Yao-ching, a peasant who learned Chinese native veterinary methods from his grandfather and his uncle. Pei has compiled or rewritten several important works on traditional Chinese veterinary practices. In 1950, he was appointed a veterinarian and later deputy chief of a veterinary hospital in central Shansi. In 1963, he became a special research worker of the Research Institute of Traditional Chinese Veterinary Science under the Chinese Academy of Agricultural Science.[10]

As a move to propagate the old agricultural techniques, the Research Institute of Agricultural Heritage was established at Nanking in 1958 by the Chinese Academy of Agricultural Science. Under the auspices of the institute, more than thirty ancient agricultural publications have been reprinted and published. Most of these publications are from a collection of old works on agriculture that formerly was maintained by the University of Nanking. These include Shou Shih T'ung-k'ao [A Comprehensive Reference Book on Agriculture], an imperial compilation by Chang T'ing-yu and others, originally published in 1742 in 78 volumes containing quotations on agriculture from old Chinese literature; Ch'i-min Yao-shu [Important Techniques of the Common People], a book on the methods of growing and processing agricultural products by Chia Szu-hsieh, originally published in the Later Wie Dynasty (sixth century); Fan-sheng-chih Shu [A Book by Fan Sheng], a work on agricultural techniques, published in the first century B. C.; Nung Shu [Book on Agriculture], by Wang Chen of the Yuan Dynasty (fourteenth century); and works on Chinese veterinary therapeutics and prescriptions, Chinese methods of cultivating various plants, and other agricultural topics. Some of these reprints have been published with interpretations and suggestions as to how some of the old farming practices may be adopted for Chinese agriculture today.[11]

The Chinese Communists have followed the principle of subservience of scientific research to the requirements of the state. The pursuit of scientific research generally is based on the country's political, military, and economic development plans rather than on the interests of individual scientists. In agriculture, the policy has aimed at agricultural research for the sake of agricultural production. Research and experimentation with the objective of immediate increase

in agricultural production has been emphasized, although more basic
or theoretical studies have not been entirely neglected.

Since the principle of subservience requires centralized direction
and control to ensure fulfillment of plans, virtually all research institutions and projects are under the supervision of Party cadres, most
of whom are not scientists. Science that pre-supposes slow, pains-
taking work and fails to show immediate results in helping economic
development is not appreciated by the cadres. On the other hand,
many of the scientists strongly feel that they should devote themselves
to research on basic and theoretical problems rather than give their
time to problems of economic development and elementary scientific
training.

Latent differences between scientists and the Communist Party
broke into a bitter struggle during the movement of "Letting a Hundred
Flowers Bloom and a Hundred Schools Contend" in 1956. As the out-
come of the controversy, Communist China's political planners and
policy-makers took firmer control in the direction and administration
of scientific research. During the Leap Forward campaign, many
scientists were seized by the mania for speed under the slogan of
"producing more, better, faster, and economically." As pointed out
by a correspondent of the People's Daily with reference to a study
on the deterioration of potatoes conducted by the Research Institute
of Microbiology, the scientists "had to abandon the original basis of
study and tried to work out a simple method which would put a stop
to the deterioration at one blow. For the sake of speed, they sacrificed
the verification of results. This demand for speed was in obvious
contradiction to scientific work. The only result of it was waste of
manpower and waste of time with an unfortunate influence on research
work."[12]

AGRICULTURAL EDUCATION

Prior to the Communist takeover, China had 25 national colleges
of agriculture (21 Chinese and 4 missionary) and nearly 20 provincial
and private agricultural colleges. These higher educational institutions provided training in agriculture at the undergraduate level,
and by the end of 1946 they had graduated more than 6,000 students.
Some of the graduates received further training abroad. In addition
to these colleges, there were also a number of agricultural vocational
schools of intermediate level. Although some of these institutions,
such as the University of Nanking, did outstanding work, the system
of agricultural education as a whole was inadequate. Moreover, many

of the graduates were not in positions where they could best utilize
their training.[13]

Large numbers of technical workers of all levels were reported
to have been trained in the agricultural fields since 1949. As a result
of the drastic reorganization of China's educational system, which
began in the latter part of 1950, virtually all of the original institutions
of learning have been merged or abolished and many new ones have
been established. The number of higher educational institutions in
agriculture increased from 23 (one university and 22 colleges) in
1957 to 42 (7 universities, 26 colleges of agriculture, and 9 colleges
of agricultural mechanization) in 1966. Facilities as well as faculty
varied widely among these universities and colleges. For example,
in addition to trained personnel, many "native experts" (peasants
who are experienced in local farming) have been appointed to give
instruction and lectures at some colleges.[14]

Table 1 shows the annual number of graduates from institutions
of higher learning in the agricultural fields as compared with the
number of graduates in all fields in 1949-58, 1961, and 1962. The
annual number of agricultural graduates represented only 4.8 to 8.2
percent of the total number of graduates in all fields during the period
1949-61, partly because under the industrialization program there
was a greater demand for technical personnel in nonagricultural
fields. The proportion of agricultural graduates rose to 11.8 percent
in 1962 following the adoption of the policy of "developing agriculture
as the foundation of the national economy."

The training of postgraduates has progressed very slowly in
all fields. Before the Sino-Soviet split, such training was carried out
mainly by sending students to the Soviet Union and other Communist
countries. In recent years, Communist China has increasingly relied
on its own efforts in training postgraduates, but has admitted that
the program is far from adequate, both quantitatively and qualitatively.[15]

The Chinese Academy of Sciences was the first institution to
recruit postgraduate students. In 1955, the academy offered a four-
year curriculm to 50 candidates for the degree of "Associate Doctor
of Science."[16] The following year, four institutes of the Chinese
Academy of Sciences recruited 361 postgraduates for advanced studies
on 18 specialized courses.[17] Since then, the academy has continued
such recruitment every year.

TABLE 1

Number of College Graduates
in Communist China,
1949-58, 1961, and 1962

Year	Total Graduates Number	Agricultural Graduates	
		Number	Percent of Total Graduates
Peak Year Before 1949	25,000	2,064	8.3
1949	21,000	1,718	8.1
1950	18,000	1,477	8.2
1951	19,000	1,538	8.1
1952	32,000	2,361	7.4
1953	48,000	2,633	5.5
1954	47,000	3,532	7.5
1955	55,000	2,614	4.8
1956	63,000	3,541	5.6
1957	56,000	3,104	5.3
1958	72,000	3,513	4.9
1961	162,000	10,000	6.2
1962	170,000	20,000	11.8

Sources: Figures for the peak year before 1949 and for 1949-58 are from State Statistical Bureau, Ten Great Years, English edition (Peking: 1960), pp. 194, 196. Figures for 1961 and 1962 are from JMJP, August 4, 1961, p. 4, and August 29, 1962, p. 1, respectively.

The recruitment of postgraduates by the institutions of higher education began in 1956, when several universities and colleges offered for the first time a four-year curriculum for advanced degrees. In the first two years, the candidates were required to study dialectical materialism and historical materialism, foreign languages, and basic specialized subjects. The latter two years were spent mainly for the preparation of theses.[18]

In recent years, both the number of institutions recruiting postgraduates and the number of postgraduates enrolled have increased considerably. In 1964, more than 180 institutions of higher education and research organs recruited 1,280 postgraduates, as compared with 160 institutions and 800 postgraduates in 1963.[19] No data are available to indicate how many of these were in the agricultural fields.

Below the college level, in addition to the regular middle schools there are a number of technical middle schools that give short courses on various subjects, including agriculture. The number of students enrolled in these technical middle schools increased from 230,000 in 1949 to 1,470,000 in 1958, and the number of graduates increased from 72,000 to 191,000 during the same period.[20]

Since early in 1958, more than 200,000 agricultural middle schools have been established in the communes as the most important institutions for the training of intermediate technical personnel in agriculture. Boys and girls thirteen to sixteen years of age who work in the communes are selected to spend half of their time in the schools, that is, for six months of each year for three years. The level is equivalent to that of junior middle schools, and the curriculum includes basic agricultural techniques as well as politics, Chinese, and mathematics. Emphasis is given to the special farming problems and crops of the particular locality. Most of these schools arrange their schedules so that the students can work full time in their communes during the busy farming season. At the end of 1964, some 400,000 students had graduated from the agricultural middle schools in Kiangsu, the first and model province for such institutions, and another 200,000 were still studying in the schools. The Communist government hopes that these students will form a major force of technical workers on the farms when China's agriculture becomes more modernized.[21] But press reports indicate that the academic standards of these agricultural middle schools, as well as their accommodations and facilities, are generally low. Moreover, many cadres in charge of the schools, teachers, and students are not enthusiastic about their work.[22]

Since 1964, the system of combining study with farming has been expanded to educational institutions of all levels in the rural areas, in pursuance of the Chinese Communist Party's policy that education must serve proletarian politics and be linked with productive labor. By September 1965, the system had been adopted by 37 of the 66 agricultural colleges or institutes in the country with 11,800 students or 15 percent of the total enrollment and by 220 of the 307 agricultural middle schools with 41,600 students or 52 percent of the total enrollment.[23] At the same time, the whole country had a total of 17 million children attending the part-farming and part-study primary schools.[24] In 1965, 90 percent of middle schools and primary schools and 80 percent of their total enrollments were in the countryside.[25]

To strengthen the political control of agricultural education, the Ministry of Education issued a directive in March 1966 calling on all educational agencies in the country to consolidate and improve the farming-study primary schools and agricultural middle schools. Specifically, the directive called on the educational agencies (1) to bring politics to the fore and implement the Party's policies on education; (2) to strive to uphold firmly the method of work that combines the leadership with the masses; (3) to firmly observe the principle of running schools on the basis of industry and thrift; (4) to establish a new force of teachers who think revolutionary and are willing to take part in physical labor; and (5) to have the teachers rely on the leadership of the Party.[26]

During the Cultural Revolution, primary and middle schools in the countryside were placed under the management of the poor and lower-middle class peasants because the Communist authorities considered them "the most reliable ally of the working class." In accordance with Mao Tse-tung's instructions, the period of schooling has been shortened and the curriculum has been changed drastically. The instructions have further intensified political indoctrination, military training, and programs for promoting class struggle at the expense of basic education.

AGRICULTURAL EXTENSION

The earliest agricultural extension work in China was done in the 1910's by a few private educational and missionary institutions, including the former University of Nanking. In 1929, the first official extension regulations were issued by the National government. This

was followed by the establishment of the Central Extension Committee
in Nanking and extension services in sixteen provinces. However,
their work was brought to a standstill by the Sino-Japanese War,
which began in 1937.[27]

Agricultural extension service in Communist China did not
begin until 1951 when the "agricultural technique extension stations"
were established in Manchuria on an experimental basis. More
stations were later set up in other areas, and at the end of 1954 their
number throughout the country exceeded 4,500. In general, these
stations were poorly organized and equipped, and most of the workers
were Party cadres whose technical level was low. In 1954, only about
10 percent of the 600,000 agricultural producers' cooperatives and
mutual-aid teams were served by the stations.

In an effort to strengthen the agricultural extension system,
the Ministry of Agriculture issued a directive in 1955 urging all
provinces, special districts, and hsien to set up agricultural technique
extension stations. The functions of the stations were stipulated as
follows: to coordinate the production experience of local peasants;
to propagate modern agricultural science and technology; to help
peasants increase their production and income; to promote agricultural cooperativization; and to assist local Party leaders in
improving agricultural techniques and management. The directive
provided that the stations generally should be located in villages and
rural towns with better foundations for cooperativization and better
natural conditions; that in general the staff of a station should consist
of no more than five persons, including technicians and one accountant,
all of whom should have strong political leadership and be familiar
with agricultural management; and that the technicians should be
graduates of secondary agricultural schools or progressive peasants
with long experience of agricultural production and at least six months
of political training.[28]

The total number of extension stations increased rapidly, from
43 in 1951 to 13,669 in 1957.[29] But their operation as a whole was
not efficient. In another directive issued by the Ministry of Agriculture on December 26, 1962, the stations were instructed to make
administrative and personnel improvement. They were urged particularly to popularize agricultural techniques by means of demonstration and propaganda rather than by coercion and to take local
conditions into consideration.[30]

The crop failures of 1959-61 and the departure of Russian experts
in the early 1960's made it necessary in 1963 for the Communist

government to adopt the policy of "combining the three," under which Party cadres, the scientists, and the masses were urged to cooperate and to pool their ideas. To implement this policy, research and extension systems have been reorganized and many yang pan t'ien (demonstration farms) have been set up. Agricultural scientists have been sent to these farms to try out the results of research, as well as the peasants' experience, before deciding whether or not certain agricultural techniques should popularized in larger areas. These demonstration farms, which vary in size from a few score to several thousand mou, are described as bridges between experimentation and extension. They are designed to supplement rather than to replace the experimental farms, research bases and extension stations.[31]

During the 1960's, more than ten large demonstration farms were established in the Peking municipal area, Northeast China, the Szechuan Basin, the Taihu area, the Pearl River delta, Hainan Island, Northwest China, and many smaller demonstration farms also were set up in other areas.[32] At the end of 1964, one-fourth of China's agricultural research workers and one-half its agricultural extension workers were stationed at the some 5,400 demonstration farms set up by various agricultural institutions in 12 provinces, autonomous regions, and municipalities. In 1965, it was planned to extend the land under the guidance of demonstration farms to 50 million mou and to allocate one-half of the personnel of agricultural scientific institutions to run demonstration farms.[33]

Many scientists doubt the wisdom of their participation in the demonstration farm work and maintain that research and experimentation should be continued in the laboratories. But the authorities regard this as a bourgeois attitude.[34] It appears that one of the principal reasons for establishing the demonstration farms is to seek to fulfill a mission that state farms are supposed to fulfill but in which they apparently have failed: namely, to serve as models of efficient agriculture.

For the dissemination of agricultural knowledge, provinces, municipalities, and autonomous regions have been urged to compile and publish local experiences in agricultural production, to hold agricultural exhibitions, to give awards to model peasants, to arrange for exchange of information between the cooperatives (now the communes), and to encourage peasants and cadres to study the advanced experience of other localities in farm management and techniques. (Article 4, National Program for Agricultural Development, 1956-67). A National Agricultural Exhibition Center has been constructed on the eastern outskirts of Peking, including five pavilions dealing with agriculture in general, rural sideline occupations, water conservation, agricultural mechanization, and animal husbandry. The predominating theme in all five pavilions is self-reliance.[35]

Radio broadcasts have been used by the government as a means for the dissemination of agricultural knowledge as well as for political propaganda and mass indoctrination in the countryside. The National Program for Agricultural Development provided that in the seven or twelve years beginning in 1956, depending on local conditions, the radio diffusion network was to be extended to virtually all rural areas and the majority of the cooperatives (now the communes) were to be enabled to receive the radio programs (Article 32). It was reported in 1963 that more than 80 percent of the country's 2,309 counties had built broadcasting stations and that many communes had installed amplifiers so that all production brigades and production teams could listen to broadcasts. More than 500,000 loudspeakers were located in China's countryside.[36]

Since literacy plays a key role in the dissemination of agricultural knowledge, the National Program for Agricultural Development required that illiteracy among young and middle-aged people be virtually wiped out in the twelve years beginning in 1956. (Article 31). By the end of 1959, more than 110 million, or two-thirds of all young and middle-aged people in the countryside, had been "freed from the state of illiteracy," according to Vice-Premier T'an Chen-lin.[37]

Despite the reportedly impressive networks of agricultural research, education, and extension, the quality and competence vary greatly among institutions. Some have made considerable progress, but others have accomplished very little or simply have not had many activities because of the shortage of funds and trained personnel. On the whole, a slow but steady improvement seems to have been made in the 1950's and 1960's. However, the progress has been far from adequate for carrying out the arduous task of the technical transformation of agriculture.

Among the serious drawbacks are the requirements in the selection of staff members for the research, educational, and extension services. The most important requirement is "political level." Persons coming from an acceptable class background, especially the former poor and low-middle class peasants, are given high preference. Next to political standing is physical fitness--the ability to work long hours at manual labor. Technical qualification is only a poor third in the list of requirements.

Another drawback in the development of agricultural research, education, and extension is the lack of a clearly articulated organizational structure in these three services, as well as the lack of coordination among them. Progress could have been speeded up if more effective administration and management had been provided.

SOVIET ASSISTANCE

As in other fields, the influence of the U.S.S.R. on agricultural techniques in Communist China was substantial during the "Economic Recovery Period" and the First Five-Year Plan period. In addition to the Sino-Soviet Protocol for Scientific and Technical Cooperation signed in 1954, an agreement for technical cooperation was reached in 1957 by the academies of agricultural science in the two countries. Russian experts have assisted in planning and carrying out many agricultural projects, and Chinese students and special missions have been sent to the U.S.S.R. to study Russian agricultural techniques. Russia also has supplied Communist China with improved seeds, farm machinery, and equipment.[38]

The departure of Russian experts beginning in the 1960's was a severe blow to the technical transformation of agriculture in Communist China. The progress of many important projects was affected. For example, work at the Sanmen Gorge project, scheduled to be completed in 1961, was never finished, partly because of the withdrawal of the Russians. The construction of some of the large chemical fertilizer plants slowed down for the same reason. The supply of Russian equipment and scientific research materials also declined drastically.

Even before the Sino-Soviet split, the relationship between scientists of the two countries was not always harmonious. Many Chinese scientists frequently expressed their regret for the Party cadres' absolute obedience to Russian experts. During the 1956 movement of "Letting a Hundred Flowers Bloom and a Hundred Schools Contend," numerous complaints along these lines were published in newspapers and scientific journals.[39]

In the case of the Yellow River water conservation plan, some Chinese engineers considered the presence of Russian experts as harmful. The Sanmen Gorge project was suggested by the Russians as the first project for the control of the Yellow River. Many Chinese engineers expressed the opinion that the reservoir would be filled

with silt.[40] Their view was supported by some foreign observers who
believed that the life of the Sanmen reservoir would be a mere half-
century or so unless energetic measures in agriculture, forestry, and
animal husbandry, as well as in engineering, were taken to combat
silting.[41] This objection was dismissed by the Russians on the ground
that soil conservation work would be undertaken. Another objection--
that millions of people would have to be moved--was answered by
the Russians with the argument that no large reservoir can be constructed without this problem. But perhaps the most serious objection
on the part of Chinese engineers was that the Russians made recommendations without proper technical preparation. In an unmistakable
tone of irony, Ch'eng Hsüeh-min wrote:

> Upon their arrival at Peking, the [Russian] experts imme-
> diately plunged themselves into intensive work. They lis-
> tened to oral reports and at the same time studied all the
> data already compiled. After one month of investigation
> of the situation and of the research materials, the experts
> recommended that the existing data were sufficient for
> drawing up a plan for the Yellow River. The leadership
> accepted the view of the experts and decided to begin the
> preparation of the report on the Yellow River Plan.[42]

A number of publications on Chinese agriculture have been
prepared by Russian experts during or after their visits to Communist China. Ocherki Prirody i Pochv Kitaia [Soils and Natural
Environment of China] was prepared by V. A. Kovda in collaboration
with Chinese soil scientists during a four-year period. It was published in 1959 by the Publishing House of the Soviet Academy of
Sciences in Moscow.[43] Another publication, by Yu N. Kapelinskiy
et al., deals with the development of the economy and foreign economic
contacts of China and contains discussions on agricultural problems.[44]
A third publication, Nekotorye Voprosy Razvitiia Sel'skokhoziaistvennoi
Nauki v KNR [Some Questions on the Development of Agricultural
Sciences in the People's Republic of China], was published in Moscow
in 1959. It contains three long reports based on the authors' surveys
and observations in China: "Socialist Reform and Problems Involved
in the Technological Revolution of Agriculture in the Chinese People's
Republic," by V. A. Zhamin and L. A. Volkova; "Progress in Plant
Physiology in the Chinese People's Republic," by B. A. Rubin; and
"Accomplishments in Phytopathology and the Organization of Plant
Protection in the Chinese People's Republic," by M. V. Gorlenko.[45]

Chinese translations of Russian publications played a predominant
role in introducing scientific materials from abroad, especially during

the "Economic Recovery" and First-Year Plan periods. Chao Chung-chih of the Science Press reported that many people were reluctant or did not dare to translate scientific literature from capitalist countries. From January 1, 1950, to June 30, 1956, only 11 of the 330 translations published by the Chinese Academy of Sciences and the Science Press were from publications written in capitalist countries. Some publishers accepted translations of Soviet writings only. In order to avoid "errors," writings of capitalist countries were translated from Russian translations rather than from the original language into Chinese. For example, Principles of Insect Pathology by Edward A. Steinhaus published in New York in 1949 by McGraw-Hill, was translated into Chinese from a Russian translation. The Chinese translation, published in Peking in 1959 by the Science Press, is without many original sections deleted by the Russian publisher and yet includes footnotes and other materials added by the Russians.[46]

Reflecting at least a temporary cooling of the relationship between scientists of the two countries, several Chinese publications bearing the title of "Soviet" have been renamed. For example, Su-lien Nung-yeh K'o-hsueh (Soviet Agricultural Science), which began publication in 1954, was renamed Nung-yeh K'o-hsüeh (Agricultural Science) in January 1959 "with a view to including new theories, techniques and accomplishments of other countries in addition to the Soviet Union," according to an editor's note.

NOTES

1. Edgar Snow, "Talks With Chou En-lai: The Open Door," The New Republic, March 27, 1971, pp. 20-23.

2. JMJP, August 22, 1965, p. 1.

3. Snow, op. cit., pp. 20-23.

4. Office of Foreign Agricultural Relations, U.S. Department of Agriculture, Report of the China-United States Agricultural Mission, (Washington, D. C.: 1947), pp. 70-73, 231-37.

5. Chung-kuo Nung-pao [Chinese Agriculture Bulletin], Peking, No. 6, 1957, pp. 4-6.

6. Ch'eng Chao-hsuan, "China's Great Leap Forward in Agricultural Science," K'o-hsueh Hsin-wen [Scientific News], No. 30, 1959, pp. 18-21.

7. NCNA, Nanking, August 11, 1963.

8. Kuang-ming Jih-pao [Kuang-ming Daily], Peking, March 16, 1962, p. 1; JMJP, March 22, 1962, p. 2.

9. JMJP, October 29, 1963, p. 1.

10. NCNA, Taiyuan, March 27, 1963.

11. Wan Kuo-ting, "General Preface for the Series of Selected Works on China's Agricultural Heritage," in Ch'en Tsu-kuei, ed., Tao: Chung-kuo Nung-hsueh I-Ch'an Hsuan-chi Chia-lei Ti-i-chung [Rice: China's Agricultural Heritage Series, No. A-1] (Peking, 1958), pp. 1-3.

12. JMJP, July 19, 1961, p. 4.

13. Office of Foreign Agricultural Relations, U.S. Department of Agriculture, op. cit., pp. 61-70, 229-30.

14. Wang Chun, "Reform of Agricultural Universities and Colleges in Communist China," Chung-kung Yeh-chiu [Studies on Chinese Communism], Taipei, Vol. IV, No. 10 (1970), pp. 100-12.

15. "Rely on Our Own Efforts to Train More Postgraduates of Better Qualifications," editorial, Kuang-ming Jih-pao [Kuang-ming Daily], Peking, January 17, 1966, p. 1.

16. JMJP, September 1, 1955, p. 1, and September 2, 1955, p. 1.

17. JMJP, August 25, 1956, p. 1.

18. Kuang-ming Jih-pao [Kuang-ming Daily], Peking, July 18, 1956, p. 1.

19. Kuang-ming Jih-pao [Kuang-ming Daily], Peking, October 14, 1963, p. 1; JMJP, October 22, 1964, p. 3.

20. State Statistical Bureau, Ten Great Years, English edition, (Peking, 1960) pp. 192, 194.

21. NCNA, Peking, August 23, 1961; Jen-min Shou-ts'e [People's Handbook] (Peking, 1962), pp. 313-14; Kuang-ming Jih-pao [Kuang-ming Daily], Peking, April 2, 1963, p. 1; Ouyang Hui-lin, "A New Type of

Schools With a Bright Future," JMJP, April 2, 1963, p. 2; Ch'en Kuang, "The Seventh Anniversary of the Founding of the Agricultural Middle Schools in Kiangsu," Hung Ch'i [Red Flag], Peking, No. 4, 1965, pp. 36-47.

22. Kuang-ming Jih-pao [Kuang-ming Daily], Peking, July 17, 1961, p. 2.

23. Chiang I-cheng, "Positively and Steadily Push Forward the Revolution of Agricultural Education; Render Still Better Service to Socialist Agriculture," Kuang-ming Jih-pao [Kuang-ming Daily], Peking, August 19, 1965, p. 2.

24. JMJP, September 28, 1965, p. 2.

25. Ho Wei, "Properly Manage Part-Farming and Part-Study Schools; Promote Revolution of Rural Education," JMJP, July 13, 1965, p. 5.

26. JMJP, March 9, 1966, p. 1.

27. Office of Foreign Agricultural Relations, U.S. Department of Agriculture, op. cit., pp. 76-79.

28. Ministry of Agriculture, People's Republic of China, "Directive on the Work of Agricultural Technique Extension Stations, April 1, 1955," Jen-min Shou-ts'e [People's Handbook] (Peking, 1956), p. 482; "Agricultural Technique Extension Stations Must Be Properly Operated," editorial, Chung-kuo Nung-pao [Chinese Agriculture Bulletin], Peking, No. 5, 1955, pp. 22-24.

29. State Statistical Bureau, Ten Great Years English edition, (Peking, 1960), p. 136.

30. Ministry of Agriculture, People's Republic of China, "Directive on the Strengthening of Agricultural Technique Extension Stations and Improvement of Their Work, December 26, 1962," Chung-hua Jen-min Kung-ho-kuo Fa-kuei Hui-pien [Compilation of Laws and Regulations of the People's Republic of China], Volume XIII (January 1962-December 1963) (Peking, 1964), pp. 199-202.

31. Hsi Feng-chou, "Improve the Extension Work for Agricultural Techniques," Nung-yeh Chi-shu [Agricultural Techniques], Peking, No. 1, 1964, pp. 2-5.

32. "Demonstration Farms Are the Main Centers Through Which Agricultural Science May Serve Production," editorial, JMJP, October 25, 1964, p. 1.

33. K'o-hsueh T'ung-pao [Scientia], Peking, No. 5, 1965, pp. 459-61; Chia Pei-hua, "Farm Scientists Run Rural Demonstration Fields," Peking Review, No. 27, 1965, pp. 15-17.

34. "Properly Manage Demonstration Farms and Positively Unfold the Movement of Agricultural Science Experimentation," editorial, Kuang-ming Jih-pao [Kuang-ming Daily], Peking, March 28, 1965, p. 2.

35. NCNA-English, Peking, April 12, 1966.

36. Kuang-ming Jih-pao [Kuang-ming Daily], Peking, August 16, 1963, p. 2.

37. T'an Chen-lin, "Strive for the Fulfillment, Ahead of Schedule, of the National Program for Agricultural Development," JMJP, April 7, 1960, p. 1.

38. Jen-min Shou-ts'e [People's Handbook] (Peking, 1952), pp. 354-55; Hsia T'ing, "Ten Years of Soviet Unselfish Assistance to Chinese Agriculture," Nung-yeh K'o-hsueh T'ung-hsun [Agricultural Science Bulletin], Peking, No. 19, 1959, pp. 662, 674.

39. K'o-hsueh T'ung-pao [Scientia], Peking, No. 8, 1956, pp. 63-71; No. 9, 1956, pp. 54-63; No. 10, 1956, pp. 80-83.

40. Li Jui, "Several Basic Problems Concerning the Multi-Purpose Plan for the Yellow River," Hsin Chien-she [New Construction], Peking, No. 11, 1955, pp. 29-32.

41. Jean Messines, "Forest Rehabilitation and Soil Conservation in China," Unasylva, Rome, Vol. XII, No. 3 (1958), pp. 103-20.

42. Ch'eng Hsueh-min, "Great Assistance of the Russian Experts to the Yellow River Plan," in Ken-chih Huang-ho Shui-hai K'ai-fa Huang-ho Shui-li [Fundamentally Curing the Yellow River's Destructiveness and Developing the Yellow River's Water Conservation] (Peking: Propaganda Section of the Ministry of Water Conservation, 1955), pp. 74-84.

43. English translation by the U.S. Joint Publications Research Service, JPRS No. 5957, (Washington, D. C., October 31, 1960).

44. English translation by the U.S. Joint Publications Research Service, JPRS No. 3234, (Washington, D. C., May 23, 1960).

45. English translation by the U.S. Joint Publications Research Service, JPRS No. 9717, (Washington, D. C., July 20, 1961).

46. Chao Chung-ch'ih, "Scientific Publication Work and 'Letting A Hundred Schools Contend,'" K'o-hsueh T'ung-pao [Scientia], No. 11, 1956, pp. 48-50.

4

Compared with raising the yield per unit of land, expansion of the area under cultivation is a longer and more costly process to increase agricultural production. Despite this fact and despite China's limited potentialities of additional land for agricultural uses, the Communist government has made strenuous efforts to bring new land under cultivation. The general situation of China's arable land and cultivated land and the progress of the land reclamation program in the 1950's and 1960's will be discussed in the sections that follow.

Until a nationwide survey is made, any enumeration of the total area of China's arable land and cultivated land must be only a rough estimation. Table 2, based on estimates from various sources, indicates that at present China's land suitable for farming is only about 15 percent of its total land area and that one-fourth of the land area presently classified as arable is still uncultivated.

ARABLE LAND

China is a rugged country for the most part, a land of mountains. Level land is found along some river valleys, in delta regions, and in a few other areas. The largest of the level areas is the compound delta that reaches from northern Chekiang Province northward into Manchuria. It includes the North China Plain, which is the most important region in the production of producing wheat and cotton. There are basins around Poyang and Tungting Lakes and a few alluvial areas south of the Yangtze Valley, including small deltas in the vicinity of Swatow and Canton. West China has limited level areas in the alluvial fan of the Chengtu Plain in Szechuan and the plateau of Yunnan. In Inner Mongolia, Sinkiang, and Tibet, there are some areas of level or rolling country, mostly in the form of high plateaus. Otherwise, the country is mountainous.

TABLE 2

Land Use in Mainland China

	Thousands of Mou	Percentage of Total
Arable land	2,200,000	15.28
Cultivated	1,650,000	11.46
Uncultivated	550,000	3.82
Forest area	1,140,000	7.92
Land suitable for afforestation	4,500,000	31.25
Grassland	4,000,000	27.78
Other (deserts, etc.)	2,560,000	17.77
Total	14,400,000	100.00

Sources: Chao Shih-ying, "Searching the Direction of China's Agriculture," K'o-hsueh T'ung-pao [Science Bulletin], Peking, No. 8, 1963, pp. 1-5; Food and Agriculture Organization of the United Nations, FAO Production Yearbook, 1969, Vol. XXIII (Rome, 1970), p. 6; Chao Hsi, "Our Country's Agricultural Future Is Infinitely Good," K'o-hsueh Ta-chung [Popular Science], Peking, No. 5, 1963, pp. 1-3; Sung Chia-t'ai, "Change the Appearance of Our Country's Geography by Using Land Rationally," Ti-li Chih-shih [Geographical Knowledge], Peking, No. 4, 1956, pp. 144-49; Chia Sheng-hsiu, "Grassland," K'o-hsueh Ta-chung [Popular Science], Peking, No. 9, 1964, pp. 323-324.

Table 3 shows China's land area classified according to elevation by Wong Wen-hao, a well-known Chinese geologist. Areas below 500 meters are mostly suitable for farming. Areas between 500 and 1,000 meters are for the most part hilly, but agriculture can be operated profitably in these areas with the help of terracing and other water and soil conservation devices. Areas with 1-2,000 meters of elevation contain mostly plateaus where animal husbandry is more profitable than farming. The bulk of the remaining land consists of mountainous areas with very little agricultural productivity.

Thus, from the topographical viewpoint, only 14 percent of China's land is suitable for farming. Even with the possible addition of 18 percent of land with 500-1,000 meters of elevation, the total area suitable for farming is still less than one-third of China's total land area. Moreover, a substantial portion of the land under 1,000 meters of elevation is located in the areas where climatic and soil conditions

TABLE 3

Elevation of China's Land Area

Elevation (meters)	Area (square kilometers)	Percentage of Total Land Area
0-500	1,344,000	14
500-1,000	1,728,000	18
1,000-2,000	3,360,000	35
2,000-3,000	768,000	8
3,000-4,000	480,000	5
4,000-5,000	384,000	4
Over 5,000	1,536,000	16
Total	9,600,000	100

Source: Chang Lun-p'o, Chung-kuo ti Tzu-yuan [China's Resources], (Peiping, 1947), p. 1, based on estimates made by Wong Wen-hao.

are not favorable for farming because of such factors as uneven distribution of precipitation throughout the year, short growing season, and
poor soils. Another problem is that most of the arable land considered
suitable for expansion is in Manchuria and Sinkiang, where a number
of obstacles must be overcome before any large-scale reclamation
program can be carried out effectively. Most of the areas lie in the
frontiers, away from trade routes and good harbors. To use the land,
agricultural development must be accompanied by transportation,
housing, public health facilities, local industry, and electric power.

CULTIVATED LAND

The total area of a country's cultivated land, like that of arable
land, can hardly remain static for any length of time. It fluctuates in
response to the interplay of many factors, including land reclamation
policy, success or failure of harvests in recent years, rates of rent,
political stability or instability, migration program, and changes of
agricultural techniques.

In 1947, China's cultivated land was estimated by the National
government at 1,410,731,000 mou (235,122,000 acres) or about 10 percent of the total land area of the country.[1] Official data reported in
Table 4 indicate that China's cultivated land increased slowly but
steadily from 1,468,220,000 mou (244,700,000 acres) in 1949 to 1,677,
450,000 mou (279,575,000 acres) in 1957, or from 10.20 percent to
11.65 percent of the total land area (14,400 million mou or 2,400 million
acres). Thus, the average annual increase from 1949 to 1957 was less
than 0.2 percent. The slow increase was confirmed by Vice-Premier
Teng Tzu-hui, who stated at the National Conference on the Work of
State Farms and State Pastures held in 1957: "For the past few years,
the total area of our country's cultivated land increased less than 1
percent annually, and yet her annual population increase was about
2.5 percent."[2]

In 1958, the total area of cultivated land decreased to 1,616,800,
000 mou (269,467,000 Acres) or 11.23 percent of the total land area.
The decline was not explained, but it could have been caused, at least
in part, by the short-lived campaign to "sow a smaller acreage, realize
a higher yield, and reap a greater harvest," launched late in 1958.
Under the "three-thirds system," the communes were asked to use
one-third of the existing farmland for growing principal crops, one-
third to lie fallow or for growing fodder crops and green manure, and
one-third to be dug into reservoirs or for growing trees and ornamental
plants. However, several months later a policy to the opposite extreme

TABLE 4

Cultivated Land in China, 1949-58

Year	Cultivated Land Thousands of Mou	Percentage of Total Land Area
1949	1,468,220	10.20
1950	1,505,340	10.45
1951	1,555,070	10.80
1952	1,618,780	11.24
1953	1,627,930	11.31
1954	1,640,320	11.39
1955	1,652,350	11.47
1956	1,677,370	11.64
1957	1,677,450	11.65
1958	1,616,800	11.23

Source: State Statistical Bureau, Ten Great Years, English edition, (Peking, 1960), p. 128. Percentages are based on the estimated total land area of 14,400 million mou.

was adopted, and the communes were urged to "sow a larger acreage and reap a greater harvest."[3]

Official data on the total area of cultivated land have not been released since 1958. On the basis of estimates made by various sources and figures used in the Communist Chinese press, it would appear that, throughout the 1960's or so, China's total area of cultivated land has lingered around 1,650 million mou (275 million acres) or 11.5 percent of the country's total land area. Thus, China's cultivated land is less than two-thirds that of the United States, although China has a population more than three times as large as that in the United States.[4]

Moreover, much of the cultivated land in China is of poor quality. According to the National Soil Survey conducted in 1958, 400 million mou, or nearly one-fourth, of the 1,650 million mou of the cultivated land in Mainland China needed immediate improvement; 1,200 million mou, or three-fourths of the total, needed crop rotation; and 200 million mou, or one-eighth of the total, needed to be graded to make irrigation and drainage more effective. Also, the fragmentation of much of the farmland in the south had to be readjusted to facilitate cultivation.[5]

It was also reported in 1958 that more than one-third of the farmland in Mainland China as a whole was low-yielding--saline, alkali, acidic, sandy, swampy, or erosive (see Table 5). Low-yielding farmland constituted large portions of the cultivated land in virtually all the provinces and autonomous regions and the three largest municipalities--Shanghai, Peking, and Tientsin. The Muncipality of Peking had the lowest ratio; 10 percent. Figures for other political divisions ranged from 21.4 percent for Tientsin to 52.5 percent for Kwangtung.[6] In 1962, there were about 300 million mou of alkali and saline soils in Northwest, Northeast, and North China and the coastal areas of northern Kiangsu. Of this total, nearly one-third, or 100 million mou, were in the cultivated land in North China and 20 percent of its irrigated area.[7]

RECLAMATION OF WASTELAND

Of China's some 1,500 million mou (250 million acres) of wasteland, about 800 million mou had been preliminarily surveyed by the end of 1957 and 500 million mou could be reclaimed "at a comparatively low capital cost," according to Chiang Ch'i-hsien, Vice-Minister of State Farms and Land Reclamation. These 500 million mou are presumably the land generally referred to as arable but uncultivated.[8]

TABLE 5

Low-Yielding Farmland in Mainland China, 1958

	Cultivated Land (in thousands of mou)	Low-Yielding Farmland (in thousands of mou)	Low-Yielding Farmland as a Percentage of Cultivated Land
eking	2,000	200	10.0
ientsin	1,402	300	21.4
iaoning	72,390	18,750	25.9
onan	134,616	35,000	26.0
hensi	67,181	17,870	26.6
hantung	138,000	40,000	29.0
opei	133,400	40,300	30.2
upeh	64,725	20,000	30.9
unnan	42,368	13,600	32.1
iangsu	94,273	30,450	32.3
iangsi	42,424	14,000	33.0
nhwei	89,021	30,000	33.7
irin	70,716	24,680	34.9
inkiang	27,933	10,000	35.8
unan	58,300	21,570	37.0
weichou	30,763	11,600	37.7
hekiang	33,766	13,000	38.5
eilungkiang	110,204	43,200	39.2
hinghai	7,576	3,000	39.6
hanghai	514	210	40.8
ner Mongolia	83,398	34,110	40.9
ansu	72,639	30,000	41.3
zechuan	115,418	51,130	44.3
hansi	66,208	31,250	47.2
ukien	22,363	10,600	47.4
wangsi	38,000	19,000	50.0
wangtung	59,048	31,000	52.5
Iainland China	1,678,686	594,820	35.4

Sources: Chung-kuo Nung-pao [Chinese Agriculture Bulletin], Peking, No. 8, 1958, p. 25; nd No. 10, 1958, p. 20.

Major portions of the wasteland already surveyed are in Manchuria, the Sinkiang-Uigur Autonomous Region, Chinghai, the Corridor
west of the Ordos Bend of the Yellow River in Kansu, the tropical and
subtropical areas of Fukien, Kwangtung, Kwangsi, and Yunnan, the
areas near the Gulf of Po Hai along the Liaoning, Hopei, and Shantung
seacoasts, and some areas in Szechuan, Hupeh, and northern Kiangsu.[9]

The National Program for Agricultural Development provided
that in the twelve years beginning in 1956 the area reclaimed by state
farms should be increased from the 1955 figure of over 13 million mou
(2.2 million acres) to about 100 million mou (16.7 million acres). The
Program also urged the agricultural producers' cooperatives (now the
communes) to make full use of scattered bits of idle land, such as
ridges and corners of land plots, the edges of ponds, land along ditches,
and unused threshing grounds. Also, factories, mines, commercial
and agricultural enterprises, departments of education, culture, public
health, water conservation, communications, and military affairs, and
mass organizations were asked to exercise the strictest economy in
using land for capital construction and particularly to refrain from
using cultivated land for such purpose (Article 16).

While the communes enforce the collective ownership system,
a number of state farms have been established as "enterprises under
the ownership of the whole people." The main functions of the state
farms are to reclaim land, as well as to supply the state with agricultural products for export, to serve as showplaces for modern farming
techniques, and to supply improved seeds and animal breeds and to
render technical assistance and guidance to the communes (agricultural
producers' cooperatives prior to the establishment of communes).
State farms also help assist in solving such problems as migration, the
the rehabilitation and resettlement of demobilized soldiers and returned
overseas Chinese, and the unemployment of urban people.

The state farms are far less significant than the communes in
both the total acreage of cultivated land and agricultural production.
In 1957, for example, the state farms had only 15 million mou of cultivated land, or 0.89 percent of China's total cultivated land, which is
estimated at 1,677 million mou. In the same year, the state farms
produced only 1,190 million chin of grain, or 0.30 percent of China's
total grain production, which was 370 billion chin. On the other hand,
state farms had a much higher degree of agricultural mechanization.
In 1957, state farms had 10,177 tractors, or 40 percent of all the 24,629
tractors operated in Communist China in that year (see Table 6).
Another source indicated that in 1964 the total acreage of cultivated
land on the state farms was 290 percent of that in 1957 but still was

TABLE 6

State Farms and State Pastures in Communist China,
Selected Years, 1949-60

	Unit	1949	1952	1957	1958	1960
Number of state farms and pastures		18	404	710	1,442	2,490
Tractors	15-hp. units	401	1,792	10,177	16,955	28,000
Harvester-combines		13	283	1,537	1,982	3,300
Trucks		28	229	3,444	4,284	n.a.
Land used for production	thousands of mou	460	8,480	17,990	39,820	n.a.
Cultivated land	thousands of mou	460	3,820	15,380	34,080	78,000
Reclaimed land	thousands of mou	n.a.	2,240	4,060	12,430	n.a.
Number of employees	thousands	4	390	500	990	2,800
Total grain production	millions of chin	n.a.	n.a.	1,190	2,170	5,000

Note: State farms and state pastures refer to those under the direct supervision of the Ministry of Agriculture prior to 1956 and the Ministry of State Farms and Land Reclamation in 1956 and thereafter but not to those administered by provinces, autonomous regions, municipalities, and other local authorities.

Sources: All figures for 1960 and the figure for grain production in 1957 are from Wang Chen, "Strengthening the Construction of State Farms," Hung Ch'i [Red Flag], Peking, No. 7, 1961, pp. 1-7. The figure for grain production in 1958 is from "March Forward Bravely on the Land Reclamation Front," editorial, Chung-kuo Nung-k'en [China Reclamation], Peking, No. 18, 1959, pp. 1-2. All other figures are from State Statistical Bureau, Ten Great Years, English edition, (Peking, 1960), p. 134.

"only a fraction of the total acreage of cultivated land for the country as a whole." In the same year, state farms owned 32 percent of the country's tractors; 50 percent of mechanical farm tools; 82.5 percent of combines; 68 percent of heavy-duty motor trucks; "several hundred thousand units" of irrigation and drainage equipment, livestock machinery, power-generating equipment, and processing equipment; and several hundred repair shops of various sizes.[10]

Large state farms generally are under the direct supervision of the Ministry of State Farms and Land Reclamation, established in May 1956, while smaller farms are administered by provincial, municipal, special district, and hsien authorities. Most of the large state farms are in one of the four major reclamation areas established by the Ministry. The Sinkiang Reclamation Area, the largest of the four, is operated by the Sinkiang Production-Construction Corps, under the Sinkiang Military Area Command of the People's Liberation Army, with a total sown acreage in 1961 of 8 million mou of corn, spring wheat, cotton, soybeans, rapeseeds, and sugarbeet. The other three areas, operated by the Northeast General Bureau of Land Reclamation, are the Mutankiang and Hokiang reclamation areas in Heilungkiang Province and the Hulunbar reclamation area in Inner Mongolia. Each of these areas sowed some 4 million mou of grains and soybeans in 1961.[11]

In addition to the goals for land reclamation prescribed in the National Program for Agricultural Development, 1956-67, the First Five-Year Plan (1953-57) also called for the expansion of 38,680,000 mou of cultivated land, mainly through reclamation of small pieces of wasteland by organized peasants, so that at the end of 1957 the total area of cultivated land would be increased to 1,657,450,000 mou, as compared to 1,618,780,000 mou in 1952.[12] The increase actually accomplished in the First Five-Year Plan period was reported to be 58,670,000 mou, bringing the total area of cultivated land at the end of 1957 to 1,677,450,000 mou.[13]

It was planned to reclaim 50 million mou during the Second Five-Year Plan period (1958-62).[14] According to a report by Vice-Premier Po I-p'o, for 1958 alone the goal was 17,735,000 mou, of which 7 million mou were to be reclaimed by the state farms under the Ministry of Land Reclamation and 10,735,000 mou by the state farms under local governments and by peasants and migrants.[15] The total acreage of wasteland actually reclaimed during the First Five-Year Plan period and the acreage expected to be reclaimed during the Second Five-Year Plan period was thus 108,670,000 mou. However, another source reported that during the eleven years 1949-60 only 70 million mou

(11.7 million acres), or less than 5 percent of the estimated total area of wasteland (1,500 million mou), were reclaimed.[16]

Data on the progress of land reclamation are fragmentary and, in many cases, conflicting. Following are brief accounts of the accomplishments and problems in Manchuria, Sinkiang, and other areas, as given in various publications and press reports.

Northeast China (Manchuria)

The Northeast China (Manchurian) plain consists of the flat valleys of Nonni, Sungari, and Liao with a total area of about 460 million mou, which is comparable in size to the North China Plain and even larger than the lower Yangtze Valley. A large part of the plain, especially in Heilungkiang Province, has rich virgin soil. The rolling country is suitable for mechanized farming. Although the climate here is cold and the frost-free period is short, the hot summer has long hours of sunshine. And the rainfall in the area is more abundant than in North China, ranging from 20 to more than 30 inches per year.

Manchuria has about 230 million mou of arable wasteland already surveyed.[17] Of this total, 100 million mou are in Heilungkiang Province, where reclamation work began even before the Communist takeover of Mainland China. During the blockade of the Sino-Japanese War, a brigade of the Communists' Eighth Route Army was sent to Nanniwan, near Yenan in Shensi Province, to reclaim wasteland for food production. In 1946, the Chinese Communists established a "Hua Ch'uan Water Conservation Farm" on the grassland in the part of Heilungkiang Province that is commonly known as the "Northern Great Wilderness." Several collective farm groups were later set up in the area.[18]

In 1964, there were more than 400 state farms of various sizes in Manchuria, cultivating a total of some 15 million mou.[19] Many of the state farms are located in the Sanchiang [Three-River] Plain Reclamation Area, with the Heilungkiang River in the north, the Ussuri River in the east, and the Sungari River running through the area. The plain occupies about 24 million mou, of which 15 million mou are arable. One of the largest state farms in the Sanchiang Plain Reclamation Area is the much publicized Friendship State Farm, which 492,000 mou of land, established in 1954 with technical aid and a supply of tractors, harvesters, threshers, mechanized five-share plows, trucks, and other equipment from the U.S.S.R.[20]

In 1965, there were 36 state farms in the Sanchiang Plain Reclamation Area, equipped with more than 6,500 tractors, 1,500 combine-
harvesters, and a network of farm machinery repair plants. In 1964,
the area produced nearly 1,000 million chin of grains and soybeans and
delivered more than 500 million chin of grains to the state, the largest
quantity ever delivered.[21]

But, according to a Soviet technical team that participated in
setting up the Friendship State Farm, although most of the Sanchiang
area is suitable for farming, there are certain unfavorable climatic,
soil, and hydrological conditions in the area that must be overcome in
order to obtain higher and more stable yields of the principal crops.[22]
One of the main obstacles to the reclamation of this area is waterlogging in the summer, which forms marshes in places. In 1957 and
1958, for instance, waterlogging brought heavy losses to the Friendship
State Farm and its sown acreage and grain production decreased considerably.[23]

Low labor efficiency is another problem in operating the state
farms. The reclamation of the Sanchiang area is said to be undertaken
by "volunteers"--demobilized soldiers and young people. But, ever
since the early period of the Communist regime, the Sanchiang area
has been a center where "rightists" and cadres who have committed
serious ideological mistakes are reeducated under forced labor. In
official reports, those who undergo labor reform in the area are
described as people who are reclaiming the wasteland for farming by
"fighting amidst hardships and exerting their efforts to achieve success
in the exploitation of the frontiers and the development of agriculture.
They are optimistic even under difficulties and have a fervent love for
the soil and grain. They are loyal to and persist in the revolutionary
enterprise and have made their pledge to build the Northern Great
Wilderness into a great granary." However, press reports indicate
that most of the participants were reluctant to stay.

Sinkiang

Although the Sinkiang-Uighur Autonomous Region occupies about
one-sixth of China's total land area, its dry climate, rough mountains,
and extensive deserts make agriculture profitable only in small areas
along the foot of the Kunlun and Tienshan mountains. The region is
the driest part of China, with an average annual rainfall of 5-6 inches.
Deserts occupy about one-third of the land. The rate of evaporation
under the scorching desert sun is very high, and irrigation is indispensable to agriculture. For centuries, farming in this region has depended

.on melted snow and glaciers from the Tienshan Mountains, which flow
through a few inland rivers, and on numerous irrigation canals and
ditches. But most of these waterways have become seriously silted.
Melted snow rushes down the mountains in summer, often causing
floods. In the spring and autumn, when water is most needed, periodic
drought threatens.[24]

Sinkiang has some 100 million mou (16.5 million acres) of wasteland with soil sufficiently fertile to support agriculture, according to a
survey conducted in the 1950's by the Chinese Academy of Sciences.
Since 1956, the academy has sent groups of scientists to Sinkiang to
study the problems of developing wasteland for agricultural uses,
such as the possibility of utilizing the glaciers and snow for farming
in a section of the Tienshan range near Urumchi; measures for protecting farmland against sandstorms in the desert areas of southwestern
and northern Sinkiang; conditions of the grasslands in the livestock
breeding hsien of T'oli in northern Sinkiang; and methods of improving
alkaline soil in other parts of the autonomous region.[25]

An important portion of the land reclaimed in Sinkiang is under
the administration of the Sinkiang Production-Construction Crops (PCC)
of the People's Liberation Army. In 1961, the PCC administered more
than 18,900,000 mou, or one-third of the cultivated land in Sinkiang.[26]
Of Sinkiang's estimated 1968 population of 8 million, about 1.2 million,
or one-seventh, were PCC workers and members of their families.[27]

The PCC concept stemmed from the Yenan period prior to World
War II, during which the Red Army cooperated closely with civilians
in agricultural and other production work. In 1953, the first PCC unit
was formally installed in Sinkiang and was assigned to carry out programs for industrial and agricultural development, including the operation of state farms. Thus, while retaining its status as a national
defense unit of the People's Liberation Army stationed in Sinkiang, the
PCC also plays an important role in economic reconstruction under the
supervision of relevant agencies of the State Council and the Sinkiang
Committee of the Chinese Communist Party. Since the eruption of the
Sino-Soviet clash at Chenpo Island in 1969, the PCC has been introduced
into the other frontier regions, including Inner Mongolia, Heilungkiang,
Chinghai, and Tibet.

Chinese youngsters have been drafted in increasing numbers
from all parts of the country to join the PCC for hard labor. By May
1965, their number exceeded 260,000, including 50,000 from Shanghai.
The PCC serves as an organization for settling boys and girls, mostly
from middle (secondary) schools, who are recalcitrants or who did not

go further in their studies. A land reclamation college for the training
of agricultural personnel in Sinkiang was established at Tarim in 1958
by the Production-Construction Corps. The college combines education
with productive labor through the part-time work and part-time study
system. In 1965, it had 670 students and a teaching staff of 90. By the
end of that year, it had graduated 950 students of intermediate and higher
levels in the fields of plant science, agricultural mechanization, water
conservation, animal husbandry, agricultural economics, and forestry.
Students of the college are mostly children of lower-echelon cadres,
farmers, and state farm and reclamation area employees.[28]

Since adequate irrigation is prerequisite to the expansion of
cultivated land in Sinkiang, numerous canals, ditches, and reservoirs
have been constructed by the communes and state farms to improve
the water supply of the region as well as to harness the Tarim, the
Manass, the Urumchi, and other principal rivers.[29] In recent years,
emphasis has been given to the digging of wells in order to utilize
more of Sinkiang's underground water. The communes and the state
farms were reported to have sunk thousands of wells, many of which
are artesian wells with a depth of up to a hundred meters.[30]

As a result of improved water conservation and increasing
mechanization, Sinkiang's total area of cultivated land was reported
to have doubled from 18,110,000 mou (3,018,000 acres) in 1949 to
36,170,000 mou (6,028,000 acres) in 1964.[31] By the end of 1963, the
Sinkiang Production-Construction Corps had established more than
140 mechanized state farms and had reclaimed some 11 million mou
(1,830,000 acres) of wasteland.[32]

The major portions of wasteland reclaimed in Sinkiang during
the 1950's and 1960's included: (1) areas totaling more than 1.5 million
mou (250,000 acres) along the Tarim, Sinkiang's principal river, producing grains and oil-bearing, industrial, and fodder crops; (2) the
Urumchi River basin, and important supplier of grains, vegetables,
and meat for Sinkiang's capital city of Urumchi; (3) the Khotan (Hotien)
area, a narrow greenbelt of oases extending 600 kilometers from east
to west and fringing the southern part of the Taklamakan Desert,
producing wheat, cotton, and oil-bearing crops; (4) some 850,000 mou
of wasteland in the Masowan area reclaimed for growing wheat, cotton,
and corn; (5) the Kawako reclamation area of some 16,000 mou established in 1960 within the Taklamakan Desert, producing grains, cotton,
and oil-bearing crops; (6) areas at the foot of the Tienshan, Kunlun,
and Altai Mountains; and (7) the Ili and Manass Valleys.

Land reclamation and increased yield per unit of land reportedly
have enabled Sinkiang to produce three times as much grains and six

times as much cotton in 1965 as in 1949 and to be self-sufficient in
both.[33] The region has been developed into an important producer of
long-fiber cotton so that some of the cotton fields in other provinces
can be used for growing grains and other principal crops. Cotton production has been particularly successful in the Turfan Basin, the Manass
River Valley, Ku-erh-le, and Agsu because these areas have plenty of
sunshine and irrigation facilities are available. The average annual
increase of cotton output during the First Five-Year Plan period was
16.54 percent, and the average yield of 410,000 mou of cotton farms
operated by the Sinkiang Production-Construction Corps in 1957 was
68.8 chin per mou, which was about double the yield of many cotton
farms in the interior. But the costs of reclaiming land for growing
cotton in Sinkiang--including the costs of land leveling, soil improvement, farm machinery, draft animals, and construction of canals,
ditches, roads, and houses--were much higher than in the interior.[34]

   One source estimated that the total area suitable for growing
cotton in Sinkiang may reach 23 million mou, mostly in the southern
part of the region. On the basis of an average yield of 70 chin per mou,
the annual output would be 16 million tan.[35] But a number of problems
must be solved before cotton production in Sinkiang can be substantially
increased. These include fertilization, cultivation technique, and control
of diseases and insect pests, especially Agrotis Segtis Hubner, which
is the insect most harmful to cotton in Sinkiang.[36]

   In livestock industry, as a result of artificial insemination and
control of animal diseases, Sinkiang has become a supply center of
fine breeds of sheep and horses for the entire country. In 1966, Sinkiang
had the second largest number of sheep, ranking after Inner Mongolia.
But it ranked first in the production of fine and semifine wool. The
autonomous region has developed the gungnais sheep, the first fine-wool
breed of sheep in China, and the famous Ili horse. The gungnais sheep
is well-known for its large size, delicious mutton, adaptability to different natural conditions, and high propagation rate. The fineness, color,
and length of the wool are suitable for making high-grade woolen fabric.
The Ili horse can cover 30 to 40 kilometers a day for three or four days
in a row and can draw a load of 1,500 kilograms.[37]

   Despite the reported accomplishments, reclamation work in
Sinkiang has confronted extreme hardship, especially along the Tarim,
the principal river of the region, with a total length of 2,750 kilometers.
The Tarim's major tributaries, including the Khotan, Yarkand, Kashgar,
and Agsu rivers, have the greatest flow in the late spring and early
summer, when they are fed by melting snow and glaciers from the
northern slopes of the Tienshan mountains. The water hurtles down
the mountain slopes in heavy torrents, causing serious floods in some

areas. In the dry season, a large part of the river water evaporates
or disappears in the desert sand before reaching the Tarim, causing
serious droughts in many places. Moreover, because of the rapid
evaporation of underground water, land easily becomes alkaline.
Various water and soil conservation measures have been taken, but
land conditions have not improved very much. A similar situation
exists in other reclaimed areas in Sinkiang.[38]

Like land reclamation workers in Manchuria, the Production-
Construction Corps workers in Sinkiang generally are inefficient because
they are expected to participate in intense physical labor as well as to
receive political indoctrination and military training. The PCC units
usually are located in camps in the most desolate areas, where workers
must adjust to extremes in climate and a lack of modern conveniences
in their work.

From the viewpoint of agriculture, Sinkiang is not an asset to
China. Land reclamation in the region has not been successful even
at high cost because of the unfavorable natural and economic conditions.
But the Communist Chinese government apparently is building up the
region at all costs because of its strategic importance vis-à-vis the
Soviet Union, as well as the minor nationalities and anti-communist
or anti-Mao elements.

Other Areas

In addition to the land reclamation projects in Manchuria and
Sinkiang, many have been carried out or planned in other provinces
and autonomous regions. The more important projects include the
following:

1. Some 90,000 mou of sandy wasteland near the Ulanpuho Desert
in eastern Inner Mongolia.[39]

2. Some 300,000 mou of wasteland in the Karmu Area south of
the Tsaidan Basin in Chinghai.[40]

3. Areas near the Maowusu Desert bordering northern Shensi,
Inner Mongolia, and Ninghsia.[41]

4. Areas on the edge of the Scrub Desert, locally known as "the
Hunger Desert," in Ninghsia.[42]

5. Some 900,000 mou of saline wasteland along the Yellow River
in Ninghsia.[43]

6. A narrow strip of land extending 2,400 shih li (750 miles) from east to west in the Kansu Corridor, which was China's ancient route to the West.[44]

7. Some 19,500 mou of marshy, alkaline wasteland, formerly the abandoned course of the Wei River, a tributary of the Yellow River, in Shensi.[45]

8. Vast stretches of saline wasteland along the North China coast have been transformed into rice fields. This is continuation of a project started by a Japanese reclamation company to produce rice for Japanese troops during World War II. Included in the project was the reclamation of more than 500,000 mou of saline wastelan 1 in the northern Shantung Peninsula along the shores of Pohai Bay, from which the sea receded centuries ago.[46]

9. The Yellow River Delta, known among local peasants as the "Isolated Island" and formerly a desolate delta at the estuary of the Yellow River in Shantung. The entire area was almost untouched before 1950.[47]

10. About 1,250,000 mou along Tungting and Poyang lakes, two of China's largest freshwater lakes.[48]

11. More than 2,250,000 mou of seacoast and lakeside wasteland in Kiangsu.[49]

12. Nearly 130,000 mou of land along Hangchou Bay at the mouth of the Chientang River.[50] Hangchou Bay is a major cotton and hemp growing area in China.

13. Some area on Hainan Island and the Luichow Peninsula in Kwangtung for growing rubber, spices, coconut, coffee, and other tropical and subtropical crops.[51]

Exactly how much wasteland has been reclaimed by the state farms is not known. Many of the figures released are conflicting and confusing. In some cases, for example, it is not clear whether a figure refers to the acreage of land reclaimed in a specific year or to the total acreage so far reclaimed. In other cases, it is not clear whether a figure refers to the land reclaimed by the state farms only or to that reclaimed by the communes as well as the state farms. In light of the available data, it seems certain that the pace of land reclamation by state farms has been far behind the target prescribed in the National Program for Agricultural Development, i.e., to increase reclaimed wasteland from 13 million mou in 1955 to 100 million mou in 1967.

The slow pace is evidenced by the fact that from 1949 to 1958 cultivated land in China increased by only a little over one percent (see Table 4, above); by the admissions of several high government officials, including Chou En-lai and Teng Tzu-hui; and by the reticence about the progress of land reclamation since the Leap Forward period.[52]

There have been numerous claims about the yields of the principal crops produced by state farms. In 1952, the average yield of wheat produced by the mechanized state farms was reported to be 21.7 percent higher than that of wheat produced by all farms in Mainland China; the average yield of cotton, 48.7 percent higher; and the average yield of soybeans, 11.0 percent higher. In 1956, the average yield of grain crops produced by the state farms was reported to be 4 percent higher than that of grain crops produced by the agricultural producers' cooperatives, and the average yield of cotton, 66 percent higher.[53] In 1957, Vice-Premier Teng Tzu-hui revealed that the average yield of grains produced by the state farms in that year was 220 chin per mou; that of soybeans, 120 chin per mou; and that of cotton, 57 chin per mou.[54] These compare with the average yield of grains for all farms in the country in that year, which was 204 chin per mou; that of soybeans, 105.1 chin per mou; and that of cotton, 37.9 chin per mou.[55]

Despite these claims, it has been reported that the labor efficiency of the state farms in general is low. Many of them spend extravagantly and have suffered a deficit.[56] Also, the use of farm machinery and the methods of cultivation and management need improvement, according to Wang Chen, Minister of State Farms and Land Reclamation.[57] At a national conference on state farms and land reclamation held in Peking in March 1966, some achievements of state farms were praised but it was pointed out that for many of the state farms politics had not been brought to the fore, management and operations needed adjustment, production level was not high enough, capital construction on farmland was not solid, and farming skills were on a "relatively crude level."[58]

Simultaneously with the land reclamation by the state farms, the agricultural producers' cooperatives (now the communes), especially those with surplus labor, have been urged to cultivate as much of the wasteland as possible, in addition to the existing farmland, in their own or neighboring areas. It was pointed out by the People's Daily that, although a major portion of China's wasteland is located in the northeast, and northwest, and other border areas, there are innumerable small pieces of wasteland, totaling some 100 million mou (16.7 million acres), that are scattered over all parts of the country, including wasteland along rivers, canals, and seacoasts and around buildings. Most of these small fragments of land are of low productivity but if cultivated they may produce 20,000 million chin (13.1 million tons) of grains each year on the basis of 200 chin per mou (1,600 pounds per acre), according to the People's Daily.[59] Very few data are available on the land reclaimed by the agricultural producers' cooperatives or communes. The total acreage of such land probably is considerably smaller than that reclaimed by the state farms.

In evaluating Communist China's land reclamation program, it is important to note that substantial portions of the land reclaimed in the 1950's and 1960's are located in sparsely populated upland areas, on the edge of deserts ravaged by shifting sands, on arid grasslands marked by drastic changes in climate, or in areas handicapped by alkaline and saline soil. Most of these lands are agriculturally unproductive.

China's deserts total approximately 1,600 million mou (265 million acres), an area nearly equivalent to the total area of existing cultivated land, and are distributed mainly in the Sinkiang-Uighur, Inner Mongolia, and Ninghsia-Hui autonomous regions and in Chinghai, Kansu, and Shensi provinces. The principal deserts include the Taklamakan Desert (the Big Gobi), China's largest desert with a total area of 450 million mou (75 million acres), the Kurbantongut Desert in Sinkiang, and the Tengri Desert, the Patachilian Desert, and the Ulanpuho Desert in Inner Mongolia. The Communist government believes that nearly 300 million mou (50 million acres) of the deserts can be improved to grow some plants or developed into livestock bases.[60]

As an initial step toward desert transformation, a surveying team composed of members of the Chinese Academy of Sciences and Soviet scientists was organized in 1957 to study deserts in Inner Mongolia, the Yülin Special District in northern Shensi, the Ninghsia Plain, and the Corridor west of the Yellow River. Among the principal subjects studied were the natural conditions of these areas and farmers experience in controlling the sand that might be adopted for improving the deserts.[61]

The schemes used for desert transformation in Communist China include the construction of irrigation and drainage systems, the extensive cultivation of grass and green manure crops, the leveling of sand dunes, and the building of tree shelter belts to ward off windstorms. Among the many desert control projects, the conquest of shifting sand to enable the Paotow-Lanchow Railroad to cross the southeastern end of the Tengri Desert in Ninghsia is considered by Communist authorities to be one of the most successful. This railroad,

China's first railroad traversing a desert, is reported to have remained open to traffic since its completion in 1958 and, according to a 1961 report, traffic was not interrupted by the desert after the spring of 1959.[62] The train passes at six places through the Tengri desert, altogether 40 kilometers long.

The method used for the project, as described by the New China News Agency, was to divide the ground along the railroad into small rectangles and surround each rectangle with half-buried wheat stalks to prevent the sand from being blown away. The checkered sandbreaks were then covered with gravel, clay, and asphalt and planted with grass, in order to slow down wind velocity by some 20 percent and greatly reduce sand movement within the sandbreaks. Among the 30 kinds of plants that were tried out in 1956-64, shrubs of clover, yellow willow, and oleaster grew well on the sand dunes, which vary in height from dozens of meters to more than 100 meters. In the sandbreaks where plants have grown, thin solidified crusts have appeared on the surface of the sand. In the opinion of Chinese scientists, this change in the formation of the soil is the result of fixing the sand and the growth of plants. They believe that, if such crusts were general, the sand would no longer move.[63]

Despite many claims, it was admitted that desert transformation remains a long and arduous task and that many problems are yet to be solved. In the first place, the methods and measures for the control of deserts have not been very efficient and the cost has been prohibitively high. Secondly, many deserts can only be transformed through the utilization of underground water, which often contains too much salt, making it difficult to develop agriculture, forestry, and animal husbandry. Finally, the development of deserts calls for large quantities of motive power. Although there is plenty of wind and solar energy in the deserts, how to make effective use of such energy remains to be studied.[64]

As already stated, mountains and hills constitute a major portion of China's land area. The Communist government has made efforts to cultivate some mountains and hills for production of grains as well as forest products, fruits, and other crops. The National Program for Agricultural Development urged the agricultural producers' cooperatives (now the communes) to develop grain production in some of the mountainous areas, provided this would not affect the water and soil conservation program; to grow timber forests in the remote mountainous areas; and to grow forests for firewood and charcoal as well as fruits in the less remote mountainous areas. In the south, emphasis has been given to the cultivation of tea-oil and tung-oil trees, bamboo,

mulberries, and tea plants; in the north, to that of walnuts, Mongolian
oaks, and wild pepper. The cooperatives were also encouraged to grow
medicinal herbs in the mountainous areas (Article 17 of the Program).

Party cadres, young intellectuals, and others have been sent to
the mountainous areas in increasing numbers, particularly during the
Leap Forward campaign, to participate in such activities as reclaiming
waste mountain valley. In South China, the cultivation of fruit trees on
hilly land has been especially encouraged in order to save as much flat
land as possible for planting grains and cotton.[65] It has been reported
that some 40 million young intellectuals were sent to the mountainous
areas for rural work during the ten years 1955-65.[66] Several other
millions were drafted during the Cultural Revolution for similar purposes.

Despite the reported progress, the surge into the mountainous
areas was greeted with little enthusiasm by the cadres and peasants.
The Communist press observed in 1958 that "conservative thinking
and inertia among some of the cadres should be subjected to excoriating
criticism."[67] The situation apparently remained the same in the more
recent years. In 1966 editorial, the Liberation Daily stated that not
enough attention had been paid to the development of mountainous areas
owing to erroneous thinking on the part of some cadres, who maintained
that the development of such areas is not worth the trouble. Other
cadres were afraid of hardship in mountainous areas and reluctant to
go there.[68]

In addition to deserts and mountains, efforts have been made to
improve China's vast area of grassland for developing animal husbandry.
China's grassland, with an estimated total area of 4,000 million mou
(667 million acres), or nearly 30 percent of the country's total land
area, is mainly distributed west of the diagonal extending from the
Greater Khingan Mountains southwestward toward the eastern foreland
of the Tibet Plateau. It constitutes a major portion of Sinkiang,
Chinghai, Inner Mongolia, Ninghsia, and the Kantze and Ahpo districts
in Szechuan.

Flat grassland makes up approximately two-thirds of the total
area of China's grassland, while the remaining one-third consists
mainly of hilly grassland. Most of the country's grassland lies in
arid zones marked by drastic changes in climate. The grass yield is
unstable and varies a great deal between years and between seasons.
Moreover, much of grassland in China is suitable only for grazing
and not for harvesting grass. For this reason, the stock of hay is
inadequate to meet the needs of the animal herds. Mismanagement

of the grassland and excessive grazing have worsened the situation. Another problem in many areas is the inadequate supply of drinking water for men and animals. In some of these areas, the underground water resources are rather abundant but their utilization has not been well developed. Rodent and insect pests also constitute a serious menace to the grassland. In Chinghai particularly, the damage to grassland by rodents has been most serious, and the grassland in Chinghai and Sinkiang frequently has been attacked by locust pests.

In recent years, measures reportedly have been taken for the improvement of grassland, with special attention given to its better cultivation and utilization. Reservoirs, wells, ditches, dams, and other water conservation projects have been carried out to store water and channel water from accumulated snow. Scientific research has been planned on methods to raise production on the grassland and establishment of grassland experimental stations.[69]

In the vast Gobi area in Bayan Naoh League of the Inner Mongolian Autonomous Region, rich underground water resources were reported to have been discovered 20 to 50 meters below the surface in 1959 by a desert control team of the Chinese Academy of Sciences. It was believed that at least one-third of the 180,000 square kilometers of the Gobi could be brought into use for grazing if water were provided. As a result of improved water supply, Bayan Naoh League's livestock increased from 1.3 million head in 1949 to 3.8 million head in 1963.[70]

Part of the 8,000 square kilometer Tamchin grassland, one of the largest arid grasslands in Inner Mongolia, was improved in 1963 through the sinking of large numbers of artesian and pump-operated wells and the construction of aqueducts, canals, and reservoirs. Formerly known as "the demon's domain" for its desolation, the Tamchin grassland rises like a flat, green terrace 100 meters above the surrounding pastures in the central part of Inner Mongolia. It does not have any river, and shortage of drinking water for men and animals was the main obstacle to using the rich grassland. Now it can feed 100,000 head of livestock every year, according to press reports.[71]

A question has often been posed as to whether some of China's grassland should be improved for animal husbandry or transformed into forests. China is short of both livestock and forest products, and the problem of soil erosion is serious. From the standpoint of ecological conditions at least, it would seem that some of the grassland, especially the hilly grassland, is rather unpromising for the development of animal husbandry. Therefore, the only use to be gained from it would be through afforestation.[72]

Since 1949, reclamation projects have been carried out on some of the alkaline and saline land with reportedly successful results. From the viewpoint of land utilization, it seems more economical and profitable for China to reclaim some of its land on the long coast than to reclaim the deserts, mountains, and grassland. Some of the low-lying marshy areas along the seacoast that are now unproductive because of poor drainage and harmful accumulation of alkali salt can be reclaimed. In Southeast China particularly, precipitation is suffi-cient to wash the salt off the reclaimed coast and the growing season for crops is long. Some alkali land can also be reclaimed in the semi-arid parts of North, Northeast, and Northwest China, where water is available and topography is favorable. Before World War II, consider-areas of saline land along the coast in northern Kiangsu were success-fully drained and irrigated for the growing of cotton, and during the Japanese occupation thousands of acres in the vicinity of Tientsin-Tangku area in Hopei and in several areas of Northeast China that formerly were considered worthless were reclaimed for growing rice.[73]

ACQUISITION OF FARMLAND FOR
CONSTRUCTION PURPOSES

As population grows, such nonagricultural land requirements as housing, government buildings, industry, highways, airports, and cemeteries steadily encroach on the arable land area. The procedure for the requisition of land for such purposes was first provided in the "Regulations Governing Agrarian Reform in Suburban Areas," approved by the State Administration Council (now the State Council) in November 1950, and again in the "Regulations Governing the Requisition of Land for State Construction," promulgated in December 1953. As the con-struction program proceeded, it became more and more apparent that these regulations were far from adequate.

The Municipality of Peking can serve as an example. Up to the end of June 1957, a total of 210,000 mou of land in Peking's suburban areas had been requisitioned for building construction. Of this total, 15,000 mou was wasteland while the remaining 195,000 mou was farm-land.[74] The arbitrary manner of the requisition can be seen in many of the notices, almost identical in form, by the Land Administration Bureau or the City Planning Commission, which appeared frequently in the newspapers. The one in the People's Daily of March 29, 1952, reads:

It has now been decided to start building construction in the following areas: [description of location and boundaries]. All land and graveyard owners in the area prescribed above

are expected to settle the transfer of land, the removal of
graves and other matters with their respective village
governments within fifteen days from the date at which
this notice first appears in the newspaper. If any owner
fails to do so, the grave will be treated as ownerless and
will be removed by the government to the People's
Cemetery.

In the pre-Communist days, it was the custom in China for each
family to have its own burial grounds. As a rule, the geomancer located
the grave site. Since he gave attention only to the feng shui (the supposed magical wind and water influences), the grave was as often
located in the center of a cultivated field as elsewhere. This practice
created a real problem not only because of the land actually taken
from cultivation but also because of the obstacle the grave presented
to cultivation. J. Lossing Buck estimated in 1937 that if the graves
could be removed China's crop area for the eight agricultural acres,
which totaled 232 million acres, would be increased by 1.1 percent or
2,552,000 acres and that this increased area could support over 400,000
additional farm families.[75]

Cremation and cemeteries have now replaced the private burial
system, but many of the lands and graveyards requisitioned during the
1950's and 1960's were left unused. Moreover, in many construction
projects too much space was allowed between buildings, causing even
greater waste. It was estimated in 1958 that, if the space between
buildings had been planned more properly, four or five thousand mou
of the arable land requisitioned in Peking's suburban areas by 33
government units and other institutions could have been saved to yield
about one million chin of grains per year.[76]

In view of the waste, in 1957, 88 government units and institutions
were asked to return land that they had requisitioned but on which
construction projects had not been started. At the end of May 1957,
a total of more than 7,800 mou of such land were reported to have
been turned over either to the agricultural producers' cooperatives
for cultivation or to the government for reallocation. However, some
pieces had to remain idle because they had been either enclosed by
buildings or divided up into too many fragmentary parts.[77]

Meanwhile, the 1953 regulations were revised in January 1958.
Under the revised regulations, the area of land to be requisitioned
must be approved by "the organ which is competent to approve the
preliminary design of the construction project concerned"; in cases
where the removal of more than 30 households is involved or more

than 300 mou of land is called for, the allotment must be approved by
the people's council at the provincial level; and a clearcut system is
provided for constant supervision and inspection of the use of land
requisitioned.

Despite these revised regulations, the situation of land acquisition
apparently has not improved very much. On June 6, 1962, the People's
Daily carried a number of letters from readers which disclosed that
in recent years some capital construction units had taken over excessive
quantities of land. Much of it was unused for a long time or was used
by government organs and factories for cultivating subsidiary food
crops with unsatisfactory harvests. The newspaper again urged the
respective units to give back the land to the production teams for
cultivation, "in accordance with the successive instructions on the
economical use of land."[78]

In another article, the authors stated:

> The economic level of our country is still not very high and
> it is impossible for the State to devote too much financial,
> material and labor resources to the reclamation of waste-
> land. Moreover, newly-reclaimed wasteland will yield a
> relatively low output in the first few years, and the use of
> one mou of cultivated land for construction purposes must
> be offset by the reclamation of several mou of wasteland.
> Thus, it is clear that we should pay full attention to the
> economical use of cultivated land for construction pro-
> jects.[79]

THE PROSPECTS FOR EXPANDING THE
AREA UNDER CULTIVATION

From the above discussion, it is apparent that the attempts by
the Communist Chinese regime to expand cultivated areas in the 1950's
and 1960's have not been successful and that the prospects for the future
are not bright. In the first place, there is very limited acreage of
uncultivated land suitable for agricultural use. In fact, a sizable portion
of the present cultivated land is not profitable for agricultural use and
should be developed for other purposes, such as forestry, animal husbandry, and recreation. Also, a substantial portion of the land presently classified as arable is marginal or submarginal land with steep
slopes, little or unreliable precipitation, and other unfavorable natural
conditions, and it is possible that such land should not be considered
arable at all. It is true that some of the land considered not arable

at present may become suitable for farming through the introduction
of modern farm machinery and other technological innovation, but the
acreage of such land is negligible and will remain so for some time.

Furthermore, the greater part of China's wasteland is situated
in remote frontier regions. Tremendous financial and technical problems are involved in any large-scale reclamation program. Surveying
work, power machinery, better transportation facilities, and well-
planned migration are needed. These, in turn, would require abundant
investment of capital, manpower, equipment, and material, as admitted
by Chou En-lai and other Communist Chinese leaders.[80]

Among Chinese scientists, the question of whether China's
cultivated land could be extended by reclaiming wasteland has been
discussed frequently. Even those who think that this could be done
raised serious problems. Huang Ping-wei, Director of the Research
Institute of Geography, Chinese Academy of Sciences, and his associate,
Shih Ch'ien, are of the opinion that the present 1,650 million mou (275
million acres) of cultivated land could be doubled. However, Huang
maintained that most of the land reclaimed would be mountainous and
erosive and that there would be too much salt in the soil. He suggested
that this could be ignored, possibly for three to five years, but in eight
or ten years' time serious damage would have occurred. Such damage
might involve not only the newly reclaimed land but also neighboring
land and even land at a considerable distance.[81] Shih Ch'ien expressed
the opinion that, owing to the shortage of machinery, reclamation of
wasteland on a large scale is not possible.[82]

The zeal to exploit wasteland has produced unfavorable results.
The dikes at the two sides of the Grand Canal have been destroyed in
many places because trees have been cut down for the planting of
wheat.[83] Several readers wrote to the People's Daily in 1962, com-
plaining that the cultivation of steep land in certain areas had caused
soil erosion. The "Provisional Regulations Governing the Conservation
of Water and Soil," issued by the State Council in 1957, specified that
reclamation of wasteland on slopes having a gradient of 25 degrees or
more generally should be prohibited. It was also provided that the
gradient of a slope on which cultivation is prohibited may be determined
variably in accordance with the condition of soil, the intensity and
volume of rainfall, the distribution of forests, farmland, and population,
and other conditions in the provinces. Apparently, the regulations were
ignored during the zeal to exploit wasteland.[84] For example, a survey
of northern Shensi and western Shansi in 1963 indicated that much of
the reclaimed land was on slopes with a gradient of 25 degrees or
more, and in some cases the gradient even exceeded 60 degrees.

The reclamation was carried out by individual production teams without coordination with water and soil conservation work. As a result, forest land and grassland were destroyed.[85] In many areas, the exploitation of wasteland has led to the permanent destruction of valuable resources in exchange for a relatively short-term gain in agricultural output.

Recognizing the difficulties of land reclamation, in recent years the Communist government has given increasing emphasis to the development of "stable and high-yielding farmland despite drought and water-logging," farmland that guarantees high yields even in the years of natural calamities. This is not an easy task either. The People's Daily noted:

> The area of farmland which is stable and high-yielding despite drought and waterlogging at present constitutes only a small part of the 1.65 billion mou of all farmland. In the near future, say in three to five years, it will still be only a small part. The development of stable and high-yielding farmland not only takes a long time but also requires a huge force of manpower and large amounts of capital and materials. In certain areas, it requires the construction of some large-and medium-sized projects for water conservation, afforestation, soil improvement and other purposes. It would be difficult for the communes and localities to initiate such large projects, although there are certain small projects in which they could actively participate, such as the digging of irrigation channels in the fields, leveling of land and heavier application of fertilizers.[86]

NOTES

1. Directorate of Statistics, National Government of China, Chung-hua Min-kuo T'ung-chi T'i-yao [Statistical Abstracts of the Republic of China] (Nanking, 1947), pp. 1, 14.

2. Teng Tzu-hui, "Great Accomplishments of State Farms and State Pastures in the Past Few Years and Their Basic Functions in the Future," Chung-kuo Nung-pao [Chinese Agriculture Bulletin], Peking, No. 8, 1957, pp. 2-6.

3. "Resolution on Certain Questions Concerning the People's Communes," Hsin-hua Pan-yueh-k'an [New China Semimonthly], Peking, No. 24, 1958, pp. 3-11; JMJP, editorial, June 11, 1959, p. 1.

4. Food and Agriculture Organization of the United Nations, FAO Production Yearbook, 1969 (Rome, 1970), pp. 4-6.

5. Ministry of Agriculture, People's Republic of China, "Notice on the Strengthening of the Planning Works in Land Utilization of the People's Communes," Chung-kuo Nung-pao [Chinese Agriculture Bulletin], Peking, No. 18, 1959, p. 18.

6. Chung-kuo Nung-pao [Chinese Agriculture Bulletin], Peking, No. 8, 1958, p. 25, and No. 10, 1958, p. 20.

7. Chang Tzu-lin and Huang Jung-han, "The Problem of Improving Alkali and Saline Land and Preventing Alkalization and Salinization in North China," Hung Ch'i [Red Flag], Peking, Nos. 15/16, pp. 47-56.

8. Chiang Ch'i-hsien, "Strive to Fulfill the Reclamation Work of 100 Million Mou of Wasteland Ahead of Schedule and to Manage Well the State Farms," Chung-kuo Nung-k'en [Chinese Argicultural Reclamation], Peking, No. 1, 1958, pp. 4-5.

9. Teng Tzu-hui, "Great Accomplishments of the State Farms and Pastures in the Past Few Years and Their Basic Functions in the Future," Chi-hsieh-hua Nung-yeh [Mechanized Agriculture], Peking, No. 4, 1957, pp. 1-5; Kuang-ming Jih-pao [Kuang-ming Daily], October 9, 1961, p. 1; Liu Huan-wen, "Miscellaneous Sketches of Hohsi," Kuang-ming Jih-pao [Kuang-ming Daily], July 20, 1965, p. 4.

10. Shang Chih-lung and Ma Ching-p'o, "Fifteen Years of Agricultural Mechanization on State Farms," Nung-yeh Chi-hsieh Chi-shu [Technology of Agricultural Machinery], Peking, No. 11, 1964.

11. NCNA, Peking, July 9, 1961.

12. Chung-hua Jen-min Kung-ho-kuo Fa-chan Kuo-min Ching-chi Ti-i-ko Wu-nien Chi-hua 1953-1957 [The First Five-Year Plan for the Development of the Economy of the Chinese People's Republic, 1953-1957] (Peking, 1955), p. 85.

13. Hsin-hua Pan-yueh-k'an [New China Semimonthly], Peking, No. 8, 1959, p. 50.

14. Chiang Ch'i-hsien, op. cit., pp. 4-5.

15. Po I-p'o, "Draft Resolution on the National Economy Plan for 1958," a report at the Fifth Session of the First National People's

Congress, February 3, 1958, Hsin-hua Pan-yueh-k'an [New China Semimonthly], Peking, No. 5, 1958, pp. 12-23.

16. Kuang-ming Jih-pao [Kuang-ming Daily], Peking, October 9, 1961, p. 1.

17. Teng Tzu-hui, "Great Accomplishments of the State Farms and Pastures in the Past Few Years and Their Basic Functions in the Future," Chi-hsieh-hua Nung-yeh, op. cit., pp. 1-5.

18. Lu Jen, Hsin-chung-kuo Ti-i-ko Chi-t'i Nung-chuang ti Ku-shih [The Story of New China's First Collective Farm Group] (Hankow, 1952), pp. 1-7.

19. NCNA-English, Shenyang, February 17, 1964.

20. Ho Hsu-chih, "The Site of the Friendship State Farm--the 'Three-River Plain' in Northeast China," Ti-li Chih-shih [Geographical Knowledge], Peking, No. 4, 1955, p. 111; Kuo Wen-yu, Kuo-ying Nung-ch'ang [State Farms] (Peking, 1957).

21. China News Service, Canton, news releases No. 4146, August 9, 1965, and No. 4174, September 6, 1965; NCNA-English, Shenyang, February 17, 1964; NCNA-English, Harbin, January 13, 1966.

22. Chang Yu-san and Wang Pao-kung, "Land Planning of the Friendship State Farm," Chi-hsieh-hua Nung-yeh [Mechanized Agriculture], Shenyang, No. 10, 1955, pp. 18-24.

23. T'ien Lien-ch'ien and Sun Kuang-hsien, "Friendship State Farm on Its Way to Healthy Development," JMJP, May, 3, 1962, p. 2; "Diversified Undertakings Centered on One Single Enterprise," editorial, JMJP, May 3, 1962, p. 1.

24. Wang Wei-p'ing and Hu Ting-mei, Hsin-chiang Wei-wu-erh Tzu-chih-chu [The Sinkiang-Uighur Autonomous Region] (Peking, 1959), pp. 14-24.

25. NCNA, Urumchi, May 11, 1961, and May 27, 1963.

26. Min-tsu T'uan-chieh [Unity of Nationalities], Peking, No. 12, 1961.

27. NCNA, Urumchi, September 6, 1968.

28. Kuang-ming Jih-pao [Kuang-ming Daily], Peking, December

29, 1964, p. 2, and March 15, 1966, p. 1; "Tarim Institute of Land Reclamation--A New Type of School in Sinkiang," Peking Review, No. 41, 1966, pp. 27-30

29. NCNA-English, Urumchi, September 16, 1965.

30. NCNA-English, Urumchi, February 24, 1966.

31. Sai Fu-ting, "Ten Years of Great Achievements in Sinkiang's Agriculture," Chung-kuo Nung-pao [Chinese Agriculture Bulletin], No. 19, 1959, pp. 19-23; NCNA-English, Urumchi, November 13, 1964.

32. JMJP, October 30, 1963, p. 1.

33. NCNA-English, Urumchi, March 19, 1966.

34. Kuo Ch'un-hua, "The Potentiality of Reducing the Cost for Constructing State Farms in Sinkiang," Chung-kuo Nung-k'en [Chinese Agricultural Reclamation], Peking, No. 1, 1958, pp. 4-5.

35. Ts'ao Tse-yuan, "The Outlook of Land Reclamation for Growing Cotton in Sinkiang," Chung-kuo Nung-k'en [Chinese Agricultural Reclamation], Peking, No. 5, 1957, pp. 29-30, 25.

36. "Several Problems of Cotton Production in Sinkiang," Chung-kuo Nung-k'en [Chinese Agricultural Reclamation], Peking, No. 5, 1958, pp. 14-15.

37. Ta Kung Pao, Peking, March 31, 1966, p. 2; NCNA-English, Urumchi, November 26, 1970.

38. Kung-jen Jih-pao [Daily Worker], Peking, September 27, 1965, p. 1.

39. NCNA-English, Huhehot, June 16, 1963.

40. NCNA-English, Sining, April 26, 1966.

41. NCNA-English, Sian, September 7, 1963.

42. NCNA-English, Yinchuan, February 27, 1964.

43. NCNA-English, Yinchuan, May 2, 1966.

44. NCNA-English, Lanchou, January 3, 1966.

45. NCNA-English, Sian, September 5, 1961.

46. NCNA-English, Tientsin, September 20, 1961; NCNA-English, Tsinan, May 22, 1963.

47. NCNA-English, Tsinan, October 17, 1961.

48. NCNA-English, Peking, December 9, 1960; NCNA-English Nanchang, January 6, 1964.

49. NCNA-English, Nanking, October 18, 1961.

50. NCNA-English, Peking, July 20, 1970.

51. Lin Hsin, "Achievements and Future Plans of the State Farms in Kwangtung," Jo-tai Tso-wu [Tropical Crops], Canton, No. 15, 1959, pp. 1-4.

52. Planning Commission, Government of India, Report of the Indian Delegation to China on Agrarian Cooperatives (New Delhi, May 1957), p. 11; Teng Tzu-hui, "Great Accomplishments of the State Farms and Pastures in the Past Few Years and Their Basic Functions in the Future," Chi-hsieh-hua Nung-yeh, op. cit., pp. 1-5.

53. Wang Chen, "Strengthening the Construction of State Farms," Hung Ch'i [Red Flag], Peking, No. 7, 1961, pp. 1-7.

54. Teng, Tzu-hui, "Great Accomplishments of the State Farms and Pastures in the Past Few Years and Their Basic Functions in the Future," Chi-hsieh-hua Nung-yeh, op. cit., pp. 1-5.

55. "Data for the National Agricultural Exhibition" Nung-yeh K'o-hsueh T'ung-hsun [Agricultural Science Bulletin], Peking, No. 2 1959, pp. 46-47.

56. JMJP, January 9, 1965, p. 2.

57. Wang Chen, op. cit., pp. 1-7.

58. JMJP, April 1, 1966, p. 2.

59. JMJP, January 16, 1958, p. 1.

60. Li Ch'iao, "China's Deserts," K'o-hsueh Ta-chung [Popular Science], Peking, No. 6, 1963, pp. 6-8.

61. Tuan Shao-po, "Transforming Deserts into Good Farms and Gobi into Grassland," K'o-hsueh Hua-pao [Science Pictorial], Peking, No. 9, 1959, pp. 330-31.

62. JMJP, September 28, 1961, p. 1.

63. NCNA, Yinchuan, October 6, 1963.

64. Lou T'ung-mao, "A Brief Account of the Deserts in North west China," Ti-li Chih-shih [Geographical Knowledge], Peking, No. 9. 1959, pp. 413-14; Li Ch'iao, op. cit., pp. 6-8.

65. Li Lai-jung, et al., Nan-fang ti Kuo-shu Shang-shan [Cultivating Fruit Trees on Hilly Land in South China] (Peking, 1956), pp. 1-120.

66. JMJP, December 9, 1965, p. 1.

67. Jen-min Shou-ts'e [People's Handbook] (Peking, 1958), pp. 528-32.

68. "A Great Deal Can Be Done in Tapping the Potentialities of Mountainous Areas," editorial, Chieh-fang Jih-pao [Liberation Daily], March 4, 1966, reprinted in JMJP, March 15, 1966, p. 2.

69. Wang Chi-wu, The Forests of China (Cambridge, Mass., 1961), pp. 171-76; Chia Shen-hsiu, "Problems on the Utilization and Improvement of Grassland in China," Kuang-ming Jih-pao [Kuang-ming Daily], Peking, February 23, 1964, p. 4.

70. NCNA-English, Huhehot, April 10, 1963; and November 27, 1964.

71. NCNA-English, Huhehot, July 10, 1963.

72. Jean Messines, "Forest Rehabilitation and Soil Conservation in China," Unasylva, Rome, Vol. XII, No. 3 (1958), pp. 103-20.

73. Office of Foreign Agricultural Relations, U.S. Department of Agriculture, Report of the China-United States Agricultural Mission, (Washington, D.C.; 1947), p. 4; Shen Tsung-han, Agricultural Resources of China (Ithaca, N.Y.; Cornell University Press, 1951), pp. 84-86.

74. JMJP, November 27, 1957, p. 1.

75. J. Lossing Buck, Land Utilization in China (Nanking: University of Nanking, 1937), pp. 178-79.

76. JMJP, January 7, 1958, p. 1.

77. NCNA, Peking, June 11, 1957.

78. "A Problem Which Should Be Speedily Solved," editorial, JMJP, June 6, 1962, p. 1.

79. Miao Hui-fen and Chang Ch'eng-p'o, "On the Economical Use of Land for Construction Projects," JMJP, March 5, 1964, p. 5.

80. Chung Chieh, "A Discussion on the Question of Agricultural Modernization in Our Country," Ching-chi Yen-chiu [Economic Research], Peking, No. 12, 1963, pp. 73-78; Planning Commission, Government of India, op. cit., p. 11.

81. Huang Ping-wei, "Several Problems to be Considered in Expanding the Acreage of Cultivated Land," JMJP, May 5, 1961, p. 7.

82. Kuang-ming Jih-pao [Kuang-ming Daily], Peking, October 9, 1961.

83. JMJP, November 13, 1961, p. 2.

84. JMJP, March 23, 1962, p. 2.

85. Chao Ming-fu, "Water and Soil Conservation in Regions Along the Middle Reaches of the Yellow River," JMJP, November 14, 1963, p. 2.

86. "Properly Manage All Farmland with a View to Building Stable and High-Yielding Farmland," editorial, JMJP, July 4, 1964, p. 1.

CHAPTER

5

RAISING
THE YIELD
PER UNIT
OF LAND

Because of the limited potentialities for expanding land under cultivation, most plans for increasing agricultural production have been geared to improving the yield per unit of land. The National Program for Agricultural Development called for higher yields of grains, cotton, and other principal crops and laid down the targets as follows:

1. During the twelve years beginning in 1956, the average annual yield of grains should be raised from the 1955 figure of 150 chin per mou to 400 chin per mou (from 1.12 to 3.00 metric tons per hectare) in the areas north of the Yellow River, the Chinling Mountains, the Pailung River, and the Yellow River in Chinghai Province. In the areas south of the Yellow River and north of the Huai River, the yield should be raised from the 1955 figure of 208 chin per mou to 500 chin per mou (from 1.55 to 3.73 metric tons per hectare). In the areas south of the Huai River, the Chinling Mountains, and the Pailung River, the yield should be increased from 1955 figure of 400 chin per mou to 800 chin per mou (from 3.00 to 6.00 metric tons per hectare).

2. In the same twelve years, the average annual yield of ginned cotton should be raised from the 1955 figure of 35 chin per mou to 40, 60, 80, or 100 chin per mou (0.30, 0.45, 0.60, or 0.75 metric tons per hectare), depending on local conditions.

3. While giving priority to increasing grain production, various localities were expected to exert efforts to develop a diversified agriculture to meet the state production targets for textile raw materials, oil-bearing crops, sugarcane, sugarbeet, tea, cured tobacco, fruits, vegetables, medicinal herbs, tropical and subtropical crops, and other economic crops (Article 2 of the Program).

MAP 2 - The Three Grain-Producing Regions of China

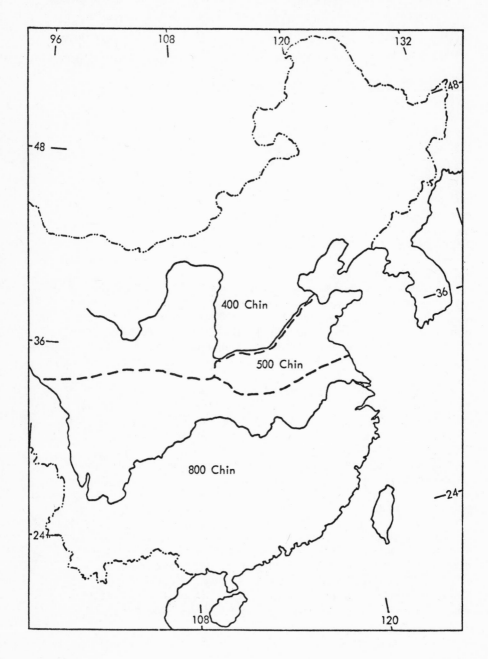

400 Chin

500 Chin

800 Chin

TABLE 7

Natural Conditions of the Three Regions Specified in
the National Program for Agricultural Development, 1956-67

	400-Chin Region	500-Chin Region	800-Chin Region
Location	Areas north of the Yellow River, the Chinling Mountains, and the Pailung River.	Areas south of the Yellow River and north of the Huai River.	Areas south of the Huai River, the Chinling Mountains, and the Pailung River.
Acreage of cultivated land	730 million mou	290 million mou	620 million mou
Annual precipitation	600 mm. in the northeast; 630 mm. in eastern Hopei; less than 200 mm. in Sinkiang; 400 mm. in other areas.	Average 600 mm.	1,000 mm. in the Yangtze River basin; 1,500-2,000 mm. in the areas further south.
Growing season	120-170 days north of the Great Wall; 200 days in the Liaotung Peninsula area and south of the Great Wall.	220 days or longer.	250-300 days in the Yangtze River basin; practically frost-free in the areas further south.
Principal crops	Wheat, corn, millet, kaoliang, soybeans, cotton, flax, sugar beets.	Food crops (about the same as those in the 400-chin Region), cotton, tobacco.	Rice, corn, potatoes, wheat, ramie, jute, sugar cane, cotton, tobacco, rapeseeds, tea, silk cocoons, rubber, coffee, citronella, tropical fruits.
Number of crops per year	Generally one crop per year north of the Great Wall; three crops in two years in the Liaotung Peninsula area and south of the Great Wall.	Three crops in two years in most areas; five crops in three years or two crops per year in some areas.	Two or three crops per year in the Yangtze River basin; three crops per year in the areas further south.

Source: Hsin-hua Pan-yueh K'an [New China Semimonthly], Peking, No. 2, 1958, p. 94.

The approximate boundaries of the three principal grain-growing regions, commonly referred to by the Chinese Communist authorities as the "400-chin region," the "500-chin region," and the "800-chin region," are shown in Map 2. Both the boundaries of these regions and their respective grain production targets appear to have been set arbitrarily, although their natural conditions as shown in Table 7, are apparently different.

To attain the goals cited above, the National Program for Agricultural Development provided various technical measures for raising yields per unit on the existing cultivated land. Eight of these measures were considered by Mao Tse-tung as the most important and, for propaganda purposes, were referred to as the "Eight-Character Charter of Agriculture." The eight Chinese characters were: shui (water conservation), fei (fertilization), t'u (soil conservation), chung (seed selection), mi (close planting), pao (plant protection), kung (tool improvement), and kuan (field management). Although these eight measures were selected on a rather arbitrary basis and do not necessarily represent all the important phases of agricultural technology, the "Eight-Character Charter of Agriculture" includes the areas of concentration in planning and carrying out the program of technical transformation of agriculture since the Leap Forward campaign. For this reason, the problems of raising the yields per unit of the existing cultivated land will be discussed in terms of these eight aspects in the following eight chapters.

CHAPTER

6

WATER
CONSERVATION

Because of the poorly distributed rainfall through the seasons and the frequent occurrence of floods and droughts, water is regarded by Mao Tse-tung as the lifeline of China's agriculture and is placed above all other factors in his "Eight-Character Charter of Agriculture." The National Program for Agricultural Development provided that in the twelve years beginning in 1956 ordinary floods and droughts should in the main be eliminated (Article 5).

During the earlier years of the regime, many large water conservation projects were carried out with great enthusiasm and fanfare. It soon became evident that many of the projects did not perform their functions as satisfactorily as expected, because of improper planning, lack of coordination, and poor quality of construction. The authorities also realized that large projects would require large amounts of funds, raw materials, and labor, and would take a long time to complete.

Therefore, in mapping out the National Program for Agricultural Development, emphasis was given to small and medium-sized water conservation projects, such as digging of wells and ponds, construction of dikes, ditches, reservoirs, and embankments, and harnessing of small rivers (Article 5). This policy of emphasizing small and medium-sized projects was reaffirmed at the beginning of the Leap Forward campaign in 1958, when a "three-priority" program of water conservation was adopted. Under the program, priority was given to the following: (1) small projects, supplemented by large and medium-sized projects, in order to gradually form coordinated networks; (2) water-storage projects, although considerable attention was also to be paid to drainage projects, in order to prevent land from being waterlogged, salinized, and alkalized; and (3) projects undertaken by the communes under the unified planning and help of the state, while only large projects were to be built by the central government.[1] This remains the guiding principle for water conservation work at present.

For the convenience of discussion, the progress of the water conservation program in Communist China may be reviewed in terms of two major aspects: (1) flood control, particularly the harnessing of the principal rivers, and (2) drought control, particularly irrigation. The two are of course interrelated, and many water conservation projects have been constructed or planned for the control of both floods and droughts.

FLOOD CONTROL

Approximately one-fourth of cultivated land in Mainland China is subject to floods and waterlogging. This land is distributed primarily in the areas along the middle and lower reaches of the Yangtze River; the Huai River basin in northern Kiangsu and northern Anhwei; the plains along the lower reaches of the Yellow River in Shantung and Honan and along the Hai River in Hopei, the Sungari-Liao plains in Northeast China, and the Pearl River delta. These are among the most populated and most fertile areas in China, and they are also the principal areas producing grains and cotton. The Yellow, Yangtze, Huai, and Hai rivers are the most treacherous rivers in China, although there is also frequent flood menace along other principal rivers.

The Yellow River

There have been nine major course changes in the history of the Yellow River, which for centuries has been known to Westerners as "China's sorrow." Until 1194, the river reached the sea at various points of the Po Hai north of the Shantung Peninsula. In that year, one arm entered the sea south of Shantung through the valley of the Huai River. After nearly seven centuries of southeasterly flow, the Yellow River resumed its northeasterly course about 1855 in what is essentially its present channel. Once again, the river was diverted toward the Huai River basin in June 1938, but this time its dike was broken intentionally at a point northwest of Kaifeng by the National government to slow the Japanese advance. The breach was sealed in March 1947 with the assistance of the United Nations Relief and Rehabilitation Administration (UNRRA), and the Yellow River returned to its former northeasterly course.

The Communist regime has given renewed attention to the problem of flood control along the Yellow River. The program includes a complex system of flood-detention reservoirs in the upper reaches, the strengthening of dikes along the lower course, and the provision of spillways, particularly near the mouth where ice jams frequently cause flooding in the spring. A multiple-purpose plan for the development of the Yellow River basin, mapped out with Soviet assistance, was adopted in 1955. The plan included the construction of reservoirs for irrigation and flood control, the development of hydroelectric power for industries, and the extension of the navigable sections of the Yellow River. One of the first projects under the plan was the much publicized Sanmen Gorge project above Loyang in Honan Province, which began in April 1957. It was expected that when completed the project could reduce the flow of the river from 37,000 cubic meters per second to 8,000 cubic meters per second. According to a Chinese Communist account the project included the construction of a dam 110 meters high and 960 meters long, to create a reservoir capable of holding 35,000 million cubic meters of water and second in size only to the largest reservoir in the world, the Kuibyshev Reservoir in the Soviet Union.[2]

In 1959, it was reported that the Sanmen Gorge project would be completed in October 1960, two years ahead of the plan.[3] But no further information about its progress has been revealed since. The project was never finished because of the departure of the Russian experts.

The Yangtze River

Although the Yangtze carries less sediment than the Yellow River (600 million tons a year compared with 4,000 million tons) and aggrades its channel to a lesser extent, it nevertheless presents a summer flood threat. In recent times, two disastrous floods have occurred, in 1931 and 1954. The most serious floods of the Yangtze River usually have occurred along its middle reaches. As a first step toward regulating the Yantze, the Ching River flood-detention project was carried out in 1952. The Ching is a section of the Yangtze between Chinkiang Hsien in Hupeh Province and Chenlingchi at the Tungting Lake in Hunan Province. Along the Ching River is an important areas of 860 hectares producing rice and cotton. It is also one of the localities of the Yangtze River basin that have been most seriously affected by floods. Principal measures taken to control the floods since 1952 were strengthening of main dikes, the diversion of the water of the river, and the construction of two main dams.[4]

For further control of the Yangtze River, a plan has been mapped
out to complete a number of reservoirs and strengthen the dikes along
the river's middle and lower reaches and to build a big dam near the
"Three Gorges" in Szechuan in order to slow down the flow of the
upper reaches. No details of the plan have been revealed. However,
it has been admitted that the plan involves many financial and technical
problems.[5]

The Huai River

The Huai is the largest river between the Yellow River and the
Yangtze River and drains the southeastern margin of the North China
Plain. A relatively short river (675 miles), the Huai is subject to
severe summer flooding. When the Yellow River usurped the channel
of the Huai before 1855 and again from 1938 to 1947, the invading
stream deposited vast amounts of sediment in the Huai channel, disrupting its natural course to the sea. The Huai discharged its water
into the fluctuating lakes Hungtse and Kaoyu, which enlarged overvast
areas in times of flood. Part of the water from the naturally mouthless
Huai followed the Chungshan River and the Grand Canal to the sea.

In response to Mao Tse-tung's call for "assuring success in
bringing the Huai River under control" in 1950, the Peking regime
embarked on an ambitious program that included the construction of
detention reservoirs (some with power-generating capacity) on the
upstream tributaries, the dredging of the main channel, the strengthening of dikes, flood-diversion dams, and reservoirs in middlecourse,
and the digging of a new outlet to the Yellow Sea. A new outlet for the
Huai, the North Kiangsu Irrigation Trunk Canal extending from Hungtse
Lake at Kaoliangchien 105 miles northeast to the sea at Pientankang,
was completed in 1952. Another important project, a dam regulating
the Chungshan River outlet of Hungtse Lake, was completed the following
year. Several major reservoirs have been completed on upstream
tributaries of the Huai, including those at Paisha, Shihmantan, Panchiao,
Pushan, Tapoling, Hsianghungtien, Fotzeling, Nanwan, and Meishan.

In the northernmost part of the Huai River lowland, on the
Kiangsu-Shantung border, new outlets were built in 1952 for the I River
and the Shu River. Both of these rivers descend in virtually parallel
courses from the Shantung upland and often have caused floods in
northermost Kiangsu for lack of direct outlet to the sea. Together,
they drain an area of 15,000 square kilometers (5,800 square miles).
Since the establishment of communes, a number of reservoirs and
ponds have been constructed. It was reported that, during the high

water season in the summer of 1963, these water conservation projects
took 44 percent of the flow of the I River and 30 percent of the flow of
the Shu River and that a serious flood was thus avoided despite the
unprecedentedly heavy rainfall.[6]

A series of water conservation projects to regulate the three
major tributaries of the Huai River--the Pi, Shih, and Hang rivers--
began in 1959 in the Liuan Special District, Anhwei. The area lies in
the region of hills and mountains that constitutes the watershed between
the Yangtze and Huai rivers and used to be constantly under the menace
of floods and droughts. Several big reservoirs and more than 2,000
kilometers of canals have been built as a part of the project for
harnessing the Huai and its tributaries. The Shuch'eng-Luchiang
Canal, 80 meters long, is the major part of the Pi-Shih-Hang irrigation
system. By the end of 1969, the Pi-Shih-Hang irrigation system,
which is one of the biggest in China, had brought more than 5 million
mou of farmland under irrigation.

The construction of a 127-kilometer canal on the northern Anhwei
Plain began late in 1966 and was completed in 1969. The canal's
purpose was to reduce the menace of flood and waterlogging in the
Pienho (Toho) River basin, shich drains 22,800 square kilometers in
Honan, Kiangsu and Anhwei. With its source in Honan Province, the
Pienho River, a tributary of the Huai River, passes through Anhwei
and empties into the Hungtse Lake in Kiangsu. In the past, the Pienho
would reach flood level during the rainy season. The completion of the
"New Pienho River," as the canal is commonly called, has enabled the
water to converge from an area of more than 6,900 square kilometers
and flow to the Hungtse Lake through the man-made waterway.[7]

The Hai River

The Hai River itself is only a short stream flowing 30 miles
from Tientsin to the sea. But it serves as the outlet for five major
rivers that drain the North China Plain and converge fanlike at Tientsin.
These are the Northern Canal, a section of the Grand Canal formed at
Tungchow, east of Peking; the Yungting River, rising in northern
Shansi as the Sangchien River; the Tach'ing River, formed in central
Hopei; the Tzuya River, formed in south central Hopei by the junction
of the Huto and Fuyang Rivers; and the Southern Canal, a section of
the Grand Canal that receives the Wei River from northern Honan. In
high water seasons, the flow on the rapid-rising upper reaches of the
tributaries is far more than the Haiho can cope with. Several disastrous
floods of the Hai River occurred in pre-Communist days. In 1917 and

1939, the floods breached the dikes and inundated most of the metro-
polis of Tientsin and vast areas of farmland in Hopei.

The multi-purpose Kuant'ing reservoir was completed in 1953
on the Yungting River, the northermost of the five tributaries. The
reservoir is located at a narrow gorge below the confluence of the
Yungting and Kueishui rivers, 47 miles northwest of Peking. It impounds
80,131 million cubic feet (2,270 million cubic meters) of water, creating
a lake of 85 square miles (220 square kilometers). The reservoir has
made significant accomplishments in regulating the once widely fluctuating flow of the Yungting, which was 176,000 cubic feet per second
at its peak and 35 cubic feet per second at the minimum, and in reducing
the silt content of the river, which used to rise to as much as 40 percent
of the volume of the water. But the reservoir has not eliminated the
danger of flood, as evidenced by the overflow of the Yungting's banks
near Lukouch'iao (the Marco Polo Bridge) on August 6, 1956, which
inundated more than seven million acres of farmland.[8]

The reservoir itself was reported to be silting up at such a rate
that it affects energy output and water control as well as the irrigation
systems. It was feared that a complete silting-up of the reservoir
might take place in 60 years unless reforestation plans were set afoot at
at once.[9]

Scores of other reservoirs in addition to the Kuant'ing Reservoir
have been constructed on the upper reaches of the Hai River tributaries
to retain heavy torrents in the summer and store water for the dry
spring months; new outlets to the sea have been built on the lower
reaches to give swifter passage for the flood waters of the river.
But these measures apparently were not enough. In 1963, unusually
heavy rains swelled the Haiho and four of its five main tributaries
spilled over, doing extensive damage to farms. In response to a directive issued by Mao Tse-tung in November of that year, the relevant
departments of the Central Committee of the Chinese Communist
Party and the State Council, together with the Hopei Provincial Party
Committee and government, mapped out a new plan for harnessing
the Hai River based on the principle of "detaining water in the upper
reaches, dredging river beds in the middle reaches, and improving
drainage in the lower reaches."[10]

The new harnessing scheme divided the Hai River and its
tributaries into two major systems, southern and northern. The
southern system consisted of the Heilungkang River, the New Tzuya
River, the New Fuyang River, the Huto River, and the Tach'ing River;
the northern system included the Yungting River, the Northern Canal,

the Chaopai River, and the New Canal. During the seven years 1964-70, the work of the southern system was carried out by draining the Heilungkang basin, freeing more than 16 million mou (2.7 million acres) of farm land from floods; by building the New Tzuya River and the New Fuyang River, which drain 10,000 cubic meters of flood water per second; by strengthening the northern dike of the Huto River; and by reinforcing the banks and deepening and widening the channel of the Tach'ing River. In addition, 218 tributaries of the main rivers were dug and dredged, and more than 73,000 canals and ditches were constructed. In all these projects, a total of 1,500 million cubic meters of earthwork was dug.[11]

Following the completion of the southern system of the Hai River harnessing project late in 1970, the work on the northern system was jointly undertaken by Hopei Province and the municipalities of Peking and Tientsin. Together, the rivers of the northern system drain an area of more than 85,000 square kilometers.

The Pearl River

The Pearl River (Chu Kiang) delta is built up by the alluvial sediments of the three main rivers in Kwangtung and Kwangsi: the Hsi Kiang (West River), Pei Kiang (North River), and Tung Kiang (East River). This delta of less than 10,000 square kilometers, covering 11 hsien and the outskirts of three cities, is important in producing rice, sugar cane, silk cocoons, and jute. The low-lying alluvial land along the coast has suffered from river flooding, typhoons, rainstorms, and the backwash of sea tides, as well as from periodic drought. A number of dams, dikes, and tidal detention projects have been completed since 1949 to protect farmland and cities from floods and tidal waves, which often threaten the area in the wake of typhoons. A network of power transmission lines and 2,500 electric pumping stations with a total capacity of 180,000 kilowatts was completed in 1964 for irrigation and drainage purposes, and the construction of additional 2,000 stations with a total capacity of 58,000 kilowatts was planned. By the end of 1963, the network had been extended to cover 23 hsien and cities, with Canton as its center. It was expected that, with the completion of the project at the end of 1964, more than half a million hectares of farmland on the delta and its adjacent areas would have mechanized irrigation and drainage. But in the summers of 1959 and 1966, as a result of heavy rain in most parts of Kwangtung, farmland was inundated in many areas, especially along the East River basin.[12]

The Sungari and Liao Rivers

A low watershed of 800 feet separates the Manchurian plain
into the Sungari lowland in the north and the Liao lowland in the south.
The Sungari, known in Chinese as the Sunghua, flows northwest until
it meets the Nun River (Nonni). It then turns sharply northeast and
receives the Mutan River before joining the Amur on the Sino-Soviet
border. In the southern part of the Manchurian plain, the Liao River
flows east and south to the Gulf of Liaotung, west of the Liaotung
peninsula.

Because of the concentration of annual precipitation in July and
August, the Sungari basin is subject to frequent summer floods.
Heavy damage was reported from floods in the area in 1951, 1953, 1956,
1957, and 1960, despite the construction and repair of nearly 600
kilometers of dikes along the river. In 1956, a plan was mapped out
for the construction of eleven multipurpose reservoirs and other flood-
control projects along the Sungari and its tributaries.[13]

The Fengman reservoir, 15 miles southeast of Kirin, the capital
of Kirin Province, was the only large reservoir in Mainland China
before the Communists took over. It is located at the point where the
Sungari River leaves the East Manchuria uplands in a rapids-strewn
section. The Japanese built the multiple-purpose project during
World War II. The dam is 3,700 feet long and 300 feet high. The
hydroelectric plant had eight turbines of 70,000 kilowatts each, but by
the end of the war only two turbines were in operation as a result of
dismantling by the Soviet Army in 1946. The reservoir sustained
damage during the decisive battle between the Nationalists and the
Communists in the Northeast. During the First Five-Year Plan period,
the Peking government reconstructed the power plant with a projected
capacity of 567,000 kilowatts. In March 1954, a 220,000-volt transmission line was installed, linking the Fengman station with the
industrial complex at Shenyang over a distance of 230 miles. The
reconstruction project was completed in October 1959.[14]

More than 200 reservoirs and 1,000 kilometers of dikes have
been built along the West Liao River, a tributary of the Liao River,
to control its periodic floods. The river's silt-laden water has been
used to transform one-third of a million hectares of sandy land along
its banks.[15]

In addition to the projects for the principal rivers, flood-control
measures also have been taken for local water bodies. But floods and
waterlogging remain a major menace to agricultural production.

According to Chang Tzu-lin, President of the Research Institute of
Water Conservation and Hydroelectric Power:

> This is because the standards for the prevention of floods
> along the big rivers are not high enough, and large num-
> bers of medium-sized and small rivers have yet to be
> brought under control. Along the southeast coast, agri-
> cultural production is still menaced by tidal waves. The
> potentials of the existing engineering projects for the
> control of floods, the elimination of waterlogging and the
> resistance to tidal waves have not yet to be carried out.[16]

IRRIGATION

A large proportion of the cultivated land in China is irrigated,
about 15 percent in North China and nearly 70 percent in the rice-
growing regions. In both the wheat and rice regions, there is urgent
need for a larger and more dependable supply of water. The National
Program for Agricultural Development provided that paddy fields and
irrigated land should be expanded in twelve years from more than
390 million mou (65 million acres) in 1955 to approximately 900 million
mou (150 million acres) in 1967. For the purpose of ensuring good
harvests, the capacity of the irrigation facilities to resist drought
generally should be raised to between 30 and 50 days, according to the
varied conditions in the different localities. In places suitable for
double-crop paddy fields, the capacity should be raised to between 50
and 70 days (Article 5 of Program).

As shown in Table 8, there was only a gradual buildup in irrigated
acreage during the period 1949-57. However, a very large increase
was reported from 1957-58 and was attributed by Communist authorities
to the Leap Forward Campaign. According to Vice-Premier T'an Chen-
lin, the irrigated area had increased by 550 million mou (91.7 million
acres) in the first two years of the Leap Forward campaign. This
increase resulted in a total irrigated area of 1,070 million mou (178
million acres), of which 610 million mou (102 million acres) were
able to withstand drought for 30, 50, or 70 days as required by the
National Program for Agricultural Development.[17] In another account,
Vice-Minister of Agriculture, Ho Chi-feng claimed an increase of
total irrigated area in China from 230 million mou (38.5 million acres)
in 1949 to more than 1,000 million mou (167 million acres) in 1959, or
from 16.3 percent to more than 60 percent of the total cultivated area.
According to his account, this meant that China's irrigated area had
reached more than one-third of the world's total irrigated area to

TABLE 8

Irrigated Area in Communist China,
1949-66

Year	Total Area Under Irrigation (in millions of mou)
1949	240
1950	250
1951	280
1952	320
1953	330
1954	350
1955	370
1956	480
1957	520
1958	1,000*
1959 (planned)	1,100*
1960	820
1961	n.a.
1962	n.a.
1963	510
1964	500
1965	520
1966	560

*See explanation on page 81.

Sources: For 1949-58, State Statistical Bureau, Ten Great Years, English edition (Peking, 1960), p. 130; for 1959, "Report on the Draft Plan for the National Economy, 1959," by Vice-Premier Li Fu-ch'un at the First Session of the Second National People's Congress, April 21, 1959, Hsin-hua Pan-yueh-k'an [New China Semimonthly], Peking, No. 9, 1959, pp. 15-20; for 1960, Communique of the Ninth Plenary Session of the Eighth Central Committee of the Chinese Communist Party, January 14-18, 1961, JMJP, January 21, 1961, p. 1; for 1963, "Actively Do a Good Job in Water Conservation for This Winter and Next Spring," editorial, JMJP, November 30, 1963, p. 1; for 1964, Economic Reporter, Hong Kong, No. 895, November 16, 1964, p. 20; for 1965, JMJP, September 30, 1965, p. 2; for 1966, JMJP, September 30, 1966, p. 3.

become one of the most developed countries in water conservation.[18]

But several later statements have discredited the claims about total irrigated areas for 1958 and 1959. For example, the Communique of the Ninth Plenary Session of the Eighth Central Committee of the Chinese Communist Party, held on January 14-18, 1961, said that the area "effectively irrigated" had increased by more than 300 million mou in the three years of 1958, 1959, and 1960.[19] On that basis and on the assumption that 520 million mou of irrigated area in 1957 were all in the "effective" group, the total irrigated area in 1960 would have been only 820 million mou.

Also, at the end of 1963 a People's Daily editorial stated that irrigated land at that time was only one-third of the cultivated land, which was equivalent to a little over 500 million mou. This meant that the figure given by Ho Chi-feng for 1959 (1,000 million mou) was grossly exaggerated and that there had been no notable progress between 1957 and 1963, as most irrigation works during that period were directed at improvement of existing projects, repairs, and maintenance.[20]

The 1958 and 1959 claims also were contradictory to the statement made by Su Tsung-sung, Director of the Research Institute of Irrigation of the Chinese Academy of Agricultural Science, that the total area effectively irrigated in 1964 was approximately 500 million mou.[21] The total irrigated area in 1965 was reported to have increased 20 million mou over that of 1964, and the increase in the total irrigated area in 1966 was reported to have doubled the increase in 1965.[22] Based on Su Tsung-sung's figure for 1964 (500 million mou), the irrigated area would have been 520 million mou in 1965 and 560 million mou in 1966. These figures compare with the 1,000 million mou claimed for 1958 and the 1,100 million mou planned for 1959.

At present, irrigation in Communist China still depends mainly on human and animal labor, while only a small portion is operated mechanically (by diesel, gas, or steam engines) or electrically. In September 1965, "power-driven irrigation and drainage systems" served a total area of 84 million mou, which was little over 16 percent of the 520 million mou irrigated and drained by all means in that year.[23]

During 1960 and 1961, the government set up more than ten electric irrigation areas, each embracing more than one million mou (167,000 acres). The electric irrigation areas were mostly in regions producing grain and cotton where adequate electric and water sources

were available or in vegetable-producing areas around the cities or
the industrial and mining districts. These included (1) the rice-
producing regions of the Pearl River Delta in Kwangtung, southern
and northern Kiangsu, and the Hangchow-Kashing-Huchow area in
Chekiang; (2) the important grain and cotton regions around Tientsin,
Tangshan, Shihchiachuang, Paoting, and Changchiak'ou in Hopei, the
Kuanchung area in Shensi, the area in northern Honan, the areas
around Chengchow, Loyang, and Sanmen Gorge in Honan, the areas
along the Shih River, the Pi River, and the Hangpu River in Anhwei
and the area in southern and central Shansi; and (3) the vegetable-
producing regions in the suburbs of Peking, Shanghai, and Tientsin.[24]

Since the mid-1960's the government has placed increasing
emphasis on the use of electric pumping facilities for irrigation and
drainage. In 1964, there were 4 million horsepower of mechanical
pumping facilities in the rural areas, as against 2.04 million horsepower
of electric pumping facilities. Thus, the ratio was about 2:1 in favor
of mechanical pumping facilities.[25] But since then electric pumping
facilities have increased more rapidly. It would seem that in the
1970's or so electric irrigation and drainage will catch up with mechanical irrigation and drainage mainly because of the lower cost of the
electric methods.

In addition to modern mechanical and electric pumping facilities,
many traditional types of irrigation and drainage equipment have been
improved or semimechanized during the 1950's and 1960's. An
improved type of waterwheel has played an increasingly important
role in irrigating and draining paddy fields. The conventional type of
waterwheel used in South China consists of a chain of wooden paddles
and a wooden trough, the lower end of which is put in water. As the
chain rotates, paddles pass through the trough and raise the water.
The new type of waterwheel replaces the wooden trough with a round
or square tube and reduces the number of paddles. The paddles are
of the same size as the inner diameter of the tube, and as they pass
through the tube below the plates becomes a vacuum, causing the
water to rise as in a pump. The new waterwheel is said to be two or
three times more efficient and to cost and weigh two-thirds less than
the traditional type. It can be made in various sizes and materials
(wood, bamboo, plastic, or steel) and in different forms for operation
by hand, treadle, a draft animal, or a motor. It can be installed and
operated almost vertically, whereas the old type can work only at a
slightly inclined angle.[26]

The use of a new type of turbine pump has been popularized in
many areas in the south and southwest for lifting water to the upland

fields. In the Kwangsi-Chuang Autonomous Region and in Fukien, Szechuan, Hunan, and Kweichow provinces, the improved turbine pumps are said to have enabled some communes to keep their paddyfields watered during an unusually severe dry spell.[27] Composed of a water turbine and a pump, the turbine pump consumes neither electricity nor oil and is capable of lifting water to higher levels through water pressure. In addition to irrigation, it is used in supplying drinking water, generating electricity, and processing agricultural products. Turbine pumps were first installed in China's hilly areas in 1956 and were popularized in 1964. In mountainous areas of Hunan Province alone, their number increased from 370 in 1963 to more than 8,300, capable of irrigating some 1.1 million mou of farm land, early in 1966. In South China's hilly provinces, there were 43,000 turbine pumps in 1966, irrigating more than 3 million mou of farm land.[28]

Raising water for irrigation is less expensive by turbine pumps than by waterwheels, internal combustion engines, or electric motors, but the turbine pump can only be used where a rapid flow of water is available to produce sufficient power. Therefore, it cannot be used for lifting water at rest.

Other kinds of pumps currently in use include chain pumps, centrifugal pumps suited for irrigation in river-covered areas in the south, hydraulic pumps operated by water power and three-part serial pumps for raising water uphill, deep well pumps of various types, submersible electric pumps, internal combustion water pumps, and dredgers that also can be used for pumping water.[29]

Along the lower reaches of the Yellow River in Shantung Province, more than 70 siphons have been built since 1965 to draw silt for fertilizing some 200,000 mou of paddy rice fields as well as to draw water for irrigating the land. The project was first experimented at Lich'eng near Tsinan, with reportedly successful results, and later was extended to 16 other hsien along the Yellow River. Power-operated irrigation and drainage equipment has been installed near the siphons to draw water when siphons fail to draw an adequate quantity during a dry season. The use of siphons for irrigation does not seem to have proceeded beyond the experimental state.[30]

For irrigation as well as for grain processing, new models of windmills have been developed and widely used in the coastal areas.[31]

OTHER MAJOR PROJECTS

In addition to the projects already discussed, many other

important ones involving both irrigation and flood control have been
planned or carried out. One of these was to draw southern waters to
the north. The annual volume of water in China totals about 2,680 cubic
kilometers (95,000,000 million cubic feet). It was estimated that
approximately 500 cubic kilometers (17,650,000 million cubic feet)
for irrigation were needed in 1958 and 700 to 800 cubic kilometers
(24,710,000 to 28,240,000 million cubic feet) in 1960. Therefore, for
China as a whole water resources are more than sufficient for irrigation
uses. However, the situation varies among the different regions. The
water in the basins of the Yellow River, the Huai River, and the Hai
River is far from sufficient for the irrigation uses. In the south, on
the other hand, water is abundant, more than sufficient for developing
cultivated and wasteland in the whole area.

Thus, a natural solution is to draw water from the rivers in the
south, particularly the Yangtze and its tributaries, to the rivers in the
north, including the Yellow River, the Huai River, and the Hai River.
Work on a preliminary plan to draw water from the upper reaches of
the Yangtze to the Yellow River through a series of canals and channels
has been started by the Yellow River Water Conservation Committee
of the Ministry of Water Conservation. A similar plan to draw the
water of the Sungari River to the Liao River has been studied jointly
by two surveying and designing institutes in Harbin and Shenyang; in
this case the direction is actually from north to south.[32]

Meantime, it has been realized that tremendous amounts of money,
materials, and labor would be needed to direct southern waters to the
north. Furthermore, although master plans of water conservaton for
some of the individual rivers concerned already have been completed,
they would have to be revised according to the changing conditions,
while plans for other rivers, including the Yangtze and the Sungari,
must be completed before the entire program to draw southern waters
to the north can be started. Therefore, the authorities have urged
that, at least for the time being, as much water as possible from the
individual rivers should be used for irrigation purposes in the respective basins.

Another plan frequently discussed was to increase the use of
ground water for irrigation. Many areas in North China and Northwest
China are subject to frequent threat of drought because of little precipitation and lack of surface water. However, some of these areas
are well-endowed with deposits of ground water that, if properly
utilized, could extend irrigation considerably.[33]

In considering this plan, the Communist authorities may not
have taken into account the possibility that the water might contain too

much salt. However, it was admitted that in Hopei Province, as more
wells were dug, less and less underground water was obtainable from
each well. In any case, like the plan to draw water from the south to
the north, the plan for increasing use of ground water has only reached
a preliminary stage because of financial and technical difficulties.

One of the most publicized water conservation projects was the
construction in 1958 and 1959 of a canal network on some 40 million
mou (6.7 million acres) of cultivated land in the area north of the
Huai River in Anhwei Province. The "canalization" project was
carried out in view of the extraordinary floods in that area in 1950,
1952, and 1956 and the equally disastrous drought in 1957. The project
consisted of the construction of 9 canals, 2,621 large ditches, 15,732
medium-sized ditches, and 111,074 small ditches. The project was
scheduled to be completed at the end of 1959. It was expected that the
"canalization" would improve the irrigation of some 42.7 million mou
(7.1 million acres) of cultivated land in the area, prevent floods and
droughts, and provide facilities for navigation and for raising fish
and aquatic plants.[34]

Eight other provinces (Hopei, Honan, Shantung, Shansi, Liaoning,
Kirin, Heilungkiang, and Shensi) and the Autonomous Region of Inner
Mongolia also were reported to have mapped out plans for the construction of canals and ditches in a total area of 366 million mou
(61 million acres), to be completed by the end of 1959.[35] No details
on the plans and their implementation have been revealed. The "canalization" project apparently did not produce good results, as evidenced
by the serious floods and droughts in these provinces in 1960. In
fact, because of improper construction and lack of drainage system,
the project has resulted in salification and alkalization of land in
many areas.

METEOROLOGICAL AND HYDROLOGICAL WORK

As an important part of the program to combat natural calamities,
increasing attention has been given to the improvement of meteorological and hydrological work. The National Program for Agricultural
Development called for the completion of the networks of meteorological
observatories and stations and hydrological survey stations in the
twelve years beginning in 1956 (Article 22). In 1965, the number of
observatories and stations in Mainland China reached 2,470, exceeding
by nearly 50 percent the number in 1957. Also in 1965, observatories
had been set up in more than 90 percent of administrative districts
(chou and leagues), and meteorological or weather stations had been
established in more than 80 percent of hsien throughout the country.

Meteorological posts also had been set up in many communes.[36]

In March 1953, a team for studying agricultural meteorology was jointly organized by the Research Institute of Geophysics of the Chinese Academy of Sciences and the former North China Research Institute of Agricultural Science. This team was expanded in 1957 to become the Research Institute of Agricultural Meteorology under the Chinese Academy of Agricultural Science. The institute, in collaboration with the Central Meteorological Bureau under the State Council, co-ordinates the work of the meteorological offices and stations in rural areas throughout the country. The institute has conducted studies on the effects of climate on the growth of principal crops, the relationship of cultivation practices to climatic conditions, measures for the reduction of forest fires, the improvement of weather forecasting, and the development of simplified, low-cost meteorological apparatus for use on farms. In 1956, a unified method of meteorological observations for agricultural purposes was adopted by the Central Meteorological Bureau as a guide to farmers.

In accordance with the "walking on two legs" policy, both modern and old methods of meteorology were adopted. Although the Western calendar is used in daily life and for all official purposes, farmers are urged to observe the 24 chieh ch'i. These are the 24 periods of approximately 15 days each that make up a year according to the Chinese calendar. Each period is supposed to be characterized by certain climatic conditions. Farmers also are urged to note the adages depicting knowledge of climate that has been learned from centuries of experience and passed on from generation to generation.[37]

Since 1958, "supplementary weather forecasts" have been developed in various provinces as part of the agricultural meteorological network. These are local weather forecasts prepared by the hsien (county) weather stations on the basis of the wide area weather forecasts prepared by the major stations but with revisions made according to local meteorological data and the experience of local peasants.[38]

At the end of 1957, there were some 8,000 hydrological survey stations throughout the country. Although this total was reported to be an increase of 22 times over that in 1949, nearly one-half of the country was still without hydrological services in 1957. The Hydrological Bureau under the Ministry of Water Conservation, in collaboration with local stations, conducts surveys on water level, flowing capacity, silting, precipitation, and evaporation of the major sources of water. In addition to compiling the current data, the bureau has reorganized and analyzed the materials prepared before the Communist takeover of Mainland China. Also, by the end of 1957 the bureau had established over 2,700 hydrological information stations for reporting and forecasting the water conditions of more than 100 rivers of various sizes.

In more recent years, emphasis has been given to the strengthening of hydrological research, the expansion of the networks of hydrological survey stations and hydrological information stations, especially those operated by local governments, and the study of underground water in view of the importance of its use in agriculture.[39]

THE PROSPECTS

Despite some improvement in water conservation work in recent years, many areas in Mainland China are still vulnerable to periodic floods and droughts. Lu Wu, Deputy Director of the Century Meteorological Bureau, revealed in 1966 that calamities from floods and droughts had not been avoided in any single year since 1949. The seasons and regions in which serious floods and droughts occurred during the period 1949-65 were given as follows:[40]

	Floods	Droughts
1949 summer	Haiho basin	
1950 summer	Huai River basin	
1954 summer	Yangtze River basin	
1956 summer	Yangtze and Huai basins	
1957 summer	Northeast China	
1957 summer-autumn		Huai River basin
1958 summer		South of the Yangtze
1959 summer		Yangtze and Huai basins
1959 spring	South China	
1959 summer	North China	
1960 spring		North China
1960 summer		Central China
1961 spring		North China
1961 summer		Central China
1963 spring		South China
1963 summer	North China	
1965 summer		North China
1965 summer	Huai River basin	

Table 9 shows the acreage of farmland affected annually by floods and droughts in 1949-61 and the number of persons so affected in 1949-56. The acreage of farm land affected during the period 1957-61 increased very rapidly, despite the claimed ability of the communes to "conquer the nature through their collective strength and self-relience." Table 10 shows the annual grain losses caused by floods and droughts in 1949-56, ranging from 2.0 percent to 6.3 percent of potential production. On the basis of the acreage of farmland affected, grain crops probably suffered greater losses from floods and droughts in 1957-61 than in 1949-56.

But it was not until the end of 1960 that the seriousness of floods and droughts was revealed. According to the official New China News Agency, the worst natural calamities in a hundred years hit China in 1960 and 900 million mou (150 million acres), or more than half of the 1,600 million mou of cultivated land, were affected with varying intensity. Of this total, 300-400 million mou (50-67 million acres) suffered heavily, and "a part of the farmland" did not produce anything.

The greatest havoc was caused by droughts, which affected 600 million mou (100 million acres). With the exception of Tibet and Sinkiang, all other provinces and autonomous regions suffered from droughts at different times and with varying intensity. Hopei, Honan, Shantung, Shansi, Shensi, Inner Mongolia, Kansu, Szechuan, Yunnan, Kweichou, Kwangtung, Kwangsi, and Fukien were affected by droughts in both the spring and summer, while parts of Kiangsu, Anhwei, Chekiang, Hupeh, Honan, and Kiangsi were affected in the summer. More than 60 percent of the cultivated area in Hopei, Honan, Shantung, and Shansi was affected by droughts lasting for seven or eight months. In some areas, such as Linhsien and Ch'angkeh in Honan, the droughts lasted for more than a year. During the worst period of the droughts, eight of the twelve principal rivers in Shantung and certain sections of the lower reaches of the Yellow River had virtually no water.

Twenty provinces and autonomous regions were invaded by typhoons and floods in 1960, most seriously in Liaoning, Kirin, Heilung-kiang, Kwangtung, Fukien, Kiangsu and Shantung. Eastern Liaoning suffered the worst floods in the hydrological record of the province. The floods were aggravated by eleven devastating typhoons, the number being the highest for one year in the previous fifty years.[41]

In some cases, the Communist authorities might have exaggerated the seriousness of the adversities for the purposes of lowering food and clothing rations, raising the quota of state purchases of grains and cotton, or using the figures as an excuse for agricultural failures.

TABLE 9

Farmland Area and Number of Persons Affected by Floods
and Droughts, 1949-60

Year	Farmland Area Affected (thousands of mou)			Number of Persons Affected (thousands)		
	Total	Floods	Droughts	Total	Floods	Droughts
1949	127,870	127,870	--	45,550	45,550	--
1950	76,830	70,650	6,180	33,840	32,050	1,790
1951	56,630	22,140	34,490	30,340	10,440	19,900
1952	66,490	27,660	38,930	27,600	10,710	16,890
1953	58,090	47,970	10,120	17,250	14,760	2,490
1954	177,640	172,750	4,890	63,150	62,230	920
1955	108,100	46,090	62,010	24,950	13,530	11,420
1956	230,000	170,000	60,000	70,000	n.a.	n.a.
1957	200,000	n.a.	n.a.	n.a.	n.a.	n.a.
1958	570,000	100,000	470,000	n.a.	n.a.	n.a.
1959	650,000	n.a.	n.a.	n.a.	n.a.	n.a.
1960	900,000	300,000	600,000	n.a.	n.a.	n.a.
1961	900,000	n.a.	n.a.	n.a.	n.a.	n.a.

Source: For 1949-55, Hsü K'ai, "Irrigation Work in China," Chung-kuo Shui-li [China Water Conservation], No. 10, 1956, pp. 5-18, (there are considerable discrepancies between the figures for 1953-55 given here and those given by Chou Po-p'ing in "State Purchases and State Sales of Grains Should Not be Opposed," Liang Shih [Grains], Peking, No. 7, 1957, pp. 1-4); for 1956, Chou En-lai, "Report to the Fourth Session of the First National People's Congress, June 26, 1957," Hsin-hua Pan-yüeh-k'an [New China Semimonthly], No. 14, 1957, pp. 1-16; Wang Kuang-wei, "Simultaneous Development of Industry and Agriculture, with Heavy Industry as Foundation," in 1956-1967-nien Ch'uan-kuo Nung-yeh Fa-chan Kang-yao (Hsiu-cheng Ts'ao An) Chiang-hua [Lectures on the National Program for Agricultural Development, 1956-1967 (Revised Draft)] (Peking, 1958), p. 21. For 1957, Hsü Ti-hsin, Chung-kuo Kuo-tu Shih-ch'i Kuo-min Ching-chi ti Fen-hsi [An Analysis of China's National Economy During the Transitional Period], revised (Peking, 1959), p. 129. For 1958, Chu Hsien-li "In Celebration of the National Agricultural Exhibition," Nung-yeh K'o-hsueh T'ung-hsun [Agricultural Science Bulletin], Peking, No. 2, 1959, pp. 44-45, 56. For 1959: JMJP, January 23, 1960, p. 2. For 1960: JMJP, December 29, 1960, p. 1. For 1961: Ta Kung Pao, Hong Kong, April 1, 1964.

TABLE 10

Grain Losses Caused by Floods and Droughts,
1949-56

Year	Grain Production (millions of chin)	Grain Losses (millions of chin)	Losses as a Percentage of Potential Production
1949	216,200	11,400	5.0
1950	249,400	5,200	2.0
1951	270,100	6,300	2.3
1952	308,800	n.a.	n.a.
1953	313,800	15,000	4.5
1954	320,900	17,700	5.2
1955	349,600	12,800	3.3
1956	365,000	24,400	6.3

Sources: Ten Great Years (English edition) (Peking, 1960),
p. 119; Hsin-Hua Pan-yueh-k'an [New China Semimonthly], No. 2,
1958, p. 109; Chou Po-p'ing, "State Purchases and State Sales of
Grains Should Not be Opposed," Liang Shih [Grains], Peking, No. 7,
1957, pp. 1-4.

But in any case it was noticeable that the haphazard and rash handling
of water conservation work had contributed to the deterioration of
water and soil conditions and had intensified the droughts and floods.
Many of the projects did not perform their functions as satisfactorily
as expected because of improper planning, lack of coordination, and
poor quality of construction.

While making fabulous claims, Vice-Minister of Agriculture
Ho Chi-feng admitted that, although nearly two-thirds of the country's
cultivated land had been equipped with irrigation facilities, irrigation
could only be carried out in a normal manner on less than one-third of
of this land. Many of the projects had not developed their usefulness
in time or had begun to irrigate with only low resistance to drought.[42]

The situation apparently did not improve in most recent years;
in 1962 the People's Daily revealed that only one-third of all cultivated
land throughout the country was effectively irrigated and that the
efficiency of and benefit from the water conservation projects had not
been fully exploited because of improper planning, incomplete

assembling of facilities, untimely maintenance and repair, and inadequate management.[43] In another editorial, the paper revealed that, although water conservation facilities were well managed on the Manass River in Sinkiang, west Urumchi, in the Lohui canal irrigation area in Shensi, and in the Ch'ienchin Reservoir in Hunan, many other works were not well done and had very limited usefulness.[44]

Moreover, improper construction and mismanagement of water conservation projects have caused salification and alkalization of land in many areas. In the latter part of 1959, when 70 million peasants were reported to be working on the "canalization" project, some individuals issued warnings that this would bring disaster. But these people were called "rightists."[45] It was not until the early part of 1961 that the damage was admitted. In an article in the People's Daily, Huang Ping-wei, Director of the Research Institute of Geography, Chinese Academy of Sciences, stated: "A secondary cause of alkaline soil is to be attributed to improper action by man, chiefly to improper arrangement of irrigation."[46]

An article in the Kuang-ming Daily by Hsiung I and Wang Tsunch'i described the situation as follows:

There are many regions in which one can find examples of the soil becoming alkaline because it was irrigated but was not drained at the time of drought of semi-drought. In some places, the water rose suddenly and irrigation was stopped. In other places, salt water lay on the land for a long time and improvement of the soil was not attempted; there are regions where arable land is continually shrinking and alkali soil spreading. Agricultural work is badly affected.[47]

A more specific statement on the degree of alkalization of soil was later given by the People's Daily, which said that owing to the wrong irrigation system there was a considerable increase of alkaline land in Northern Kiangsu, in the North China plain of Hopei, Shantung, and Shansi, in the plains along the Sungari and Liao rivers, in the valleys of Inner Mongolia, and in Shensi, Kansu, Chinghai, and Tibet.[48]

Since the failure of the "canalization," the overall policy for the improvement of water conservation programs has been to emphasize the organization and management of various irrigation and drainage projects, including the following aspects: designing, planning, installation, repair, maintenance, and financing. Special attention has been given to the completion of the constituent parts of certain existing projects to make them work more effectively and to link them into integrated systems. Also, a number of drainage projects have been carried out along with irrigation projects in order to reduce water-logging and to expedite desalinization, especially in the depression areas along the coasts of Liaoning, Hopei, Shantung, and northern Kiangsu and in the beach areas around Tungting, Poyang, Hungtze, and other principal lakes. In the meantime, because of the shortage of steel, cement, stone, timber, and other necessary materials as well as financial and technical difficulties, the government has continued to depend heavily on small projects that can be built by the collective efforts of the communes. Mass campaigns have been launched through-out the country for sinking pump wells, dredging river courses, and draining flood water. In the north, wells of both traditional and semi-mechanical types remain the most important tools for irrigation, while turbine pumps are widely used in the south to bring water uphill. Since cement reinforcement and stone dikes are expensive, the old method of earth banking is adopted for controlling floods. Machines are seldom used for dredging rivers.[49] Very few large projects were carried out or planned during the late 1960's, as such projects would involve tremendous outlays of funds on the part of the central govern-ment.[50]

In view of these limitations, it is highly doubtful that ordinary floods and droughts could have been eliminated by the end of 1967, as anticipated in the National Program for Agricultural Development. In fact, it seems very unlikely that the requirements for floods and drought control could be fulfilled within the next few decades by depending mainly on small projects constructed with mass labor and materials available locally. Without modern methods and materials as well as better management, only limited progress can be made in the water conservation program.

NOTES

1. Ho Chi-feng, "Glorious Achievements of Water Conservation in Rural China for the Past Ten Years," Shui-li Shui-tien Chien-she [Water Conservation and Hydroelectric Construction], Peking, No. 18, 1959, pp. 13-17.

2. NCNA-English, Sanmen Gorge, Honan, April 13, 1957.

3. JMJP, April 25, 1959, p. 9.

4. "No Miracle Is Impossible," China Reconstructs, No. 10, 1970, pp. 19-25.

5. Yang Jen-chang, Ch'ang Chiang [The Yangtze River] (Peking, 1958), pp. 22-26.

6. NCNA, Tsinan, October 8, 1963.

7. NCNA-English, Hofei, Anhwei, May 15, 1966; NCNA, Peking, December 2, 1969.

8. Fang Tsung-tai and Jen Tao-heng, "A Study of the Overflow of the Yungting River and the Functioning of the Kuant'ing Reservoir," Chung-kuo Shui-li [China Water Conservation], Peking, No. 5, 1957, pp. 66-73.

9. Jean Messines, "Forest Rehabilitation and Soil Conservation in China," Unasylva, Rome, Vol. XII, No. 3 (1968), pp. 103-20.

10. NCNA-English, Peking, November 23, 1966.

11. " A New Chapter in the History of River Regulation--A Report on the Great Struggle by the People in Hopei Province to Regulate the Haiho," Kuang-ming Jih-pao [Kuang-ming Daily] Peking, November 18, 1970, p. 1.

12. Yang-ch'eng Wan-pao [Canton Evening Post], June 24, 1966, p. 1; June 26, 1966, p. 1; June 27, 1966, p. 1. NCNA-English, Canton, October 24, 1961; November 12, 1963.

13. Ch'iang Hsiao-ch'u (Secretary of the Heilungkiang Provincial Committee of the Chinese Communist Party), "Immediately and Fundamentally Control the Sungari," statement made at the Eighth National Congress of the Chinese Communist Party, September 1956, Jen-min Shou-ts'e [People's Handbook] (Peking, 1957), pp. 502-3; Chang Tzu-lin, "Universal Construction of Water Conservation Projects and Technical Transformation of Agriculture," Shui-li yu Tien-li [Water Conservation and Electric Power], Peking, No. 16, 1963.

14. JMJP, October 6, 1959, p. 1.

15. NCNA, Huhehot, June 15, 1963.

16. Chang Tzu-lin, "Universal Construction of Water Conservation Projects and Technical Transformation of Agriculture," Shui-li yu

94 AGRICULTURE IN COMMUNIST CHINA

Tien-li [Water Conservation and Electric Power], Peking, No. 16, 1963; Chang Tzu-lin, "Water Conservation and Agricultural Production," JMJP, August 29, 1963, p. 5.

17. T'an Chen-lin, "Strive for the Fulfillment, Ahead of Schedule, of the National Program for Agricultural Development," JMJP, April 7, 1960, p. 1.

18. Ho Chi-feng, "Glorious Achievements of Water Conservation in Rural China in the Past Ten Years," Shui-li Shui-tien Chien-she [Water Conservation and Hydroelectric Construction], Peking, No. 18, 1959, pp. 13-17.

19. JMJP, January 21, 1961, p. 1.

20. "Actively Do a Good Job in Water Conservation for This Winter and Next Spring," editorial, JMJP, November 30, 1963, p. 1.

21. Economic Reporter, Hong Kong, No. 895 (November 16, 1964), p. 20.

22. JMJP, September 30, 1965, p. 2; September 30, 1966, p. 3.

23. Special NCNA report on the occasion of the sixteenth anniversary of the founding of the People's Republic of China, NCNA-English, Peking, September 16, 1965.

24. JMJP, December 23, 1961, p. 1.

25. NCNA, Peking, September 20, 1964.

26. Peking Review, No. 34, 1965, p. 23.

27. Peking Review, No. 20, 1964, p. 29; JMJP, April 19, 1964, pp. 1, 4.

28. NCNA, Peking, June 11, 1966; NCNA-English, Changsha, June 2, 1966.

29. Liu Pang, "Paving a Way to Agricultural Mechanization in China," JMJP, April 13, 1966, p. 2.

30. JMJP, May 23, 1965, p. 1.

31. Wu Sheng-hsun, "Windmills Currently Used in China's Rural Areas," JMJP, June 22, 1964, p. 5.

32. "Certain Questions Concerning the Future Development of China's Water Conservation Work," a statement by the leader of the Soviet water conservation team at the National Conference on Hydro-electrics held in Tientsin in January 1959, Shui-li Shui-tien Chien-she [Water Conservation and Hydroelectric Construction], Peking, No. 6, 1959, pp. 36-42.

33. Ho Ch'ang-kung, "Investigate Ground Water Resources; Aid Agricultural Production," Hung Ch'i [Red Flag], Peking, Nos. 9/10, 1961, pp. 42-47.

34. Chang Tso-yin, "Canalization of Huaipei," Chung-kuo Nung-pao [Chinese Agriculture Bulletin], Peking, No. 15, 1958, pp. 3-6.

35. "Canalization--A Measure for Water Conservation on the Plains," editorial, Chung-kuo Nung-pao [Chinese Agriculture Bulletin], No. 15, 1958, p. 2.

36. JMJP, April 23, 1965, p. 2.

37. Research Institute of Agricultural Meteorology, "Accomplishments in Agricultural Meteorology Since the Founding of the People's Republic of China," Nung-yeh Hsueh-pao [Acta Agriculturae Sinica], Peking, Vol. X, No. 5 (1959), pp. 353-59.

38. Tan Wen-kuang, "On the Development of Supplementary Forecasting by Minor Meteorological Stations," K'o-hsueh T'ung-pao [Scientia], Peking, No. 17, 1958, pp. 529-31.

39. Wang Tsu-p'ing, "Functions of Hydrology," 1956-1967-nien Ch'uan-kuo Nung-yeh Fa-chan Kang-yao (Hsiu-cheng Ts'ao-an) Chiang-hua [Lectures on the National Program for Agricultural Development, 1956-1967 (Revised Draft)] (Peking, 1958), pp. 155-61.

40. Lu Wu, "China's Climate and Calamities of Floods and Droughts," JMJP, January 26, 1966, p. 5.

41. JMJP, December 29, 1960, p. 1.

42. Ho Chi-feng, "Glorious Achievements of Water Conservation in Rural China in the Past Ten Years," Shui-li Shui-tien Chien-she [Water Conservation and Hydroelectric Construction], Peking, No. 18, 1959.

43. "Actively Do a Good Job in Water Conservation for This

Winter and Next Spring," editorial, JMJP, November 30, 1963, p. 1;
"The Major Keys to Increasing the Efficiency of and the Benefits
from Water Conservation Projects," editorial, JMJP, April 10, 1962,
p. 1.

44. "Water Conservation and Stable and High-Yielding Farms,"
editorial, JMJP, August 5, 1964, p. 1.

45. JMJP, September 28, 1959, p. 9; December 30, 1959, p. 1.

46. Huang Ping-wei, "Several Problems to be Considered in
Expanding the Acreage of Cultivated Land," JMJP, May 5, 1961, p. 7.

47. Kuang-ming Jih-pao [Kuang-ming Daily], April 20, 1961.

48. JMJP, November 8, 1961, p. 2.

49. JMJP, October 16, 1965, p. 2; October 18, 1965, p. 3.

50. "Rely on 500 Million Peasants for Management of Water
Conservation," editorial, JMJP, March 11, 1966, p. 2; Liu Shen, "The
Policy of Emphasizing Small Projects Should Be Continued in Managing
Water Conservation," Ta Kung Pao, Peking, March 11, 1966, p. 3.

"Water decides whether there will be a harvest, and fertilizer decides whether the harvest will be good or bad," says an old Chinese farm adage. For centuries China has struggled to maintain a moderate level of soil fertility by the use of human and animal wastes. However, years of cropping and heavy erosion have greatly reduced the soil fertility. To rebuilt depleted soils, large quantities of chemical fertilizers are required in addition to the usual organic fertilizers. Under the "walking on two legs" policy, the Communist government has placed equal emphasis on the use of chemical fertilizers and organic fertilizers, but the latter group--including human and animal excrements, green manure, pond and canal sediment, ashes, and industrial wastes-- remains the principal source of soil fertilizer.

The National Program of Agricultural Development urged the agricultural cooperatives (now the communes) to produce locally as much as possible of the farm manure and chemical fertilizers they needed (Article 6). During the Leap Forward campaign, almost every-one in the countryside took a hand in helping to accumulate animal manure or manufacture chemical fertilizers in local plants. Factory and office workers, students, housewives, and members of army units from towns and cities joined the rural population in a massive cam-paign of manure collection and fertilizer production. On January 28, 1959, an order was issued to the communes to the effect that, in the allocation of manpower for the winter work program, priority should be given to manure collection and fertilizer production over work on irrigation and deep plowing. "Manure can be found everywhere and fertilizers can be made from almost anything," said the People's Daily, exhorting Communist China's millions to heed the directive.[1]

ORGANIC FERTILIZERS

Hog raising has been encouraged as an important source of manure as well as meat, bristles, and hides. The National Program for Agricultural Development required each household in the country-side to raise an average of 1.5 to 2 hogs by 1962 and 2.5 to 3 hogs by 1967, except in the Moslem areas where for religious reasons the communes and their members were urged to raise sheep (Article 6).

The number of hogs at the end of 1949 and each year from 1952 through 1959 are given in Table 11. According to Vice-Premier T'an Chen-lin, 270 million hogs were raised in 1959 and there were 180 million hogs in the sties at the end of that year. Thus, on the basis of 120 million farm households in the country, the average number of hogs raised by each household during the year was more than two, and that of hogs in the sties at the end of the year was 1.5. Thus, the target set for 1962 was reached ahead of schedule.[2]

Despite this claim, there has been an almost constant shortage of manure and the communes and their members frequently have been urged to raise more hogs through good care of sows, multiplying of shoats, improvement of fodder supply, proper maintenance of hog pens, and other measures. The shortage of fodder in particular has been a major problem in raising hogs as well as other domestic animals. Efforts have been made to improve the feeding of livestock by means of analysis of the chemical composition of feed from different parts of the country and study of methods to expand the cultivation of high-quality feed.

In the 1950's and 1960's, the number of hogs in Communist China has fluctuated, generally in response to changes of government policy on hog raising. During the early years of the Communist regime when hogs were mostly raised by individual farmers, the hog population grew steadily from 58 million in 1949 to 102 million in 1954. It declined to 88 million in 1955 and again to 84 million in 1956, because of agricultural cooperativization. In 1957, the government restored the emphasis on private hog raising and the number of hogs rose sharply to 146 million. Communization probably has resulted in a decline in the hog population, although official figures for both 1958 and 1959, like many other figures for the Leap Forward period, showed substantial increases. Data for the years after 1959 are not available, but it has been admitted that the number of hogs in 1960 dropped disastrously to fewer than 40 million, partly because of collective raising. Following the crop failure of 1959-61, it was necessary to adopt the policy of

Table 11

Number of Hogs at the End of the Year,
1949 and 1952-59

Year	Number of Hogs
Highest before 1949	78, 530, 000
1949	57, 750, 000
1952	89, 770, 000
1953	96, 131, 000
1954	101, 718, 000
1955	87, 920, 000
1956	84, 026, 000
1957	145, 900, 000
1958	160, 000, 000
1959	180, 000, 000

Sources: For the highest figure before 1949 and the figures for 1949, 1952, and 1957, State Statistical Bureau, Ten Great Years, English edition (Peking, 1960), p. 132; for 1953-56, Hsien-hua Pan-yueh-k'an [New China Semimonthly], Peking, No. 17, 1956, p. 43; for 1958, Ts'ai Tzu-wei, "Accomplishments in Animal Husbandry in the Past Decade," Chung-kuo Hsu-mu-hsueh Tsa-chih [China Animal Husbandry Magazine], Peking No. 10, 1959, pp. 289-93; for 1959, JMJP, January 23, 1960, p. 1.

simultaneous collective and private raising with emphasis on the latter. This policy was continued until the end of the Cultural Revolution, when collective raising again was stressed. However, it would appear that, continued emphasis on private raising would be necessary in order to increase the hog population.[3]

In addition to the accumulation of animal manure and night soil, the planting of green manure crops has been encouraged not only as a source of organic substances but also as a measure for water and soil conservation and to provide a feeding material for animals. The communes have been encouraged to grow green manure on fallow land and land between rows of other crops, and to raise hydrophytic green manure in bodies of water. Such green manure crops as sweet clover, cow vetch, and milk vetch traditionally are cultivated on winter fallow land in the rice-growing Yangtze River basin. These crops have proved effective in improving the acid red soils in South China and the saline land in North China. In recent years, they have been introduced in some areas in Kwangtung, Kwangsi, Shensi, and a few other provinces. In 1964, green manure crops were grown on more than 80 million mou of land, an increase of 1.37 times as compared with the acreage in 1952. The communes have been asked to further expand their produc- tion of these crops.[4]

But the production of green manure crops has been limited by seed shortage, cultivation systems, and natural conditions. Moreover, more than one-half the acreage of land growing these crops is in Kiangsi, Hunan, Chekiang, and a few other provinces, and its distribu- tion is very uneven.[5]

Other materials suggested as sources of organic fertilizers include wastes from food processing and other industries.[6]

CHEMICAL FERTILIZERS

The highest annual production of chemical fertilizers in Mainland China before the Communist takeover in 1949 was 227,000 tons In the period 1928-36, the average annual importation of chemical fertil- izers into the country, excluding Manchuria and Taiwan, was about 25,000 tons.[7] Thus, the use of chemical fertilizers in China before World War II was insignificant when compared to the vast agricultural area of the country.

Estimates on China's annual requirements for chemical fertilizers have differed widely, ranging from a few hundred thousand tons to as

much as 35 million tons. The National Program for Agricultural
Development urged the central and local authorities to produce approximately 5 to 7 million tons of chemical fertilizers annually by 1962 and
15 million tons annually by 1967. According to the "Report on Actual
Implementation of the 1959 National Economic Plan," released by the
State Statistical Burea on January 22, 1960, chemical fertilizer was
one of a few key industries whose output was far short of the goal for
the final year of the Second Five-Year Plan (1962). The production of
most other industries--including steel ingot, coal, electricity, metal-
lurgical equipment, generating equipment, and metal-cutting machin-
ery--was reported to have already either reached or exceeded the
1962 target. The 1959 output of 1,333,000 tons of chemical fertilizers,
on the other hand, represented only 19-27 percent of the goal for 1962,
which was between 5 and 7 million tons, or 9 percent of the target of
15 million tons set for 1967 in the National Program for Agricultural
Development. In view of the slow progress in 1958-59, the production
target for chemical fertilizers in 1962 was revised from 5-7 million
tons to 3-3.2 million tons.[8]

No actual amounts of annual chemical fertilizer production after
1959 have been released, and the figures for recent years shown in
Table 12 are based on the percentage increases or decreases over the
preceding years, according to various Communist sources. After a
slight increase in 1960, there was a decline in 1961 because of the
withdrawal of Soviet assistance and the general industrial recession.
Production in 1962 and 1963 was reported to have increased considerably as a result of the first-stage installation of the Wu Ching Chemical
Plant, the second-stage installation of the Kirin Chemical Fertilizer
Plant, and the trial production of the Canton Nitrogen Fertilizer Plant.
Production continued to increase until the Cultural Revolution, during
which very little information was released. It was not until 1970 that
the target of chemical fertilizer production set for 1967 in the National
Program for Agricultural Development was reported to have been
nearly fulfilled. According to Premier Chou En-lai, in 1970 production
was approximately 14 million tons, as compared with the 1967 target
of 15 million tons.[9]

The fundamental question as to what kinds of chemical fertilizers
should be produced in China has been discussed frequently. Field tests
conducted by the National Agricultural Research Bureau before World
War II indicated that the use of nitrogen fertilizers would give significant increase in yields in most area. Phosphorus fertilizers were
needed in a fewer number of cases, and potassium fertilizers still
less frequently.[10]

TABLE 12

Chemical Fertilizer Production
in Communist China, 1949-70

Year	Chemical Fertilizer Produced (tons)
Highest annual production before 1949	227,000
1949	27,000
1950	70,000
1951	129,000
1952	181,000
1953	226,000
1954	298,000
1955	332,000
1956	523,000
1957	631,000
1958	811,000
1959	1,333,000
1960	1,676,000
1961	1,431,000
1962	2,147,000
1963	3,000,000
1964	3,600,000
1965	6,400,000
1966	8,100,000
1970	14,000,000

Sources: For the highest annual production before 1949 and for annual production in 1949-58, State Statistical Bureau, Ten Great Years, English edition (Peking, 1960), pp. 97, 103 (all figures do not include ammonium nitrate); for 1959; JMJP , January 23, 1960, p. 1; for 1960, figure is derived by deducting the 1958 and 1959 figures from 3,819, 000 tons, which was the total production for 1958, 1959, and 1960, Ta Kung Pao, Hong Kong, October 1, 1962, p. 15; for 1961, figure is based on the statement that "production in 1961 was 52 times more than that in 1949," Ta Kung Pao, Hong Kong, October 1, 1962, p. 15; for 1961, figure is based on the statement that "the 1962 production of chemical fertilizers increased by 50 percent over that of 1961," NCNA, Peking, January 2, 1963; for 1963, "Keep On Winning the Victory," editorial, JMJP, January 1, 1964, p. 1; for 1964, "Premier Chou En-lai's Report on the Work of the Government, at the First Session of the Third National People's Congress," JMJP, December 31, 1964, pp. 1-2; for 1965, JMJP, December 18, 1965, p. 1; for 1966, JMJP, December 30, 1966, p. 3; for 1970, Edgar Snow, "Talks With Chou En-lai: The Open Door," The New Republic, Washington, D.C., March 27, 1971, pp. 20-23.

This question was again discussed at a national conference on fertilizer research held on August 1-9, 1957, under the auspices of the Chinese Academy of Agricultural Science. The participants agreed that practically all the soil in China is deficient in nitrogen; that red and yellow soils along and south of the Yangtze River and slightly acidic soil in Northeast China are generally deficient in phosphorus; and that potassium fertilizers are effective for increasing the production of certain crops in some regions. The conference recommended that priority be given to the production of fertilizers of nitrogen, phosphorus, and potassium, in that order.[11] Li Ch'ing-k'uei, President of the Chinese Society of Soil Science, estimated that 80 percent of the soil in China is deficient in nitrogen, 50 percent deficient in phosphorus, and 15 percent deficient in potassium.[12] Chang K'ai-yen, a member of an investigation tean on phosphorus fertilizer in Szechuan and Hupeh sponsored by the Ministry of Chemical Industry and the Ministry of Agriculture in 1961, was of the opinion that the manufacturing of both nitrogen and phosphorus fertilizers should be promoted.[13]

In 1957, the Chinese Academy of Agricultural Science set up a national network for experimentation with chemical fertilizers. The network was composed of agricultural research units in 27 provinces, autonomous regions, and municipalities. The major function of the network was to study the effective use of chemical fertilizers for different crops in different regions and on different types of soil. Experiments have been conducted on 19 crops. The results of the experiments were thoroughly discussed at a conference convened by the Academy in March 1963.[14]

Prior to the Communist regime, ammonium sulfate was the only chemical fertilizer produced in China, with the highest annual output estimated at 227,000 tons. Ammonium nitrate and calcium superphosphate were produced for the first time during the First Five-Year Plan, and ammonium bicarbonate, fused phosphate, ammonia water, and ammonium chloride during the Second Five-Year Plan. In 1962, nitrogen fertilizers produced in Communist China included ammonium nitrate, ammonium sulfate, ammonium chloride, calcium cyanamide, urea, ammonia water, and ammonium bicarbonate; phosphorus fertilizers included defluorinated phosphate fertilizer, superphosphate, and mixed nitrogen and phosphorus fertilizers; and potassium fertilizers included potassium sulfate, potassium chloride, and mixed nitrogen and potassium fertilizers.[15] Since 1962, successful trial production of triple superphosphate, calcium metaphosphate, granulated calcium superphosphate, and ammonium molybdate has been reported.

At present, Communist China is concentrating on the production of nitrogen fertilizers, although attempts also are being made to develop phosphorus and potassium fertilizers. In the production of nitrogen fertilizers, the proportion of ammonium sulfate is diminishing while that of ammonium nitrate is increasing. This is because ammonium sulfate contains a sulfate radical that tends to harden the soil and because its production requires large quantities of sulfuric acid, which is much needed by other industries. In recent years, production of liquid ammonia by small plants has been emphasized in order to reduce the cost of manufacturing and river transport.[16] But in 1970 ammonium sulfate remained the principal fertilizer produced in Communist China.[17]

Communist China also is paying considerable attention to the development of urea production. Urea is not only a highly effective nitrogen fertilizer but also an important raw material for manufacturing plastics, synthetic fibers, and pharmaceutical products, and a culture medium for the strain used in making high-grade feedstuffs. Furthermore, plant buildings for urea production require relatively little stainless steel, of which there is an acute shortage in China. A new technique in manufacturing granular urea, developed by the Nanking Chemical Fertilizer Plant in 1969, is reported to have and simplified the manufacturing and equipment.[18]

Since ammonium chloride and pure soda can be produced economically by a combined process and since the production of ammonium bicarbonate requires relatively little capital outlay or material in short supply, Communist China is also developing the production of these nitrogen fertilizers.[19]

In the pre-Communist days, China's chemical fertilizer industry consisted mainly of two nitrogen fertilizer plants, one set up by the Japanese in Dairen and the other by the Yung Li Company, a Chinese private enterprise, near Nanking. Both produced only ammonium sulfate. During the First and Second Five-Year Plans (1953-62), these two plants were expanded and three other large nitrogen fertilizer plants were constructed in Kirin, Taiyuan, and Lanchou. By the end of 1969, more than 20 large chemical fertilizer plants had been built.

In addition to these large plants, many "native-method fertilizer plants" were built in the communes during the Leap Forward campaign. These native-method chemical fertilizer plants varied widely in size, ranging from little shacks with two or three workers and few vats to plants capable of producing as much as 8,000 tons of liquid ammonia per year. The total production of the native-method plants is not known,

but it may have constituted an important portion of the total annual
chemical fertilizer production. Most of the fertilizers produced by
these plants were of low grade, only one-tenth to one-twentieth as
effective as those produced in modern chemical fertilizer plants,
according to a survey made in 1958 in Hopei, Kiangsu, Anhwei, and
several other provinces. In general, the method of preparing chemical
fertilizers in small local plants was to transform such materials as
nitrate rocks, bones, seaweed, and ashes from grasses and trees into
powder and liquids, and then to mix, boil, and drain these materials
so that finally a fertilizer containing a certain amount of nitrogen,
phosphorus, and potassium was produced. Generally, the percentages
of these elements were low. Sometimes, because of improper propor-
tions of the materials used, the fertilizer was either too acid or too
alkaline for the local soil. A similar problem existed in the preparation
of compost fertilizers, which are made from various materials including
vegetable refuse, human and animal manure, ashes, bones, feathers,
furs, industrial wastes, and mud taken from the bottom of lakes and
rivers.[20]

Because of the low efficiency of the small native-method plants,
an effort has been made since 1958 to transform as many of them as
possible into small modern-method plants. A small synthetic ammonia
plant with an annual output of 800 tons was constructed in 1959 by the
Dairen Chemical Company as an example of the modernization of
native-method chemical fertilizer plants. This plant was built under
the guidance of a work team composed of representatives of the State
Economic Commission, the State Construction Commission, the State
Planning Commission, the Ministry of Agriculture, and the Ministry
of Chemical Industry. The annual production of 800 tons of synthetic
ammonia was believed to be sufficient to meet the nitrogen needs of
some 200,000 mou (33,334 acres) of land. It was estimated that this
type of plant could be built by a commune in from four to six months
at a cost of 819,000 yuan (U.S. $335,000) and using 198 tons of steel.
However, the cost of production of nitrogen was found to be high, 400
yuan (U.S. $163) per ton as compared with 180 to 200 yuan (U.S. $74-82)
per ton at the larger plants.[21]

The attempt to improve small nitrogen fertilizer plants remained
unsuccessful until 1962, when a new process for producing ammonium
bicarbonate containing 17.5 percent nitrogen was developed by Hou
Te-pang, an American-trained engineer who also directed the operation
of the Yung Li Ammonia Plant constructed near Nanking in 1937. The
new process was first tested successfully at a chemical plant at Tanyang,
Kiangsu Province, and in 1963 the plant produced 2,600 tons of synthetic
ammonia which was used for making 10,000 tons of ammonium bicarbonate, exceeding the projected capacity by 30 percent.

The small plant is said to be superior in that it brings quicker results with less investment. It uses local resources to the full, rather than using coke and quality anthracite as in conventional plants. The small plant also economizes on equipment, raw material, and electric power. Since most of the plants are located in the countryside, the product is within easy reach of the users. Because of their small size, such plants can be built in large numbers by localities and there are no delay in supplying chemical fertilizers to the surrounding farms. Moreover, the small plant is easier to operate: most of the workers in the Tanyang Fertilizer Plant had received only a primary or junior middle school education.[22]

Because of the success at Tanyang, small nitrogen fertilizer plants using the new process have been constructed in Kiangsu, Anhwei Honan, Shantung, Shensi, Shanghai, and other important grain-producing provinces and municipalities. By June 1966, their total number exceeded 100. The total production capacity of small nitrogen fertilize plants increased from 2 percent of that of chemical fertilizer plants of all sizes in 1961 to 12.4 percent in 1965, 18 percent in 1966, 33 percent in 1968, and 43 percent in 1969.[23] At the end of 1969, Kiangsu Province alone had 40 small nitrogen fertilizer plants, 27 small phosphorus fertilizer plants, and 17 small fertilizer plants that are under construction.[24] Eighty percent of the province's hsien had their own plants.[25]

Between 300 million and 400 million mou of the cultivated land south of the Yangtze River are deficient in phosphorus, according to a survey made in 1964. To improve soil fertility, production, and use of phosphorus, in recent years fertilizers have been promoted in Kwangtung, Kwangsi, Yunnan, Chinghai, Chekiang, Szechuan, and Hunan In 1964, Communist China had nearly 100 phosphorus fertilizer plants with an aggregate annual production capacity of two million tons.[26]

Kwangtung and Kwangsi have made the most significant progress in the production and use of phosphorus fertilizers. In 1963, phosphorus fertilizers accounted for 85 percent of all the chemical fertilizers produced in Kwangtung, and they were used on 80 percent of the cultivated land in that province. In the same year, 25 of the 27 chemical fertilizer plants in Kwangtung produced mainly phosphorus fertilizers. The Chanchiang Chemical Industry Plant, with an annual production capacity of 100,000 tons of phosphorus fertilizers, was built in 1962 with state financing. Construction of the other 24 plants, with annual production capacities ranging from 3,000 to 15,000 tons was for the most part financed by district or hsien governments.[27]

In the Kwangsi-Chuang Autonomous Region, the Luchai Chemical Plant started its operation in 1965 with an annual production capacity

of 200,000 tons of calcium magnesium phosphate. Other phosphorus
fertilizer plants in the region had a total production capacity of more
than 250,000 tons annually.[28]

In Yunnan, the production and use of phosphorus fertilizers has
been popularized since 1965. Several plants have been constructed,
but the quality of their products is not high. Phosphorus fertilizers
are used in most areas of the province in conjunction with farm manure.
In 1964, the province produced more than 70,000 tons of phosphorus
fertilizers, and their use was extended to 40 hsien.[29]

There are several serious problems in the production of chemical
fertilizers in Communist China. First is the problem of inadequate
equipment. The Kirin, Lanchou, and other fertilizer plants built during
the First Five-Year Plan period were basically installed with imported
equipment. The equipment for the two nitrogen fertilizer plants in
Lanchou and Taiyuan was supplied primarily by the Soviet Union,
while that for the Szechuan Nitrogen Fertilizer Plant was imported
from Czechoslovakia.[30] In more recent years, Communist China
has imported fertilizer plants mainly from Western European countries, including in 1964; five synthetic ammonium plants from Great
Britain, each with an annual production capacity of 160,000 tons; a
urea plant from the Netherlands with an annual production capacity
of 175,000 tons; and two urea plants from Italy with a total annual
production capacity of 300,000 tons.[31]

Plans for the construction of heavy equipment for producing
chemical fertilizers were mapped out at the end of 1957 as a part of
the Second Five-Year Plan. The First Ministry of Machine Industry,
the Second Ministry of Machine Industry, the Ministry of Electric
Appliances and the Ministry of Chemical Industry formed a committee
including one vice-minister from each ministry, and technical personnel from the ministries were pooled for drawing up plans.[32] But
details of the plans and their implementation have not been revealed.

Since 1959, increasing quantities of equipment for producing
nitrogen fertilizers have been manufactured in China. Late in 1962,
Communist China claimed to be able to independently design and construct fertilizer plants of different sizes and build large high-pressure
compressors of 2,400-5,000 horsepower, high-pressure seamless
steel pipes, and high and super-pressure cast-steel containers. This
development of plant equipment was said to have helped not only the
chemical fertilizer industry but also the high-pressure organic
synthetic industry.[33]

Early in 1963, more than 100 machinery and electrical equipment factories throughout the country were assigned to produce full sets of equipment for the nitrogen fertilizer industry, These factories include boiler plants in Harbin and Shanghai, heavy machinery plants in Taiyuan and Canton, high-pressure valve factories in Shanghai and Shenyang, and air separating equipment factories in Kaifeng and Hangchow. However, most of these factories had to be remodeled before they could produce full sets of equipment for large nitrogen fertilizer plants (with each capable of producing the 25,000 tons of synthetic ammonia per year required for an annual production of 100,000 tons of ammonium sulfate fertilizer).[34]

The first-stage installation of the Wu Ching Chemical Plant at Shanghai, completed in September 1963, was the first large nitrogen fertilizer plant designed and constructed by Communist China with Chinese-produced equipment. Technical personnel from more than 90 construction and installation units in Shanghai participated in the project, and more than 100 factories in the city cooperated to manufacture the equipment, which previously had been largely imported. The equipment installed, which reportedly was capable of producing 25,000 tons of synthetic ammonia annually, included a high-pressure compressor, a large ammonia converter, and many precision meters. The completion of the project was hailed as "a momentous victory of China in her guideline of self-reliance in construction." Several ministries of the central government jointly sent a committee to Shanghai to study the method of installation.[35]

Early in 1965, a new workshop for producing 40,000 tons of urea annually went into trial operation at the Wu Ching Chemical Plant. The workshop consisted of more than 200 machines, including a huge compressor and a 36-meter high tower for recovering carbon dioxide. The largest machine weighed 120 tons. New types of stainless and alloy steel supplied by Chinese mills were used for resistance to high temperature, high pressure, and corrosion, according to China Reconstructs.[36]

With the completion of its third-stage construction in 1968, the Hopei Chemical Fertilizer Plant began large-scale production of urea. Designed, equipped, and installed by Chinese engineers, the plant was described as "having fully met advanced world standards with new processes, new catalysts and large modern equipment for producing urea and yet requiring only half as much investment, one-fourth as much plant area, and one-third as many workers as old-style factories."[37] The plant, which was reported to be one of the major projects in the Third Five-Year Plan, had begun producing ammonium nitrate earlier.[38]

Another important project using equipment designed, manufactured, and installed by Chinese technicians was the first large
modern nitrogen fertilizer plant, built in Shensi Province, which was
put into operation in 1969. The plant uses a carbonization process
for producing ammonium hydrocarbonate, which is said to be simpler
than other processes and to require less money, and time for construction.[39]

However, even with these reported accomplishments, Communist
China is still facing a serious problem of providing adequate equipment
for expanding production of chemical fertilizers.

Another serious problem is the shortage of funds for capital
construction investment. In 1961, when the policy of "developing
agriculture as the foundation of the national economy" was adopted,
41 percent of capital construction investment allowed to the Chinese
chemical industry was allocated for the production of chemical
fertilizer, a higher proportion than in any previous year.[40] Although
the actual amount of funds allocated to chemical fertilizers was not
revealed, it was obvious that this percentage was difficult to attain
because in the 1960's Communist China also gave more attention to
pesticides, plastics, textiles, rubber goods, enamelware, and other
industries, many of which require the use of chemicals.

Another difficulty is that the available supply of steel, cement,
timber, and other materials for the construction of fertilizer plants
is far below the actual need. The shortage of raw materials and
electric power for making chemical fertilizers is equally acute.
The phosphorus mines at Chinp'ing, Kiangsu Province, were reported
to have supplied 300,000 tons of pulverized rock phosphate annually,
beginning in 1958.[41] Many other phosphorus mines of various sizes
are reported to have been discovered during the 1960's, but large
portions of the deposits have low phosphorus content and are not
profitable for making phosphorus fertilizer.[42] In Chinghai, the bones
of sheep and cattle are used as the principal raw material for making
phosphorus fertilizer.[43]

With these serious problems, Communist China has been facing
a very difficult task in expanding the production of chemical fertilizers
to meet the increasing need. Table 13 shows that both supply and
production of chemical fertilizers increased steadily from 1952 to
1958. But, because of the rapidly growing demand and only slow
expansion of production, it has been necessary to import chemical
fertilizers in increasing quantities. Although data for more recent
years are not available, the deficit in chemical fertilizers apparently
has remained acute, as evidenced by the large amounts of chemical

Table 13

Production and Supply of Chemical Fertilizers,
1949-58
(thousands of tons)

Year	Production	Supply	Deficit
1949	27	n.a.	n.a.
1950	70	n.a.	n.a.
1951	129	n.a.	n.a.
1952	181	318	137
1953	226	592	366
1954	298	802	504
1955	332	1,255	923
1956	523	1,608	1,085
1957	631	1,944	1,313
1958	811	2,708	1,897

Source: State Statistical Bureau, Ten Great Years, English
edition (Peking, 1960), pp. 97, 171.

fertilizers imported. In 1969, Communist China imported 6 million metric tons of chemical fertilizers at a cost of U.S. $180 million.[44] In 1970, Communist China imported more than 8 million metric tons of chemical fertilizers, accounting for 20 percent of the world's total fertilizer imports, and became the world's largest fertilizer importer. Ammonium sulfate, the chemical fertilizer of which China produces the greatest quantities, has been the largest item among the imported fertilizers. The second largest item imported has been calcium ammonium nitrate. Imports of urea and ammonium chloride also have increased considerably.

In recent years, Japan has become increasingly important as a supplier of chemical fertilizers to Mainland China. In 1968, Japan's exports of chemical fertilizers to Communist China, in terms of ammonium sulfate, totaled 2,459,000 metric tons at a total value of U.S. $74 million. (The weight of all chemical fertilizers is commonly calculated on the basis of their active strength as compared with ammonium sulfate.) In 1969, the total weight increased to 2,848,000 metric tons and the total value to U.S. $80.8 million, accounting for 20.7 percent of the total value of all Japanese exports to Communist China.[45] In 1970, Japan exported 5,470,000 tons of chemical fertilizers to Mainland China.[46]

Also important as a supplier of chemical fertilizers to Communist China has been Nitrex, an organization of ten leading nitrogen producers and exporters in Belgium, West Germany, France, the Netherlands, Italy, Norway, Austria, and Switzerland, with headquarters in Zurich. In the fiscal year 1967/68, Nitrex sold about 3 million metric tons of nitrogen fertilizers to Communist China at a total value of U.S. $100 million, while Japan supplied Communist China with 2.25 million metric tons at a total value of U.S. $70 million.

Because the price of Japanese fertilizers, including freight, is lower than that of European fertilizers, it is likely that Communist China will increase its purchases from Japan. The FOB price of European fertilizers in 1969 was $28 per ton, while that of Japanese fertilizers was about $30. But, as a result of the closure of the Suez Canal in 1968, the price of European fertilizers including freight has risen to considerably more than that of Japanese fertilizers. Moreover, Japan uses small ships to carry fertilizers to China and therefore can deliver the goods to any port. The date of delivery is punctually observed.[47]

Among other countries that have supplied Communist China with chemical fertilizers are Morocco, the Soviet Union, Great Britain, Finland, Kuwait, Jordan, Canada, and Chile.

Even if chemical fertilizers could be provided in sufficient quantities, there remains the question of how to use fertilizers efficiently. This requires technical knowledge that is not yet common in the communes. It has been suggested that specialized personnel be entrusted with the handling of chemical fertilizers, but the suggestio only showed that even the most fundamental forms of organization are still wanting.

There was some hesitation about the use of phosphorus fertilizer particularly. In 1956, China's first plant producing calcium super- phosphate was completed in Nanking with Russian assistance, and during the Leap Forward campaign small phosphorus fertilizer plants were established in several provinces. However, the phosphorus fertilizer did not find buyers, especially after the beginning of 1961. The low sale of phosphorus fertilizer was believed to have been caused by several factors. First, its use was ineffective because of the lack of a balance between phosphorus and nitrogen fertilizers. In Szechuan Province, for example, phosphorus fertilizer was distributed equally among the communes and was not concentrated in places where the soil needed it. Another important reason was that the fertilizer produced was not of sufficiently good quality. In many cases, it burned the seed and the growing plant and resulted in decreased production. There was no standardization and inspection of quality. In many com- munes, the peasants regarded phosphorus fertilizer with great sus- picion. They thought it was just pulverized stone. Also, the communes were reluctant to buy the fertilizer because its price was high.[48]

There was also difficulty in the use of liquid ammonia in certain areas of Shantung, Szechuan, Chekiang, and Kiangsu provinces, where sulfuric acid was in short supply. The farmers initially were repelled by the offensive smell of liquid ammonia, but they were patiently taught by special teams how to use it. Some peasants complained that once they handled the fertilizer they would lose their sense of smell forever.[49]

It also was reported that, in Liaoning, Shantung, and Hopei provinces, production teams spent much money buying magnesium products for fertilizing. A reader of the People's Daily called attention to this matter, explaining that Chinese soil needs very little magnesium and that it is very doubtful whether such fertilizer could be of any use.[50]

In Fangshan and Ch'angp'ing hsien of the Municipality of Peking, some production teams used large quantities of ammonium bicarbonate to mix the seeds, with the result that the rate of germination was lowered. Other production teams spread the ammonium bicarbonate over the fields and exposed it to the air so that it rapidly decomposed. Many peasants in the hsien complained that ammonium bicarbonate had killed the crops and had not shown any fertilizing effect.[51] Finally, the inadequacy of storage and transportation facilities has resulted in heavy damages and losses of chemical fertilizers in Communist China. The conditions of many of the warehouses are poor: the floors are damp, no protective measures are taken to separate the chemical fertilizer from the floors, and as a result much of the fertilizer is moistened and decomposed. The inefficient inland river transport, system and loading and unloading methods also have caused considerable damage to chemical fertilizers. In some places in Kwangtung, the rate of damage and loss of chemical fertilizers in the course of storage and transit was estimated at more than 7 percent in 1963.[52]

THE PROSPECTS

The production, distribution, and use of chemical fertilizers in Communist China seem to have improved somewhat in the past few years. According to Chou En-lai, Communist China's chemical fertilizer production in 1970 was 14 million metric tons. This figure seems to be too high, even though it is still one million metric tons short of the goal for 1967 prescribed in the National Program for Agricultural Development. He estimated the country's annual need for chemical fertilizers at 30-35 million metric tons, which is also the production goal for 1975, the final year of the Fourth Five-Year Plan.[53] For the estimated 1,650 million mou of cultivated land, this is equivalent to 36-42 chin of chemical fertilizers per mou (273-320 kilograms per hectare), which would place Mainland China with the Netherlands, Japan, Taiwan and others among the countries applying the largest amount of chemical fertilizers to the same acreage of cultivated land. But even if Communist China's capacity for producing chemical fertilizers continues to improve, it would be a difficult task to increase its annual production from the reported 14 million metric tons at present to 30-35 million metric tons in 1975: that is, to increase production by an average of 3 or 4 million metric tons per year over five years. Because of the periodic shortage of manpower and fodder for raising hogs and other difficulties, it is also doubtful that the supply of organic fertilizers, produced mainly by the communes, could improve sufficiently to meet the increasing demand. Therefore, to make up the deficiencies, Communist China probably will have to continue to import chemical fertilizers in considerable quantities for many more years.

NOTES

1. JMJP, January 29, 1959, p. 1.

2. T'an Chen-lin, "Strive for the Fulfillment, Ahead of Schedule, of the National Program for Agricultural Development," JMJP, April 9, 1960, p. 1.

3. JMJP, August 31, 1960, p. 1. Ta Kung Pao, Peking, August 31, 1961, p. 1; January 28, 1962, p. 1; June 12, 1962, p. 1.

4. JMJP commentator, "Develop Cultivation of Green Manure to Insure Soil Fertility," JMJP, June 5, 1965, p. 2.

5. JMJP, June 5, 1965, p. 2; Chang Hsin-i, "Grow More Green Manure Crops in South China," Hung Ch'i [Red Flag], Peking, No. 18, 1962, pp. 19-29.

6. "Fertilizer Is the Key to Achievements of Continued Forward Leap in Agricultural Production," editorial, JMJP, July 19, 1960, p. 1; T'u Feng, Hung Ch'i [Red Flag], Peking, Nos. 9/10, 1961, pp. 53-57.

7. K. K. Yao, Fertilizers in China (Washington, D.C.; Food and Agriculture Organization of the United Nations, 1948), p. 19.

8. JMJP, January 23, 1960, p. 1.

9. Edgar Snow, "Talks With Chou En-lai: The Open Door," The New Republic, March 27, 1971, pp. 20-23.

10. Office of Foreign Agriculture, U.S. Department of Agriculture Report of the China-United States Agricultural Mission (Washington, D.C.; 1947), pp. 5-6.

11. K'o Hsueh T'ung Pao [Scientia], No. 17, 1957, pp. 541-42.

12. JMJP, December 25, 1962, p. 5.

13. Chang K'ai-yen, "A Discussion of Certain Questions on the Promotion and Use of Phosphorus Fertilizers," JMJP, November 15, 1962, p. 5; Li Ch'ing-k'uei, "An Examination of the Problem of Phosphorus Fertilizers in China from the Viewpoint of Soil Fertility, Properties of Phosphorus Deposits and Agricultural Conditions," K'o Hsueh T'ung Pao [Scientia], Peking, No. 24, 1959, pp. 820-23.

14. Kuang-ming Jih-pao [Kuang-ming Daily], Peking, March 22, 1963, p. 1.

15. "Chemical Fertilizer Industry Energetically Supports Agriculture," Ta Kung Pao, Hong Kong, October 1, 1962, p. 15.

16. Investigation Group of the Shanghai Municipal Revolutionary Committee, "Run Small Fertilizer Plants Well," Hung Ch'i [Red Flag], Peking, No. 12, 1969, pp. 36-42.

17. Snow, op. cit., pp. 20-23.

18. NCNA, Nanking, April 18, 1969.

19. Kao Kuang-chien, "Chemical Industry Serves Agriculture," Peking Review, No. 29, 1963, pp. 25-28.

20. K'o Hsueh T'ung Pao [Scientia], Peking, No. 21, 1958, pp. 656-57.

21. JMJP, July 19, 1960, p. 2; "Turn Out More Chemical Ferti-Lizers," editorial, JMJP, August 7, 1960, p. 1; Hua Hsueh Kung Yeh [Chemical Industry], No. 22,]959, pp. 4-6.

22. JMJP, August 4, 1964, p. 1; "A Strong Reinforcement for Nitrogen Fertilizer Industry--Development and Growth of Small Nitrogen Plants Amid the Struggle Between the Two Lines," JMJP, April 10, 1969, p. 4.

23. NCNA, Nanking, June 14, 1966; Ta Kung Pao, Peking, June 15, 1966, p. 1; "Growth of Small Nitrogen Fertilizer Plants," Peking Review, No. 24, 1969, pp. 33-35; NCNA-English, Peking, June 2, 1970.

24. NCNA-English, Peking, January 1, 1970,

25. "Fertilizer Industry Comes to the Countryside," China Reconstructs, Peking, Vol. XIX, No. 1 (1970), pp. 20-25.

26. JMJP, August 5, 1964, p. 1.

27. Ta Kung Pao, Peking, January 21, 1964, p. 1.

28. JMJP, July 26, 1965, p. 2.

29. JMJP, April 29, 1965, p. 2.

30. Hsin-hua Pan-yueh-k'an [New China Semimonthly], Peking, No. 4, 1958, pp. 97-98.

31. Arika Uchimi, "Problems in Deferred Payment to China," Ajia Keizai Jumpo [Asian Economy Thrice-monthly], Tokyo, June 1964, pp. 11-14 (translated by the Joint Publications Research Service, JPRS No. 26,466, Washington, D.C., September 21, 1964, pp. 13-18).

32. JMJP, November 25, 1957, p. 3.

33. "Chemical Fertilizer Industry Energetically Supports Agriculture," Ta Kung Pao, Hong Kong, October 1, 1962, p. 15.

34. NCNA, Peking, February 13, 1963.

35. JMJP, December 10, 1962, p. 2; June 11, 1963, p. 1; NCNA, Peking, September 27, 1963.

36. China Reconstructs, Peking, Vol. XIV, No. 6 (June 1965), p. 30.

37. "China's Nitrogen Fertilizer Industry Steps Into Top World Ranks," China Reconstructs, Peking, Vol. XVIII, No. 5 (1969), pp. 11-15.

38. NCNA-English, Peking, December 30, 1968.

39. NCNA, Sian, May 19, 1969.

40. NCNA, Nanking, August 27, 1961.

41. Hsin-hua Pan-yueh-k'an [New China Semimonthly], Peking, No. 4, 1958, pp. 97-98.

42. Li Ch'ing-k'uei, "An Examination of the Problem of Phosphorus Fertilizer in China from the Viewpoint of Soil Fertility, Properties of Phosphorus Deposits and Agricultural Conditions," K'o-hsueh T'ung-pao [Scientia], Peking, No. 24, 1959, pp. 820-23.

43. NCNA-English, Sining, January 3, 1966.

44. "China's Foreign Trade in 1969," Current Scene, Hong Kong, Vol. VIII, No. 16, (1970) pp. 1-8; "The Food and Population Balance: China's Modernization Dilemma," Ibid., Vol. IX, No. 6, 1971 pp. 1-7.

45. Chinese Affairs Division, Ministry of Foreign Affairs, Tokyo,

"The Present State of Japan-China Trade," Current Scene, Hong Kong, Vol. VIII, No. 9 (1970).

46. KYODO, Tokyo, dispatch in English, March 1, 1971.

47. YOMIURI, Tokyo, June 21, 1969; Food and Agriculture Organization of the United Nations, The State of Food and Agriculture, 1967 (Rome, 1967), p. 66.

48. Chang K'ai-yen, "A Discussion of Certain Questions on the Promotion and Use of Phosphorus Fertilizer," JMJP, April 17, 1962, p. 5.

49. Kung-jen Jih-pao [Daily Worker], Peking, September 13, 1962, p. 1.

50. JMJP, October 20, 1962, p. 2.

51. Kung-jen Jih-pao [Daily Worker], Peking, February 20, 1963, p. 1.

52. Chin Yen, "Pay Attention to Reduce the Damages and Losses of Chemical Fertilizers in Transit," Nan-fang Jih-pao [South China Daily], March 20, 1963, p. 2.

53. Snow, op. cit., pp. 20-23.

8

Through many centuries, Chinese farmers have maintained the productivity of the land by means of terracing, fallowing, manuring, crop rotation, and other soil conservation devices, but there are extensive areas where land has declined in productivity because of lack or inadequacy of drainage, irrigation, fertilization, or proper management. According to an estimate made in 1958, approximately 600 million mou (100 million acres), or more than one-third, of the cultivated land in China were of low productivity--saline, alkali, acidic, sandy, swampy, or erosive.[1]

The improvement and conservation of soil thus commands great importance in the country's agricultural development. The solution to this problem is to be found in the development of a program to promote better use of land in the adoption of practices designed to reduce water run-off. To this end, the Communist government has given considerable attention to the assessment, utilization, and preservation of soil resources, including soil surveys and various means for controlling soil erosion and improving land fertility.

SOIL SURVEYS

A soil survey includes classification, mapping, and study of the best uses to which the soil can be put. Such a study supplies information needed in highway construction and for military purposes, but its most important use is in the development of agriculture. It is an essential guide to research programs for crops, soils, and fertilizers and for planning the best use of land. The information that it supplies may prevent serious mistakes, fruitless efforts, and a waste of soil, forest, and other natural resources.

119

A program for the assessment of soil resources was begun in China in the 1930's by the newly organized Soil Survey Section of the National Geological Survey, with the assistance of several American soil experts. Charles F. Shaw, a soil scientist of the University of California who served as visiting professor at the University of Nanking in the spring and summer of 1930, was assigned the training of field enumerators in the methods of obtaining soil samples from 16,786 farms in 168 localities of 22 provinces for the study of land utilization in China, 1929-33. At Mr. Shaw's recommendation, the Soil Survey Section was created at the National Geological Survey, and Robert L. Pendleton of the University of Philippines, who had previous extensive experience in soil survey in India, was appointed for a two-year period (from spring of 1931 to spring of 1933) to continue the training of the land utilization regional investigators at Nanking. Mr. Pendleton, in collaboration with R. L. Chang, L. C. Chen, and K. C. Hou, also made intensive soil surveys of the Salach'i area in Suiyuan Province and the Tat'ung area in Shansi Province. In addition, Mr. Pendleton conducted a reconnaissance soil survey of a portion of Kwangtung Province.

During the period from the spring of 1933 to the spring of 1936, W. H. Wong, Director of the National Geological Survey, employed James Thorp of the U. S. Department of Agriculture to make an extensive soil reconnaissance survey of China. His findings and appraisal were published in 1936 by the National Geological Survey under the little Geography of the Soil of China. He also wrote a summary as a chapter on soil in Land Utilization in China, by J. Lossing Buck, published in Nanking in 1937. By the end of 1936, the National Geological Survey had published fourteen soil bulletins. Eight other intensive local soil studies all by Chinese soil scientists, were published by Sun Yat-sen University, in Canton in 1932-36.[2]

The soil survey work was interrupted by the Sino-Japanese War and was resumed by the Research Institute of Soil Science, established in Nanking in 1952 under the Chinese Academy of Sciences. For the first few years, the institute's principal work was the preparation of a new system for a nationwide soil survey, for which Li Ch'ing-k'uei, President of the Chinese Society of Soil Science, gave the following explanation:

> Between the 1930's and the 1950's, China's soil classifi-
> cation was primarily based on a combination of the
> systems designed by the world's two leading soil scien-
> tists, V. V. Dokuchaev of Russia and C. F. Marbut of the
> United States. For the major soil types, American and
> European continental names were adopted with the

supplement of some Chinese names used by local farmers.
In preparing regional or local soil maps, the types of the
soils were named after the localities where the soils were
first found. A major shortcoming of this system is that it
hardly reflects the effect of cultivation on the fertility of
each type of soil. In view of this shortcoming, another
system has to be adopted.[3]

The national soil survey, covering approximately 1,600 million
mou (267 million acres) of farmland, began in late 1958 following a
conference of soil scientists held at Hsinhsing, Kwangtung, in October
of that year under the joint auspices of the Chinese Academy of
Agricultural Science and the General Office of Land Utilization of the
Ministry of Agriculture. The survey, using a combination of native
and Western methods, was conducted under the supervision of the
Chinese Communist Party committees at different levels in all localities. Its personnel was composed mainly of some 7 million peasants
who were organized into groups each headed by a technical staff.
Emphasis was laid on investigating the changes in the soil resulting
from the methods of cultivation of various crops under different
natural conditions and in different areas. According to Vice-Minister
of Agriculture Liu Jui-lung, the survey in effect summed up the
experience of Chinese peasants in handling the soil over thousands of
years. It provided data for plowing, cultivating, fertilizing, and
irrigating different types of soil and for improving the country's
soil in a planned way.[4]

The survey, including the classification of the soils, was completed in a preliminary from during the winter of 1959-60. In the
opinion of Ch'eng Chao- hsüan, Vice-President of the Chinese Academy
of Agricultural Science, the survey laid a scientific foundation for
the practice of planting crops according to the nature of the soil, for
the practice of rational crop rotation, and for the improvement of
soil by the communes.[5] The survey also formed the basis for a
general soil map of China, regional soil maps, a map showing China's
soil fertility, a map showing the present use of land, and a book on the
experience of Chinese peasants in identifying, utilizing, and improving
soils. These publications were reported to be in preparation in early
1962.[6]

The nature of the national soil survey may be illustrated by the
provincial survey in Kwangtung, which covered all the cultivated land
in the province's 120 hsien and cities. After six months of field work
in which nearly 180,000 technicians and peasants participated, soil
maps and land utilization maps of 1:10,000 or 1:5,000 scale were

prepared for all communes, and on a smaller scale for various special districts and hsien. A 1:200,000 scale soil map for Kwangtung and a publication on the soils of the province have been completed.[7]

Another example is the soil survey conducted in the suburban areas of Peking in the winter of 1958-59. Under the direction of a soil research group of the Chinese Academy of Sciences, the Peking Municipal Academy of Agricultural Science, and the Peking Municipal Council, the survey included the participation of 39 students of the Department of Geography of the Peking Normal University, more than 2,000 peasants, 200 cadres, and a number of Party workers who had been dispatched to the rural areas for agricultural work training. The whole area under survey was divided into eight districts, each under the direction of an expert from the Chinese Academy of Sciences. Maps of 1:10,000 scale were prepared, showing the types and distribution of high-yield farmland, measures taken to improve land, distribution of canals, and other features in each commune or district.

According to Hsiung I, leader of the Soil Research Group of the Chinese Academy of Sciences, one of the problems in conducting the Peking soil survey was how to select and unify the names of various types of soil that traditionally had been used by the peasants. Many of the names sound very lively and are suggestive of the characters of the soil, but at the same time they are rather misleading and not suitable for use in the classification of soils.[8]

Other important surveys in connection with soil and water conservation conducted since 1949 included those for the areas along the Yangtze, Yellow, Huai, Heilung, Liao, and other rivers, and those for the subtropical areas of South China. During the First Five-Year Plan (1953-57), a soil survey of 640 million mou (107 million acres) of wasteland throughout the country was conducted and a total of 800 million mou (133,334,000 acres) of wasteland were surveyed for soil and water conservation purposes.[9]

One of the most important studies on the soils of China was made by a Russian agronomist, V.A. Kovda, in 1954-57. Entitled Ocherki Prirody i Pochv Kitaya (Soils and Natural Environment of China), the book is based on materials compiled by the Chinese Academy of Sciences, results of the field studies conducted by the writer in collaboration with Chinese scientists, and findings in the laboratories of the Soil Research Institute of the Soviet Academy of Sciences. The publication, which includes a map of 1:10,000,000 scale showing the geographic distribution of 64 soil types, was published in 1959 by the Soviet Academy of Sciences Press in Moscow.[10]

Despite the continued efforts to improve soil science in Communist China, there remain widely different opinions on soil classification and nomenclature among Chinese scientists. The problem was discussed at length at the annual meeting of the China Society of Soil Science held in Shenyang on August 15-25, 1963, during which a provisional system of soil classification based on "the findings of Chinese scientists and the experiences of Chinese peasants" was adopted.[11] But thus far no important development in this connection has been reported.

IMPROVEMENT OF LAND OF LOW FERTILITY

As already stated, approximately 600 million mou, or more than one-third of China's cultivated land, are of low productivity. The National Program for Agricultural Development urged the Agricultural producers' cooperatives (now the communes) and the state farms to actively improve and utilize saline and alkaline land, red-soil land, low-lying land, sandy land, and poor land of other types; to guard against the salification and alkalization of land; and to terrace hilly land energetically and in a planned manner (Article 12).

A directive issued by the Central Committee of the Chinese Communist Party and the State Council on August 29, 1958, stated that, of the 470 million mou (78.3 million acres) of saline and alkaline land, red soil land, sandy land, muddy fields, and other land of low fertility (excluding swamps) throughout the country, more than 140 million mou (23.3 million acres) had been improved by that date. It urged the communes to improve the remaining 330 million mou (55 million acres) within two or three years.[12] Toward the end of 1959, more than one-half of the 600 million mou (100 million acres) of land of low fertility had been improved by means of terracing and other processes of soil conservation, according to Minister of Agriculture Liao Lu-yen.[13] Another account given by T'an Chen-lin, Vice-Premier of the State Council, revealed that, of the more than 700 million mou (116.7 million acres) of low land subject to waterlogging and low-yielding land of various types, "initial improvement" had been effected on 450 million mou (75 million acres), or 60 percent of the total.[14]

According to an estimate made by the Research Institute of Water Conservation and Hydroelectric Power, China has some 300 million mou (50 million acres) of saline and alkaline land, of which about 100 million mou are under cultivation. Most of this land is located in the areas where the rate of evaporation exceeds that of

rainfall, including the plains of Northwest, Northeast, and North
China, basins in the interior, areas near Po Hai Bay, and the coastal
areas in norther Kiangsu. In North China, saline and alkaline land
represents about 10 percent of the cultivated land and about 20 percent
of the irrigated land.[15]

Salification and alkalization of land result from improper farming
practices, particularly improper irrigation and drainage. The peasants
in North China have generations of experience behind them in preventing
and controlling salification and alkalization. Their measures included
the leading of flood water to wash away salt, the drainage of land to
grow rice, the building of embankments to stabilize planting, and the
storage of fresh water to suppress salt. On the plain of Hopei, which
was always on the margin of salinity, the farmers kept the land
fertile by carefully constructing small dams and elevated paths around
the fields to prevent the mounting of the underground salt and by using
organic fertilizer and intensive cultivation to block the capillaries
that bring up the salt water and to reduce evaporation.[16]

These measures are effective only when they are carried out
together with the traditional methods of farming. When the communes
were set in 1958, many of these old ways were abandoned in favor
of new ways that have proved less effective, and inadequate drainage
in particular has caused the level of the underwater to rise, bringing
more salt to the surface. It was claimed that, during the first decade
of the Communist regime, some 20 million mou of saline and alkaline
land were improved.[17] But improper water conservation measures,
particularly those taken during the Leap Forward campaign, apparently
have resulted in the salification and alkalization of land in many
areas (see Chapter 6)

Red soils occupy 75 percent of all land in Kweichow, 70 percent
in Hunan, 56 percent in Kwangtung, 55 percent in Kwangsi, 46 percent
in Kiangsi, and 40 percent in both Chekiang and Fukien.[18] In 1950-61,
the Kiangsi Agricultural Research Institute made a series of studies
on the possibilities for improving the red soil (lateritic soil) land
already in use and for reclaiming some of the red soil wasteland in
Kiangsi Province. After examining the methods used by the peasants
in growing rye, peanuts, sweet potatoes, and other principal crops,
the institute recommended that proper amounts of farmyard manure
be applied on red soil in addition to chemical fertilizers and that
certain technical measures used by local farmers be adopted. It was
reported that by the end of 1961 more than two million mou of red
soil wasteland was reclaimed and several million mou of red soil
farmland was improved in Kiangsi Province.[19] In several other

provinces, vast tracts of red soil land were reported to have been improved by applications of farmyard manure and lime to increase the organic content and reduce the acidity of soil.[20]

China's low-lying agricultural land is distributed mainly along the rivers and seacoasts in the provinces of Hopei, Honan, Shantung, Shansi, Kiangsu, Anhwei, Hunan, Hupeh, Kiangsi, Kwangtung, Liaoning, Kirin, and Heilungkiang and the municipalities of Peking and Tientsin. These areas are important in producing wheat, cotton, soybeans, and other principal crops, but they are subject to frequent floods and waterlogging. Even in normal years, an average of 90-97 million mou (15-16 million acres), or 9-10 percent, of the cultivated land in the low-lying areas was flooded or waterlogged. In some years when the precipitation was extraordinarily heavy, as in 1954-56, the acreage affected reached 240 million mou (40 million acres), or 22 percent of the cultivated land in these provinces and municipalities.

In December 1957, a conference was called in Yangliuch'ing, Hopei, by the Ministry of Agriculture and the Ministry of Water Conservation to discuss measures for improving the low-lying agricultural land. The projects that had been carried out in the Tientsin Special District, the Ts'anghsien Special District, and a few other localities were used as models. The conference participants generally agreed that the peasants and local governments should play an increasingly important role in carrying out various improvement measures because the central authorities alone could not pay the heavy costs involved.[21]

In recent years, the "raised fields" method of reducing waterlogging and salinity in low-lying areas, a method evolved by peasants in North China, has been popularized in the basin of the lower reaches of the Yellow and Huai rivers. The raised fields consist of rectangular farm plots bordered on two or three sides by deep drainage ditches. Over large tracts of land, the earth dug out from the drainage ditches is used to raised the height of the fields and cover up the saline topsoil. Such fields prevent the accumulation of surface water after heavy rainfall in the low-lying acres and also reduce salinity.[22]

PROTECTION AGAINST SOIL EROSION

Approximately 2.4 million square kilometers (600 million acres), or roughly one-fourth of China's total land area, are subject to soil erosion of all kinds, and surface erosion and gully erosion are apparent over approximately 1.5 million square kilometers, or one-sixth of the total land area. The areas most affected include the basin of the

Yellow River, covering about 600,00 square kilometers, especially
within the huge loop of the river; the basin of the Yangtze River,
covering 160,000 square kilometers; an area surrounding Peking and
in the mountains to the northeast of the bend of the Yellow River,
totaling 130,000 square kilometers; and in the basin of the Huai River,
covering 75,000 square kilometers.

Among the climatic factors causing soil erosion are the frequent
and violent sandstorms and the alternation of frost and thaw. Another
cause is the varied topography, which is very mountainous in most
parts of the country. Geologically, the situation is aggravated by the
abundance of sedimentary rocks (marine facies of sandstone, clay,
and sands resulting in soft hilly relief). The deep recent quarternary
deposits--such as moraines, superficial glacial deposits, river gravels
alluvium, and loess--furnish inexhaustible matter for erosion. Finally,
erosion has been accelerated by the destruction of forest and the
formation of torrents as a result of improper clearing, grazing, and
burning.[23]

By the end of 1959, preliminary measures for water and soil
conservation had been carried out on 890 million mou (150 million
acres), or 40 percent of the total of 2,224.5 million mou (370.5 million
acres) of land seriously affected by soil erosion.[24] As already mentioned, one of the areas where soil erosion has been most serious is
the area along the middle reaches of the Yellow River in Northwest
China. This is also one of the biggest loess plateaus in the world.
It stretches from the Ch'ilien Mountains in the west to the T'aihang
Mountains in the east and from the Tach'ing Mountains in the north
to the Ch'ingling Mountains in the south. It traverses the seven
provinces and regions of Ch'inghai, Kansu, Ninghsia, Inner Mongolia,
Shensi, Shansi, and Honan, and covers a total area of about 600,000
square kilometers. On the loess plateau, there are about 26,000
square kilometers of gullies.

The Yellow River flows from the western part of the plateau
eastward down the high mountains and giant valleys. On the way, it
is joined by several score of principal tributaries which bring with
them an abundance of water from all directions. For centuries,
agricultural production in the area has been jeopardized by the loss
of water and soil on the hill slopes and gullies, and the water and
soil thus loss have greatly reduced the acreage of arable land on the
middle reaches of the Yellow River. Moreover, because of the river
bed on the middle reaches is steep, the greater part of the silt carried
away by the currents is deposited on the more gentle river bed on the
lower reaches.

It is estimated that approximately 400 million tons of silt are deposited on the lower reaches of the Yellow River every year, raising the river bed and reducing the capacity of the river course year after year. This has resulted in frequent floods, especially after the downpours during the months from June to September when 70 to 80 percent of the average annual predipitation of 300-500 millimeters is recorded. The situation has been worsened by the fact that less than 5 percent of the loess is covered by vegetation.[25]

In the late 1960's, particularly during the slack seasons, Communist China has launched a number of campaigns for the control of soil erosion on the middle reaches of the Yellow River. Such projects as the construction of terraces, check dams, ditches, and field ridges across gullies to capture rain water and the planting of trees and grass on steep slopes, have been encouraged. Many communes participated in the campaigns by dynamiting rocks and making bricks and tiles in their own kilns to provide building materials for check dams and protective walls around the terraced fields.

By the end of 1964, 20 experiment stations and 51 technical aid stations had been set up in the loess area to study water and soil conservation problems and to extend erosion control experience to the communes.[26] By the end of 1965, some 160,000 hectares of land had been terraced, turned into strip cropping fields, or brought under irrigation by more than 100 hsien marked out as key centers for anti-erosion work. Trees and grass had been planted on 52,000 hectares,[27] and a number of water and soil conservation stations and demonstration farms had been established to strengthen the anti-erosion work.[28]

Despite these efforts, water and soil conservation work on the middle reaches of the Yellow River has been sporadic, inadequate, and uncoordinated. Moreover, man-made destruction of the soil has not yet ended, and loss of soil is appearing in new areas. Since in many places communication paths have not been built between the terraces, peasants who carry fertilizer break through the barriers and therefore open the way for erosion. Afforestation in such areas is difficult because of the lack of rain. The ineffectiveness of years of afforestation in the past also was due to the improper selection of types of trees and the destruction of young trees by men and animals.[29]

In 1958, Mainland China's forested area was about 1,134 million mou, or only 8 percent of the total land area, as compared with 41 percent in the Soviet Union (1968), 32 percent in the United States (1964), 19 percent in India (1967), 69 percent in Japan (1968), and

63 percent in Taiwan (1968).[30] Although data for recent years are
not available, it is clear that China is inadequately forested. Several
projects to reconstitute and improve natural forests and to create
new forests were included in the First Five-Year Plan. These projects were expanded in 1956 into a twelve-year (1953-65) program to
"make China a green country." The program envisaged the afforestation
of 92 million hectares (227.2 million acres) in twelve years. The new
forests, together with the 76.6 million hectares (189.2 million acres)
of natural forests, would make up a forest domain of 168.6 million
hectares (416.4 million acres) by 1965, and the proportion of forested
land in China would then rise from 8 to 19 percent.

The most urgent objective of the program was to relieve the
enormous timber shortage in China, which shackled the desired
expansion of many industries, particularly building construction. The
long-term significance of the program was to lessen the possibilities
of soil erosion, floods, and droughts and to prevent the silting of
rivers and hydroelectric reservoirs. The program also was intended
to improve hygiene and public health and to beautify urban and
suburban areas.[31]

The agricultural producers' cooperatives (now the communes)
have been relied on to carry out the bulk of the afforestation program.
Of the 497,860,000 mou (82,977,000 acres) of land afforested in 1950-
58, 21,700,000 mou (3,617,000 acres), or about 4 percent, were
afforested by some 2,000 state forest farms, while the remaining 96
percent were afforested by the agricultural producers' cooperatives
(or communes).[32] In 1964, the communes had more than 30,000
forest farms and forest teams in operation, with some 200,000 commune
members engaged in the afforestation work. By the end of that year,
more than 3,000 state forest farms (six times as many as in 1957)
had been established, employing 200,000 workers.[33]

While the agricultural producers' cooperatives (or communes)
are counted on to plant trees in the villages, the state forest farms
are mainly responsible for undertaking the planting of large tracts of
timber forests, shelter belts for water and soil conservation, wind-
breaks, sandbreaks, and shelter belts along the seacoasts. State
efforts also have been directed toward the reforestation of degraded
natural forests and the afforestation of bared hills and steppe land
unsuitable for agricultural uses. The state also has the right to take
over all uncultivated land, where reforestation operations are then
carried out as a public service to protect land against erosion. The
agricultural producers' cooperatives (or communes), on the other
hand, are encouraged to participate in tree-planting work in accordance

with the national programs and plans, with financial and technical
assistance from the state.

Table 14 shows that early efforts to develop the forests did not
yield significant results but a considerable increase in forest acreage
was reported during the Leap Forward campaign. In 1958 and 1959,
approximately 542 million mou of land were afforested. But in 1964
China's forest area still constituted only about 10 percent of the
country's total land area.[34] Thus, progress was much slower than that
anticipated in the 1953-65 afforestation program, which called for
19 percent of China's total land area to be forested by 1965. The
Ministry of Forestry attributed the slow progress to the poor quality
of the afforestation work as a whole; the low rate of forest regeneration,
which did not match the rate of felling; and the serious destruction of
forests caused by such factors as fire and improper lumbering.[35]

The "Regulations Governing the Protection of Forests," promulgated by the State Council on May 27, 1963, were regarded by the
Communist Chinese press as having an important bearing on the
country's industrial and agricultural production as well as on the
people's daily life. While acclaiming the government's work of
afforestation and protection of forests during the first decade of the
Communist regime, the People's Daily, stated in an editorial that
many localities still lacked experience in this field, that "quite a
few" localities failed to pay proper attention to it, and that therefore
the work of afforestation and protection should be intensified.[36] In
a notice issued in May 1965, the Ministry of Forestry again called on
the country to "genuinely" implement the May 1963 regulations, and
in particular to strengthen field management of saplings and young
trees in order to prepare sufficient supplies for use in future large-
scale afforestation programs.[37]

Terracing remains one of the most important methods used in
China for controlling soil erosion as well as water supply. On the
loess plateau in Northwest China particularly, land is so rough that
extensive irrigation is impossible. For centuries the Chinese farmers
have met the situation with terracing. Stone-faced terraces and
bench terraces are used to hold as much water as possible. In some
areas of Shansi Province, the terraces are graded and sloped toward
the mountain to hold rainfall. At the center of each terrace is a
carefully constructed stone-faced spillway to carry off any excess
water.

In the rice-producing areas, terracing is even more extensive
because rice fields must be level to hold water. This leveling with

TABLE 14

Afforested Area in Mainland China, 1950-59
(thousands of <u>mou</u>)

Year	Shelter Belts	Timber Forests	Other	Total
1950	1,010	210	680	1,900
1951	3,790	1,150	1,820	6,760
1952	8,540	3,310	4,430	16,280
1953	6,250	6,710	3,730	16,690
1954	5,080	9,540	2,870	17,490
1955	5,900	14,210	5,550	25,660
1956	20,270	36,810	28,770	85,850
1957	14,920	26,020	24,390	65,330
1958	50,020	90,230	121,650	261,900
1959	n.a	n.a	n.a	280,000

Sources: State Statistical Bureau, <u>Ten Great Years</u>, English edition (Peking, 1960), p. 133; <u>JMJP</u>, January 23, 1960, p. 1.

plows, shovels, and a special pronged iron leveler drawn by a water buffalo remains one of the greatest aids to the conservation of both soil and water in Mainland China today. During the winter of 1957-58, more than 51 million mou of terraces were built. This was equivalent to 26 percent of the total area of hilly cultivated land.

Since early 1964, Tachai Production Brigade at Hsiyang Hsien in Shansi Province has become a pacesetter for the country's agriculture by virtue of the hand work and the self-reliant spirit that it applied to turning its loess hills into vast staircases of terraced fields to check soil erosion. Tachai is situated in the seriously eroded Taihang Mountains. The area is cut by seven ravines and dozens of gullies. The ravines and gullies are dry most of the time, but in the rainy season raging torrents used to bite into the hillsides and damage farmland on the slopes.

The project of reconstructing Tachai began in the winter of 1953-54, the first year of agricultural cooperativization, when the people of the production brigade transformed Paitokou, one of the seven ravines, by building 20 stone check-dams to retard the flow of the torrents. The fertile silt accumulating behind the dams formed small plots where crops can be grown during the dry season. Reservoirs, canals, ponds, and additional check-dams were constructed, and the fields on the slopes were terraced. All the work was done in winter so as not to interfere with agricultural production.

The project was completed in the winter of 1955, but some of the dams were damaged badly by floods in the summers of 1956, 1957, and 1963. Each time the peasants started all over again and reconstructed the dams more solidly. As a result, grain production, family income, and property value in Tachai were said to have increased considerably.[38]

MULTIPLE-CROPPING

Multiple cropping, or growing more than one crop per unit of land per year, is highly developed in some countries, particularly in East Asia, as a means of increasing agricultural production. The methods of multiple-cropping are based on such local natural and economic conditions as climate soil fertility, topography, supply of water, fertilizers, and manpower. In China, different systems of multiple cropping are found in different areas within a province. The process is not a simple matter of sowing more than one crop per year. Moreover, multiple cropping requires substantially greater inputs of capital and labor and more scientific management.

The degree of multiple-cropping is usually represented by the "multiple-sown area index," also called "multiple-cropping index," which is derived by the following calculation: sown area divided by cultivated area multiplied by 100. The targets provided in the National Program for Agricultural Development were to raise the average multiple-sown area index (including green manure crops) as follows in the twelve years beginning in 1956: (1) in areas south of the Wuling Mountains, 230 percent; (2) in areas north of the Wuling Mountains and south of the Yangtze River, 200 percent; (3) in areas north of the Yangtze River and south of the Yellow River, the Ch'inling Mountains, and the Pailung River, 160 percent; (4) in areas north of the Yellow River, the Ch'inling Mountains, and the Pailung River and south of the Great Wall, 120 percent; and (5) in areas north of the Great Wall, in general all cultivated land should be fully utilized, the area of unworked land should be reduced, and, wherever possible, energetic steps should be taken to expand the multiple-cropping areas (Article 9 of the Program).

Like the proposed boundaries dividing the country into three regions for yield targets, the boundaries dividing the country into five regions for the purpose of multiple-sown area index were drawn on a somewhat arbitrary basis. Why the Wuling Mountains (the five principal mountain ranges traversing Kiangsi, Kwangtung, Hupeh, Hunan, and Kwangsi) and the Pailung, a small river in southern Kansu, were used for the demarcation of the regions was not explained, although their natural conditions and the proposed multiple-sown area indexes were briefly indicated (see Table 15).

As shown in Table 16, the total cultivated area for China as a whole increased steadily from 1949-1957, and the total sown area increased steadily from 1952 to 1956 and then declined in 1957 and again in 1958. The resulting annual multiple-sown area index rose from 130.9 in 1952 to 145.0 in 1958. Even the highest figure during the seven years 1952-58 was still lower than the index of 149.0 given in J. Lossing Buck's study of 16,786 farms in 22 provinces for the period of 1929-33.[39] Buck's index might have been somewhat lower if all of Mainland China had been included in his study. Even so, the figures given by the Chinese Communists do not indicate much success in multiple-cropping.

In their efforts to promote multiple-cropping, Communist Chinese authorities have changed crop cultivation systems in some areas without consideration of local conditions. In many cases, the

TABLE 15

Natural Conditions of the Five Regions and Proposed Increases of
Multiple-Sown Area Indexes, 1956-67

Region	Annual Precipitation (millimeters)	Average Annual Temperature (Centigrade)	Number of Frost-Free Days Each Year	Proposed Increase of Multiple-Sown Area Index, 1956-67
1. South of the Wuling Mountains	1,500-2,000	20-24°	320	184-230
2. North of the Wuling Mountains and south of the Yangtze River	1,250-1,750	16-20°	250-300	154-200
3. North of the Yangtze River and south of the Yellow River, the Ch'inling Mountains, and the Pailung River	500-1,000	14-17°	200-250	156-160
4. North of the Yellow River, the Ch'inling Mountains, and the Pailung River and south of the Great Wall	300-500	8-15°	150-220	113-120
5. North of the Great Wall	200-750	0-8°	120-170	"as much as possible"

Source: Nung-yeh K'o-hsueh T'ung-hsun [Agricultural Science Bulletin], Peking, No. 1, 1958, p. 1.

TABLE 16

Cultivated Area, Sown Area, and
Multiple-Sown Area Index in
Mainland China, 1949-58

Year	Cultivated Area (thousands of mou)	Sown Area (thousands of mou)	Multiple-Sown Area Index
1949	1,468,220	n.a.	n.a
1950	1,505,340	n.a.	n.a.
1951	1,555,070	n.a.	n.a.
1952	1,618,780	2,118,840	130.9
1953	1,627,930	2,160,530	132.7
1954	1,640,320	2,218,880	135.3
1955	1,652,350	2,266,220	137.2
1956	1,677,370	2,387,590	142.3
1957	1,677,450	2,358,660	140.6
1958	1,616,800	2,344,020	145.0

Source: State Statistical Bureau, Ten Great Years, English
edition (Peking, 1960), p. 128.

changes have produced ill results. In the greater part of the Yellow
River Valley, for instance, the three-crops-in-two-years system was
traditionally used in the past. In recent years, the system has been
changed to that of two crops in one year. Although this change has
benefited some localities with improved soil fertility, water conservation, and manpower, it has produced undesirable effects on the
agricultural production in other areas where economic and natural
conditions remain unchanged. A survey of the Shih Li P'u Production
Brigade of the Fa Hsin Commune in Shun-i Hsien in the suburban area
of Peking revealed that the three-crops-in-two-years system (spring
corn in the first year and winter wheat and summer corn in the
second year) produced an average yearly yield of 400 chin per mou.
After the changeover to the two-crops-in-one-year system (wheat
and summer corn), the yearly yield averaged only 336 chin per mou,
or a decrease of 19 percent from the former system. The survey
also showed that, under the three-crops-in-two-years system, the production cost was 32 percent lower, the total value of production was
9 percent higher, and the net income was 115 percent higher than
under the two-crops-in-one-year system.[40]

An effort also has been made to extend the area devoted to the
production of two rice crops per year in the basins of the Yangtze
River. Two-crop rice culture has long been practiced in parts of
southern China where climate and other factors permitted. Its increase has been particularly rapid in Szechuan Province, from 80,000
mou (13,300 acres) in 1955 to 4,500,000 mou (750,000 acres) in 1956
and 8,970,000 mou (1,495,000 acres) in 1957. Two-crop rice culture
has been attempted with varying levels of success in several areas
between 32 and 33 degrees North, including Kuangyuan in northern
Szechuan, Ank'ang in southern Shensi, Kuch'eng in northern Hupeh,
Hsinyang in southern Honan, Pengfu in Anhwei, Lihsiaho in northern
Kiangsu, and the Yenmen section of Kiangyu hsien in Szechuan,
which has an elevation of 800 meters above sea level.

As a whole, the effort to extend the two-crop rice culture area
was not successful, as low yields and uncertain harvests still existed
for the late crop in many localities. In 1958, the late crop yielded
only from 150 to 250 chin per mou in various provinces, as compared
with 400 to 500 chin per mou for the early crop. For several years,
hundreds of thousands of mou of the late crop had bad harvests or
none at all. In addition to inadequate water supply and fertilization,
another reason for the low yield of the late crop is that there are few
late-crop varieties of high productivity and high quality; the grain
tends to shatter easily. Still another reason is that the time of
harvesting of the first crop and planting of the second crop comes
too late in the season.[41]

EXPANDING THE AREA SOWN TO
HIGH-YIELDING CROPS

Rice, corn, and potatoes are the most important high-yielding grain crops in Mainland China. The National Program for Agricultural Development called for the expansion of the area sown to rice by 250 million mou in the twelve years beginning in 1956. It also encouraged the development of corn, potatoes, and other high-yielding crops according to the local needs and dietary habits (Article 10).

The average yields, in chin per mou of sown area, of the principal grain crops for the seven years 1949-55 were given by Wang Shou, Director of the Research Institute of Crop Breeding and Cultivation of the Chinese Academy of Agricultural Science, as follows:

Rice	312.2
Potatoes	231.3 (converted into grain-equivalent at the ratio of four chin to one)
Corn	179.6
Millet	136.5
Kaoliang*	133.5
Soybeans	102.0
Wheat	99.7

Wang Shou indicated that under the program to promote the growth of high-yielding crops the sown area for rice in 1956 increased by 15.9 million mou over 1955; that for corn increased by 48 million mou; and that for potatoes increased by 13 million mou. As a result of the increase in sown areas for these high-yielding crops and the adoption of other measures, in 1956 China's total grain production increased by more than 15,000 million chin over that in 1955, despite the serious natural calamities in 1956. Wang Shou further revealed that in 1956 the total sown area for rice, corn, and potatoes constituted only 49.7 percent of the total sown area for all grain crops, and yet the total production of these three high-yielding crops amounted to 70.8 percent of all grain production in Mainland China. For rice, the total sown area constituted only 26.7 percent of that for all grain crops, yet the total production of rice was 45.5 percent of that for all grain crops. From these facts, Wang visualized the great possibilities for further expanding the sown areas for high-yielding crops.

---

*A kind of grain sorghum.

However, he pointed out that in 1956 many attempts to expand sown areas for corn and potatoes without consideration of local needs and dietary habits caused serious waste as well as transportation and storage difficulties. Also, the use of seeds of certain varieties not suitable to local climate and soil conditions resulted in low production of high-yielding crops, as in the case of the "Golden Queen" variety of corn (see Chapter 9).[42]

In the opinion of J. Lossing Buck, the expansion of the area sown to potatoes in Mainland China is a good practice but the attempt to increase the area sown in rice may have resulted in displacing other more profitable crops. In general, rice growing in China before World War II extended too far up on hilly land where the water supply was not dependable. Farmers in Szechuan called it "gambling with heaven," and some of them discontinued growing rice on hilly land in favor of corn and soybeans, which gave higher yield.[43]

DEEP PLOWING

On August 29, 1958, the Central Committee of the Chinese Communist Party and the State Council jointly issued a directive urging the communes to adopt deep plowing as a measure to increase agricultural production. The directive stated that all land that could be deeply plowed should be deeply plowed once every three years. The depth of plowing generally should reach more than one <u>chih</u> (14 inches), and the highly productive fields should be plowed to a depth of at least two <u>chih</u> (28 inches). In the areas with "practical difficulties," deep plowing should be carried out in two stages: first to six or seven <u>ts'un</u> (9.5 or 10.0 inches) and later to more than one <u>chih</u> (14 inches).[44]

It was estimated that by the end of 1958 more than 800 million <u>mou</u> (133.5 million acres) of land, or nearly half the total area of cultivated land, had been deep-plowed. Deep plowing was said to have improved the quality of the soil, prevented plants from bending and being uprooted, promoted microbiological activities, and aided in weed control and in the prevention of certain plant diseases and pests.[45]

According to Ch'eng Chao-hsuan, Vice-President of the Chinese Academy of Agricultural Science, surveys and experiments have proved the favorable effect of deep plowing on agricultural production and the effect of one course of deep plowing may last for about three years.[46] However, others maintain that deep plowing, like close planting, has its limitations and can contribute to agricultural productic only under certain circumstances. They argue that the depth of plowing should be based on the type of soils and the kind of crops growr among other factors, and that deep plowing should be adopted in conjunction with other measures for improving agricultural production, particularly water conservation and fertilization.[47]

During the Leap Forward campaign, explosives were used in many areas where deep plowing was practiced, in order to save labor. The communes were urged to develop explosives made of native material. A technical group in the Research Institute of Mechanical Science of the Chinese Academy of Sciences conducted a series of experiments on explosives made of low-cost chemicals, principally potassium nitrate (75 percent), sulfur (10 percent), and charcoal (15 percent). The use of explosives in cultivating land was said to be less subject to topographical limitations and to make it possible to loosen land with less labor and higher speed.[48] However, some seriou questions remain unanswered. Does the loosening of soil by means of explosion meet the requirements for crop growth? Does the use of explosives ruin the composition of soils and thus effect the growth of crops? In any case, it would appear that the experimental use of explosives in deep plowing has not become popular.

THE PROSPECTS

The soil conservation program in Communist China consists mainly of mass campaigns, with the communes and their constitutents playing a much more important role than the central government. Peasants as well as cadres and technicians have participated in a great variety of activities, including such highly technical projects as soil surveys and soil classification. The collective afforestation by the agricultural producers' cooperatives (or communes) has made a much greater contribution than the state forest farms in the program to "make China a green country." The local governments are also responsible for carrying out work to improve land of low fertility; to construct terraces, field border ridges, and silt-detention dams; and to apply farmyard manure, especially during the slack winter season.

Because of the large amount of labor needed for the soil conservation program, as well as for many other programs, there has been a constant labor shortage. One method of reducing the shortage would be to use more machines and to improve implements and tools; however, this approach has not been used successfully (see Chapter 12).

As in other aspects of the technical transformation of agriculture, much of the effort to conserve and improve soil fertility has been wasted as a result of improper planning and management. Moreover, in order to insure the success of certain key projects, such as soil erosion control along the middle reaches of the Yellow River, the central government would have to provide tremendous amounts of funds, machinery, and equipment, in addition to the contributions from the local units. Without large-scale capital investment, any substantial improvement of soil fertility in Communist China would be difficult.

NOTES

1. Liao Lu-yen, "Ten Years of Glorious Accomplishments on the Agricultural Front," Nung-yeh K'o-hsueh T'ung-hsun [Agricultural Science Bulletin], Peking, No. 19, 1959, pp. 652-58; "Improving Farmland of Low Productivity," editorial, Chung-kuo Nung-pao [Chinese Agriculture Bulletin], Peking, No. 8, 1958, p. 21.

2. Information supplied to the author by J. Lossing Buck.

3. Li Ch'ing-k'uei and Yu T'ien-jen, "Several Questions Concerning China's Soil Science in Progress," K'o-hsueh T'ung-pao [Science Bulletin], Peking, No. 2, 1964, pp. 118-26.

4. Liu' Jui-lung, "Let the Peasants Discover the Secret of Soils," Hung Ch'i [Red Flag], Peking, No. 3, 1959, pp. 26-30.

5. Ch'eng Chao-hsuan, "Basic Experience of High-Speed Development of Agricultural Science in China," Hung Ch'i [Red Flag], No. 16, 1960, pp. 24-30

6. Ch'eng Chao-hsuan, "Great Leap Forward of Agricultural Production and Accomplishments of Agricultural Research," Nung-yeh K'o-hsueh T'ung-hsun [Agricultural Science Bulletin], Peking, No. 19, 1959, pp. 659-61; NCNA, Peking, January 4, 1962.

7. Ch'eng Chao-hsuan, "Great Leap Forward of Agricultural Production and Accomplishments of Agricultural Production and Accomplishments of Agricultural Research," Nung-yeh K'o-hsueh T'ung-hsun, op. cit., pp. 659-60.

8. Hsiung I, "A Study of the Soil Classification System in the Soil Survey for the Suburban Areas of Peking," K'o-hsueh T'ung-pao [Scientia], Peking, No. 6, 1959, pp. 182-84.

9. Land Utilization Bureau of the Ministry of Agriculture, "Great Achievements of Soil Work in China," Chung-kuo Nung-pao [Chinese Agriculture Bulletin], Peking, No. 11, 1959, pp. 12-15

10. An English translation of the book was issued by the Joint Publications Research Service, JPRS No. 5967 (Washington, D.C., October 31, 1960), 739 pages.

11. T'u-jan Hsueh-pao [Acta Pedologica Sinica], Peking, No. 3, 1963, pp. 341-42.

12. JMJP, September 11, 1958, p. 1.

13. Liao Lu-yen, op. cit., pp. 652-58.

14. T'an Chen-lin, "Strive for the Fulfillment, Ahead of Schedule, of the National Program for Agricultural Development," JMJP, April 7, 1960, p. 1.

15. Chang Tzu-lin and Huang Jung-han, "The Improvement of Saline and Alkaline Land and the Prevention of Salification and Alkalization in North China," Hung Ch'i [Red Flag], Peking, Nos. 15/16, 1962, pp. 47-56.

16. Hsiung I, "The Problem of Improving Saline and Alkaline Land in Hopei Province," Kuang-ming Jih-pao [Kuang-ming Daily], Peking, July 10, 1962, p. 2.

17. Chang Tzu-lin and Huang Jung-han op. cit., pp. 47-56.

18. Lin Nung, "Poor Land Becomes Good Farms," Chi-hsieh-hua Nung-yeh [Mechanized Agriculture], Peking, No. 3, 1957, pp. 4-5.

19. Kuang-ming Jih-pao [Kuang-ming Daily], Peking, January 19, 1962, p. 1.

20. NCNA, Peking, December 7, 1962; NCNA, Nanchang, Septembe 15, 1963.

21. Ho Chi-feng, "Great March Forward to the Low-Lying Land," Chung-kuo Nung-pao [Chinese Agriculture Bulletin], Peking, No. 7, 1958, pp. 8-12; Li Ching-yu, "Improving Low-Lying Swampy Land and Converting Low Yield to High Yield," Chung-kuo Nung-pao [Chinese Agriculture Bulletin], Peking, No. 7, 1958, pp. 13-17.

22. NCNA, Peking, November 16, 1965; NCNA-English, Peking, June 11, 1966.

23. Jean Messines, "Forest Rehabilitation and Soil Conservation in China," Unasylva, Rome, Vol. XII, No. 3, 1958, pp. 103-20.

24. T'an Chen-lin, op. cit., p. 1.

25. Chao Ming-fu, "Let Us Change the Look of the Loess Plateau," K'o-hsueh Ta-chung [Popular Science], Peking, No. 6, 1963, pp. 1-3.

26. Chia Chen-lan, "An Inquiry into the Question of Building Steady and High-Yielding Farmland on the Northwest Loess Plateau," JMJP, May 19, 1964, p. 5; NCNA, Peking, December 3, 1964.

27. NCNA, Peking, January 9, 1966.

28. Peking Review, No. 28, 1965, p. 21.

29. Chang Sen, "Several Problems of Water and Soil Conservation on the Middle Reaches of the Yellow River," JMJP, June 4, 1963, p. 5.

30. Messines, op. cit., FAO Production Yearbook, 1969, Vol. XXIII (Rome, 1970), pp. 3-6.

31. Messines, op. cit.

32. "Celebrating Our Country's Ten Great Years," editorial, Chung-kuo Lin-yeh [Chinese Forestry], Peking, No. 19, 1959, pp. 2-7.

33. JMJP, January 8, 1964, p. 2; JMJP, September 26, 1964, p. 2.

34. JMJP, January 23, 1960, p. 1; News Release, China News Service, November 16, 1964, p. 4.

35. "Conscientiously Protect the Forests," editorial, JMJP, May 29, 1962, p. 1; Ministry of Forestry, People's Republic of China, "Summing Up Forestation Work in the Past Thirteen Years," Chung-kuo Lin-yeh [Chinese Forestry], Peking, No. 5, 1963, pp. 1-5.

36. "Regulations Governing the Protection of Forests," released by NCNA, Peking, June 22, 1963; "It is Everybody's Responsibility to Protect Forests," editorial, JMJP, June 23, 1963, p. 1.

37. NCNA, Peking, May 23, 1965.

38. Land Utilization Bureau of the Ministry of Agriculture, op. cit., pp. 12-15; NCNA, Peking, February 10, 1964.

39. J. Lossing Buck, Land Utilization in China, (Nanking: University of Nanking, 1937), p. 274.

40. Kao Hui-min, "Crop Rotation Systems in China's Agricultural Production," Hung Ch'i [Red Flag], Peking, No. 24, 1961, pp. 18-24; Kao Hui-min, "A Discussion on the Coordination Between Agriculture and Animal Husbandry in Relation to the Crop Rotation System," K'o-hsueh T'ung-pao [Scientia], Peking, No. 4, 1964, pp. 283-87.

41. Pai Szu-chiu, "How to Produce Two Abundant Crops in a Two-Crop Rice Culture Program?" Chung-kuo Nung-pao Tseng-k'an [Supplement to the Chinese Agriculture Bulletin], Peking, No. 2, 1958, pp. 1-3, 6.

42. Wang Shou, "A Discussion on the Growing of More High-Yielding Crops," in 1956-1967-nien Ch'uan-kuo Nung-yeh Fa-chan Kang-yao (Hsiu-cheng Ts'ao-an) Chiang-hua [Lectures on the National Program for Agricultural Development, 1956-1967 (Revised Draft)] (Peking, 1958), pp. 90-94.

43. Information supplied to the author by J. Lossing Buck.

44. JMJP, September 11, 1958, p. 1.

45. Land Utilization Bureau of the Ministry of Agriculture, op. cit., pp. 12-15.

46. Ch'eng Chao-hsuan, "Basic Experience of High-Speed Development of Agricultural Science in China," Loc. cit.

47. Chu Chien-nung, T'u-ti Fei-li Ching-chi Yuan-li [Economic Principles of Land Fertility] (Shanghai, 1964), pp. 281-91.

48. Research Institute of Mechanical Science, Chinese Academy of Sciences, "The Use of Explosives in Agriculture," K'o-hsueh T'ung-pao [Scientia], Peking, No. 13, 1960, pp. 408-11.

Because of its large territory and wide variation in natural conditions, China has a great wealth of plant materials. Many kinds and varieties of plants thrive and are used for food or other purposes. However, little work has been done to evaluate the overall plant resources of the country and to undertake intensive research programs for the improvement of species and varieties. Since the country depends so much upon rice and wheat for food and cotton for clothing, more attention has been given to the improvement of these crops. Rice breeding in particular was a field in which considerable progress had been made prior to the Communist regime.

The National Program for Agricultural Development provided that the use of all sorts of existing improved strains of farm crops whose adaptability to local conditions had already been proved by selected experiment should be extended before 1962. In the case of improved strains whose use had in the main been popularized (cotton for example), steps should be taken to strengthen the work of invigorating and varying strains. Major efforts should be made to cultivate new, improved strains from other parts of the country and from abroad.

The program further provided that the agricultural cooperatives (now communes) should set aside land especially for growing seed, should strengthen the work of seed selection among the masses, and should institute a system for propagating improved strains of seed and their alternate use. In areas with unreliable harvests, attention should be paid to storing up good strains of seed. State farms should make themselves centers for propagating good strains of farm crops and should take energetic steps to increase the available supplies and extend the use of improved strains of crops suited to local conditions. All provinces, municipalities, autonomous regions, special administrative

143

regions, autonomous chou, and hsien were urged to set up special se
agencies. (Article 8 of the Program).

At the outset of the Communist regime, the progress of the see
selection program was rather slow. During the Economic Recovery
Period (1949-52), emphasis was given to the selection and populariz:
of seeds developed by the farmers. In the First Five-Year Plan per
(1953-57), the exchange of improved seeds between provinces and
between hsien (counties) was encouraged and there was popularizatio
of 380 new varieties of rice, wheat, corn, millet, kaoliang, sweet pot
atoes, soybeans, cotton, and other crops developed by agricultural
colleges and research institutions and 104 varieties developed by far
ers.

Like other major agricultural activities, the seed improvement
program was speeded up during the Leap Forward campaign. Agricultural universities, research institutions, and peasants throughout
the country selected and cultured more than 1,000 improved varietie:
In addition to improved varieties selected from within China, 72 improved varieties had been introduced from abroad by the latter part
1959, including varieties of cotton, sunflowers (from Hungary), and
sugar beets (from the Soviet Union and Poland). The acreage sown t
these varieties was expanded steadily.[1]

At the second national conference on the cultivation of crop
strains, held in Peking in January 1964, 146 strains of 22 crops deve
loped by Chinese scientists were recommended for propagation. The
crops included rice, wheat, corn sorghum, millet, sweet potatoes,
soybeans, cotton, tobacco, sugar beets, sugar cane, rapeseeds,
sesame, peanuts, and hemp.[2] Prior to 1949, China used mainly impo
strains in the cultivation of cotton, potatoes, tobacco, sugar cane, an
sugar beets.

Some 1,600 model stations for the multiplication of improved
seeds were reported to have been set up in practically all hsien in
fifteen province and muncipalities by the end of 1963. In addition, ma
production teams had established special farms for selecting and
preserving improved seeds.[3] By August 1965, more than 1,780 hsien
had established stations for multiplying improved seeds, nearly 10,00
communes or production brigades had established improved seed
stations or teams, and about one-half of production teams had set up
seed fields.[4]

Table 17 shows the total acreage and percentage of the area sow
to improved seeds of all crops in 1952 and 1955-59. Figures for mor

Table 17

Area Sown to Improved Seeds,
1952 and 1955-59

Year	Area Sown to Improved Seeds (thousands of mou)	Area Sown to Improved Seeds as a Percentage of Total Sown Area
1952	126,680	6.2
1955	878,000	38.7
1956	1,006,000	42.1
1957	1,200,000	55.9
1958	1,750,000	76.0
1959	1,800,000	80.0

Sources: Liu Ting-an, "Great Achievements in Seed Improvement Work in China in the Past Decade," Chung-kuo Nung-pao [Chinese Agriculture Bulletin], Peking, No. 15, 1959, pp. 22-23, 27; T'an Chen-lin (Vice-Premier), "Strive for the Fulfillment, Ahead of Schedule, of the National Program for Agricultural Development," a report at the Second Session of the Second National People's Congress, April 6, 1960, JMJP, April 9, 1960, p. 1; State Statistical Bureau, Ten Great Years, English edition (Peking, 1960), p. 128.

recent years are not available, but it is generally believed that there was an acute shortage of seeds of all kinds during and shortly after the three consecutive years (1959-61) of crop failure and that the situation improved gradually in the early 1960's. In 1965, the acreage sown to improved seeds of rice, wheat, corn, koaliang (a kind of grain sorghum), millet, and soybeans amounted to one-half of the total acreage sown to these six principal crops and was nearly 200 million mou more than in 1964.[5]

Table 18 shows the percentages of acreage sown to improved seeds of various principal crops in 1952-58. In 1952, the last year of the Economic Recovery Period, the area sown to better seeds for cotton had already 50.2 percent. This percentage was far ahead of that for any other major crop because of the fact that, prior to World War II, improved varieties of cotton had been introduced from abroad mainly from the United States, and popularized over a large area of cotton fields in China. The percentages of acreage sown to improved seeds for all major crops (rice, wheat, miscellaneous grains, potatoes cotton, and oil-bearing crops) rose steadily and rapidly during the First Five-Year Plan period (1953-57). The even more conspicuous rise in 1958 was again attributed by the Communists to the Leap Forward campaign. In that year, the area sown to better seeds for cotton reached 97.0 percent, and that for other major crops ranged from 61.6 percent for oil-bearing crops to 86.1 percent for wheat.

Claims about the improvement of individual crops in recent years are too numerous to mention; only the three most important crops--rice, wheat, and cotton--are briefly discussed here. Rice was first planted in China some 50 centuries ago. The cultivation was broadened in the twenty-sixth to twenty-second centuries, B.C. By the time of the Chou dynasty (1111-256 B.C.), many writings on the cultivation, fertilization, seed selection, irrigation, harvesting, processing, and storage of rice appeared. Today, rice is China's most important crop in production and its acreage is substantially greater than that of wheat.

Many new high-yielding varieties of rice are reported to have been developed since 1949, but some of the varieties developed prior to the Communist regime remain the most widely planted. For example the cultivation of Nant'echao (Southern Special), an early-ripening, disease-resistant variety developed in Kingasi Province before World War II, has been extended to South China and the middle and lower reaches of the Yangtze River. The total acreage of Nant'echao in these areas in 1961 was estimated at 50-60 million mou, and the yield averaged 500-600 chin per mou, with the highest yield exceeding 1,000 chin per mou.

TABLE 18

Percentage of Area Sown to Improved Seeds of Principal Crops, 1952-58*
(total area sown to each crop-100)

Year	Rice	Wheat	Coarse Grains	Potatoes	All Grains	Cotton	Oil-Bearing Crops
1952	5.4	5.1	5.0	0.4	4.7	50.2	1.9
1953	7.9	7.4	8.0	2.2	7.4	61.4	2.4
1954	12.0	23.5	12.9	9.9	14.9	67.7	2.9
1955	19.0	32.7	16.5	13.8	20.6	70.5	4.0
1956	41.3	58.7	21.4	38.3	36.4	89.5	31.5
1957	62.9	68.7	42.5	56.5	55.2	93.9	47.7
1958	81.9	86.1	67.9	81.5	77.5	97.0	61.6

Source: State Statistical Bureau, Ten Great Years, English edition (Peking, 1960), p. 131.

In the development of new rice strains, special attention has been given to strains that ripen in 110 days and are suitable for cultivation in cold Northeast China, and to strains with short stalks, that withstand typhoons and heavy rains and are suitable for cultivation along the coastal areas.[6]

The cultivation of wheat as one of China's principal crops was recorded in as early as the Yin Dynasty (1384-1112 B. C.). Today, more than one-third of the Chinese population consumes wheat as its most important staple food. Many new varieties are reported to have been developed since 1949, and some of the varieties introduced prior to the Communist takeover have been popularized. Nanta 2419 winter wheat, originally planted only in the Yangtze River basin, now is also sown in the spring wheat areas of the northeast and northwest. This variety is insect-resistant because the inner and outer glumes of the plant's ears are closely woven so that wheat aphids have no place to lay their eggs.[7] Pima No. 1 winter wheat was grown over only a few small areas in the Yellow River basin in 1950. Its acreage reached 90 million mou in 1959. Compared with other strains, Pima No. 1 has bigger ears, heavier grains, thinner husks, higher flour yield harder stalks, and stronger resistance to smut and spring cold. In Northwest China, the yield from Pima No. 1 winter wheat averaged 200-300 chin per mou in 1961, with the highest yields reaching 700 chin per mou.

Although China is one of the leading cotton producers in the world, cotton is not a plant native to China. During the T'ang dynasty (618-905), only mulberry and hemp were mentioned in Chinese writings as the country's principal fiber crops. It was not until the end of the T'ang dynasty that cotton was introduced to China from Arabia via Iran and Central Asia to Sinkiang and Kansu. Between the Sung (960-1126) and Yuan (1206-1367) dynasties, cotton also was introduced from India over a sea route to Kwangtung, Kwangsi, Fukien, and Yunnan. Later, cotton growing spread to Central China, and during the Ming dynasty it spread north of the Yangtze River.[8]

Toward the end of the nineteenth century, American cotton was introduced into China by a few missionaries and industrialists. Thereafter, the United States played an increasingly important role in developing cotton production in China by providing technical advice and superior seeds. When the Communists took over in 1949, the acreage of American cotton planted in China totaled 10.5 million mou (1.75 million acres), or more than one-fourth of the total cotton area of the country.[9]

Since 1949, cotton planting in China has undergone two major changes. In 1950-55, the planting of Stoneville 4, Deltapine 14, and Coker 100, all of which were introduced from the United States, was further extended to replace native cotton and degenerated foreign cotton. In 1956-60, Deltapine 15 was used in the Yellow River basin and the Yangtze River basin to replace Stoneville 4, Delfos 531, and Acala, while such early ripening varieties as Chinyü No. 5, 611 P'o, and Kuochi No. 1 were popularized in areas where the growing season is short, and certain new long-fiber varieties were introduced in areas where the growing season is long and the temperature is high. In more recent years, more than 20 new cotton varieties were popularized in various areas. In the meantime, Deltapine 15 was extensively planted in Kiangsu, Chekiang, Anhwei, Hupeh, and Hunan to replace other Deltapine varieties that had become impure or had degenerated.[10]

In 1956, the Ministry of Agriculture established a network of cotton experiment stations for the study of new varieties developed in China or introduced from abroad. Since 1958, the project has been undertaken by the Cotton Research Institute of the Chinese Academy of Agricultural Science in collaboration with more than 70 agricultural research units and state farms throughout the country. By the end of the first half of 1962, 18 varieties had been selected for popularization in various regions. Thirteen of these were developed in China, while the other five were introduced from abroad. Of these varieties, Hsuchou 209 and Shihtuan 5 have done particularly well. In 1961, 100,000 mou of Hsuchou 209 were planted in Honan, Hopei, Shansi, and Shensi, while 360,000 mou of Shihtuan 5 were planted in the Shihchiachuan District of Hopei.[11]

It has been suggested that Communist China may have used the high-yielding strains of rice and wheat developed by the International Rice Research Institute in the Philippines and the International Maize and Wheat Improvement Center in Mexico, which have been used by many countries in increasing quantities. Although both institutions are financed by the United States, seeds of the new strains they have developed are available to all countries. The description of some of the new strains used in Communist China in recent years seems to fit the strains developed by the two institutions.[12] However, in May 1971 leaders of the communes near Peking, Shanghai, and Canton told foreign visitors that they had never heard of the "miracle" rice and wheat developed in the outside world and that for high yields they relied on new strains developed in their own areas.[13]

As already mentioned, plant breeding, especially rice breeding, had made considerable progress in China prior to the Communist regime and development in this field stood well ahead of that in other lines of agricultural science. Numerous studies in recent years by Ting Ying (1888-1964), a well-known rice breeder, and others indicate(that Communist China had continued to make substantial progress in the development of new strains of principal crops. As early as the 1950's, for example, Communist China was already paying much attention to the development of early rice strains that are high-yielding and can withstand typhoons and heavy rains.[14] It is possible that Communist China has developed new strains similar to those developec by the two American institutions.

But, even if Communist China has succeeded in plant breeding, the mismanagement of seeds has been and still is a serious problem. In 1959, Liu Ting-an, Director of the Seed Administration of the Ministry of Agriculture, admitted that the development was too hasty and that "there was a lack of healthy systems of multiplication, inspection, storage, transportation and utilization, thus creating much confusion."[15]

One well-known example of seed mismanagement was the "Golden Queen Incident," which stirred up a nationwide clamor in 1956. The Golden Queen variety of corn was imported from the United States in 1931 for an experiment at Ming Hsien School in Shansi. It had been grown in some areas of the province with high yield. In 1956, the variety was further popularized in Shansi during the high tide of the agricultural cooperativization movement. As a result, the total area sown to corn in the province increased from 6,200,000 mou (1,033,000 acres) in 1955 to 9,160,000 mou (1,526,700 acres) in 1956, which was 17 percent of the total sown area for all grain crops. Corn seeds of the Golden Queen variety were sown on some 5 million mou (833,00 acres), or about 55 percent of all the land sown to corn. In the Yenpei area, where elevation is high and temperature is low, the acreage sown for corn increased six times from 140,000 mou (23,000 acres) in 1955 to 860,000 mou (143,000 acres) in 1956. Close planting, artificial pollination, and large amounts of labor, fertilizer, and water were applied in an attempt to promote the growth of corn, but in some areas of the province the harvest of corn in that year was unsatisfactory. Many plants did not even sprout or form ears. This drew bitter complaints and criticism from the farmers, and the total sown acreage for corn was reduced from 9,160,000 mou (1,526,700 acres) in 1956 to 6,520,000 acres) in 1957. The Shansi Agricultural Reconstruction Bureau, while blaming the inclement weather for the bad corn harvest in 1956, admitted that the practice of indiscriminate popularization of the "Golden Queen" variety regardless of local conditions should be discontinued.[16]

The popularization of the Ch'ingsen No. 5 variety of rice in Hunan and Hupeh in 1956 and 1957 also stirred up a heated debate. Ch'ingsen No. 5 is an early-ripening variety of upland rice that has grown well in Kirin Province. The cadres decided to introduce it to the south as a double-cropping variety in an attempt to increase rice production and save labor. Some scientists maintained that Ch'ingsen No. 5 was not suitable for large-scale planting in the south, although fairly high yields had been reported in a few experimental fields in Hunan and Hupeh because of extra fertilization and other favorable conditions. The cadres in charge of the seed popularization program accused the scientists of being "conservatives," saying that the low yield of Ch'ingsen No. 5 in some areas was due to improper cultivation methods. Therefore, it was planned to plant Ch'ingsen No. 5 in 1958 on 10.3 million mou (1.7 million acres) in Hupeh and 5 million mou (830,000 acres) in Hunan. The relative success of the program to popularize Ch'ingsen No. 5 is not known, but it was a typical case of adopting "superior seeds" regardless of local conditions.[17]

A number of good strains were reported to have degenerated because of natural mixing with inferior strains, unfavorable climatic conditions, or improper cultivation techniques. Among them are Victory 100 sweet potatoes, Nant'ehao paddy rice, and Deltapine cotton.[18] The seeds in many cotton fields have decome impure and have degenerated to varying degrees, thus adversely affecting output and quality. In 1963, Deltapine cotton gave about 34 percent pure cotton as compared with over 38 percent in the previous years. Compared with the past, three to five chin of ginned cotton were lost for every tan of raw cotton, and the quality of cotton was lowered by one or two grades. In Hsinchou chü, Hsinchou hsien, Hupeh, the total output of unginned cotton in 1962 exceeded that in 1957 by 50,000 chin, but ginned cotton was 140,000 chin less than in 1957.[19]

Mismanagement has resulted in an acute shortage of seeds, although this was not openly admitted in a general statement until the beginning of 1961, when the situation became very serious. An editorial in the People's Daily, speaking of the preparation of seed for spring sowing, stated that after two years of natural calamities this was a difficult task. Calamity-stricken areas had no seeds left or had only seeds of very low quality for spring sowing. Moreover, the shortage of seeds was not confined to regions that had suffered natural disasters. In Hopei, Shansi, Kirin, Hupeh, Hunan, Ninghsia,

and other provinces, many of the high-quality seeds that had been
propagated a few years earlier had been spoiled by heat or by insects
or in the damp granaries and could not be used for sowing. In some
areas, high-quality seeds had deteriorated because they were sown
together with other types of seeds. In other areas, the high-quality
seeds were not well selected at the time of harvest, or people in
charge did not care.[20]

During the Leap Forward campaign, party cadres in many
localities urged or ordered the communes to discard certain inferior
seeds in favor of the improved seeds even though the latter were not
available in sufficient quantities. This zeal to introduce and popularize
new varieties of crops, in many cases totally ignoring local conditions,
worsened the seed situation and drew many criticisms. In an article
entitled "Guidance of Agricultural Production Should Be Started
From Practicality," Lu Li stated that seeds of inferior varieties should
not be discarded at will before better seeds were available:

> We should positively breed new varieties and at the same
> time continue to use old varieties. For example, in some
> mountainous areas, there is a type of bean called "kun
> shan chi" (mountain-rolling pheasant), which is generally
> regarded as an inferior crop. But because it grows on
> any soil, this crop should not be discarded. Without it,
> some areas would have no harvest of any kind. Another
> example is kaoliang, a grain sorghum. Compared with
> crops of high yield, one may think that kaoliang should be
> discarded. But kaoliang is indispensable, particularly in
> the hilly areas. Its stalks may be used as fuel and for
> building construction, and for making mats, cooking
> utensil covers, brooms, and many other daily necessities.
> Without kaoliang, people's life in some areas would be
> difficult. Still another example is "wan tou" (field peas).
> Its yield is much lower than that of wheat and some other
> crops, but it ripens early and is important not only as
> food but also as a substitute for soap. It should therefore
> not be disregarded.[21]

In an article in the Kuang-ming Daily, Ts'ai Hsü and Chang
Shu-ch'in of the Peking University of Agriculture suggested that in
popularizing seeds, attention should not be confined to a few newly
developed varieties and that numerous kinds of "farm household seeds"
also should be used according to local geographical and climatic
conditions and cultivation systems. A newly developed strain may
increase production in certain areas but may produce very little in

other areas. On the other hand, "farm household seeds," also known as "local seeds," were developed by peasants to meet certain local requirements and therefore should be included at least as part of the seeds used. These seeds are especially important in provinces or regions where a great variety of local conditions exist. In Hunan, for example, 62.7 percent of all seeds used in the province are farm household seeds because of the wide range among the different localities in latitude, elevation, temperature, soil moisture, number of croppings, sowing period of rice (which extends from the middle of March to the end of June), period of transplanting (from the middle of April to the beginning of autumn), period of harvesting (from the middle of July to November), and growth period of rice (from 110 days to 180 days). A similar situation exists in the Kwangsi-Chuang Autonomous Regions. In areas subject to natural calamities, farm household seeds are especially important because of their strong resistance to unfavorable environment.[22] The importance of farm household seeds in China was clearly indicated in a list compiled by the Seed Administration of the Ministry of Agriculture in 1958 (including a supplement compiled in 1959), which covered 2,449 superior varieties of 32 crops. Of these, 1,834 varieties, or three-fourths of the total, were local varieties.[23]

On December 20, 1961, the Chinese Society of Crops was founded as a branch of the Chinese Society of Agriculture. Its first meeting was held in Changsha, Hunan, on December 20-28, 1961, to take up the subject of seed development. The discussion centered around the policy pursued by the government during recent years, a policy that now met wholesale condemnation. Participants in the meeting agreed virtually unanimously that future development of new seeds should be carried out in view of the standard of production over wide areas and should be adopted to different regions; in other words, that it is as important to develop seeds for production over a wide area as to follow the present practice of producing special high-yielding seeds.[24]

Commenting on the conference, the Peking journal Scientia stated:

In recent years there was a one-sided emphasis on the selection and breeding of new types of seed which would give high productivity. This had produced good results, but seeds so developed, if used under unfavorable circumstances of fertilization and water supply, might produce not more but less than the ordinary seeds used locally. Therefore the questions, what policy our country should take in the future in plant breeding, what

standards should be followed in developing new seeds, and
in general what measures should be taken, drew broad
attention at the conference.

Experts from all over the country, putting together
their experiences, carried out lively discussions, and on
the above questions they reached a relatively unanimous
view. The majority held that, in order to guarantee production increase in large areas, the direction of our country's plant breeding work in the future should be toward
the development of new varieties suitable for the production in large areas, with both higher and lower levels of
production taken into consideration. New varieties should
be developed to give much higher production than the
original varieties over large areas and for many crops,
in order to meet the need of different areas.[25]

This approach would mean that consideration should not be
confined to a few isolated areas nor to some so-called "high-yielding"
varieties and that the matter of seed development should be dealt
with for the country as a whole and adapted to different circumstances,
including local farming systems.

PLANT GENETICS

The development of genetics under the Chinese Communist
regime should be reviewed here at least briefly because the subject
is closely linked with the question of seed improvement. Before
1949, Chinese geneticists were mostly followers of the school of
Gregor J. Mendel and Thomas H. Morgan. When the Communists
took over the country, the "bourgeois" scientific schools were expelled
and the Russian Michurin-Lysenko school was introduced as the only
approach corresponding to materialist philosophy. The China Michurin
Society was established in Peking in 1951 with dozens of Chapters
throughout the country, and a large number of "Michurin Youth Farms"
have been organized by the Young Pioneers.

In the spring of 1952, the Ministry of Agriculture invited A. P.
Ivanov, a Soviet specialist in Michurin genetics, to serve as an advisor.
Accompanied by Ivanov, a joint technical group of the Ministry of
Agriculture, the Chinese Academy of Sciences, the North China Insti-
tute of Agricultural Science, the North China Institute of Agricultural
Science, the Peking Agricultural University, and other institutions
made a survey of agricultural conditions in many areas during the

months April-August, 1952. In its report, the group urged the intensive study and adoption of Michurin's theories in improving agricultural techniques. The survey was followed by a special training class in Michurin's methods of seed selection and multiplication, which lasted four months (from October 21, 1952, to February 20, 1953) and was attended by more than 1,000 technical workers from all parts of the country, including Inner Mongolia and Tibet. Lectures on Michurin's theories and their application were delivered by several Soviet experts.[26]

In an article on China's achievements in Michurin genetics during the first decade of the Communist regime, Liang Cheng-lan gave a rather detailed account of the work that done by Chinese scientists in various major aspects of genetics, including the control of individual plant development, vegetative hybridization in animals and plants, research on predetermined cultivation, and research on intra-varietal crossing. He also cited several examples of experiments conducted by advanced farmers on the basis of Michurin principles. But he admitted that the research as a whole was not well organized and "lacked depth."[27]

Tsu Te-ming, a genetics specialist of the Chinese Academy of Agricultural Science, stated that, whereas foreign data exclusively were used in lectures on genetics in China before 1949, since then more and more experimental results with regard to chromosomes and nucleo-acids and preliminary results on artificially induced variations have been obtained in China. According to Tsu Te-ming, results of studies of ontogenesis, directive breeding, and sexual and asexual hybridization have become even more varied. Since 1958, Chinese scientists have been carrying out a host of experiments in distant hybridization, an important aspect of genetics. Studies in phase development were made on wheat, rice, millet, corn, soybeans, cotton, and other principal crops. The results provided data for improving the techniques of cultivation and seed breeding and laid a scientific basis for the introduction of crops from distant places. According to Tsu Te-ming, the accuracy of the position that organic matter and environmental conditions are intimately connected could be clearly seen from the analysis of phase development of local strains of wheat, rice, and soybeans.[28]

After the death of Stalin in 1953, Trofim D. Lysenko fell from grace, and in April 1956 he was removed from his post as President of the Soviet Academy of Agricultural Sciences. Four months later, on August 10-25, 1956, a conference on genetics was held at Tsingtao under the sponsorship of the Chinese Academy of Sciences and the

Ministry of Higher Education. A large number of biologists, animal
breeders, plant breeders, and geneticists attended, and some who
had maintained silence for years were called upon to address the
audience. One of the speakers, Fang Chung-hsi, Professor of Biology
at Shantung University, who was a Michurinist prior to the conference
and had written several articles supporting Lysenkoism, revealed
that the following basic points were clarified during the two-week
discussion:

1. The controversy between Michurinists and Mendelianists
is not a struggle between materialism and idealism biology, as claimed
by Lysenko. The difference between the two schools is a scientific
problem, not a philosophical one and still less a political one.
Morganists are not reactionary.

2. Morganian genetics has never been "beaten down" by Lysenko.
In fact, it has developed into a highly refined level far beyond chromo-
somology. It should not be discriminated against or prevented from
further development.

3. There is some justification for the theory of unification of
the organism with its living conditions, as claimed by the Michurinian
school, and Lysenko's theory of phase development of plants, although
not perfect, is not without foundation. However, these should be
further investigated, particularly by refined experimental methods.

4. The recognition of the possibility of directed cultivation
does not exclude Mendelism, mutation, or random variation. Proper
utilization of existing variations can achieve the purpose of directed
cultivation. A dictatorial attitude is harmful to the development of
science.

5. Vegetable hybridization and the inheritance of acquired
characteristics may be explained in various ways; none of the facts
cited by Lysenko invalidates the chromosome and gene theory.

6. Darwin's theory of natural selection is still correct.
Lysenko's contention that there is no competition within a species is
not adequately supported by evidence.[29]

Although advocating further research and application of
Michurin's theories, Tsu Te-ming maintained that the Mendel-Morgan
school should not be ignored and that some of their theories definitely
should be used for reference.[30] In his opinion, the questions in dispute between the Morgan and Michurin schools had changed somewhat

in the late 1950's. The two schools had shown a tendency to approach one another, although some differences continued to exist in their viewpoints on the relationships among the material basis for heredity, hereditary variation, and environmental conditions; the hereditary nature of acquired properties; the possibility of directive breeding; and other important problems.[31]

Lysenko somewhat regained his influence in Soviet biological and agricultural circles in 1960 and was again appointed President of the Soviet Academy of Agricultural Sciences in August 1961. He resigned from the presidency on April 5, 1962, because of "health reasons."[32] However, through the years since the 1956 Tsingtao conference, Chinese Michurinists have been losing ground and Mendelianists have increasingly dominated the scene. In the third-year course of biology at Peking Normal University, theories of both schools of genetics were taught in the academic year 1960-61.[33] Professor Li Ching-hsiung, at Peking Agricultural University, stated: "For some years now, Morgan's theories of genetics have enjoyed the sympathy and patronage of Party and government."[34]

In a review of genetics work in China in 1961 and 1962, Fang Chung-hsi revealed that many essays on both schools were published, and forums were held in Kwangtung, Fukien, Chekiang, Kiangsu, Shantung, and other provinces. He stated:

Through discussions, we have realized that both Michurin-ian and Morganian schools have their strong and weak points, and one is not contradictory to the other. We have not only better understood the development and trends of genetics in the world, thus raising the standard of our career and broadening the scope of our knowledge, but also are more aware than before that "Let a hundred flowers bloom and let a hundred schools contend" is our Party's basic policy for developing science and culture, a means to direct research work under Marxism and Leninism, and a mass line of conducting scientific work.[35]

The reason for this definitely relaxed atmosphere in genetics may be sought in the general alienation from the slavish imitation of everything Russian that existed prior to the breach of the Sino-Soviet relations, and also in the realization that the theories of Michurin have not produced the expected miracles in agriculture.

NOTES

1. Liu Ting-an, "Great Achievements in Seed Improvement Work in China in the Past Decade," Chung-kuo Nung-pao [Chinese Agriculture Bulletin], Peking, No. 15, 1959, pp. 22-23, 27.

2. NCNA, Peking, January 27 and 30, 1964.

3. JMJP, December 1, 1963, p. 1.

4. JMJP, August 3, 1965, p. 1.

5. Ibid.

6. Shen Hsueh-nien, Shui-tao [Paddy Rice] (Peking, 1955), pp. 3-4, 18-28; Tseng Kwang-hui, "Some of China's Superior Strains of Rice," Nung-yeh K'o-hsueh T'ung-hsun [Agricultural Science Bulletin], Peking, No. 2, 1958, pp. 84-86; Cheng Chao-hsien, "Three Years of the Agricultural Charter," China Reconstructs, Peking, No. 10, 1961, pp. 6-10; NCNA, Peking, April 25, 1966.

7. Tai Sung-en, "Fully Develop the Use of Superior Varieties for Increasing Crop Production," Hung Ch'i [Red Flag], Peking, No. 2, 1963, pp. 25-34.

8. Hu Ching-liang, Chung-kuo Mien-ch'an Kai-chin-shih [History of the Improvement of China's Cotton Production], revised edition (Shanghai, 1947).

9. Feng Tse-fang, Ho-yu Chung-kuo Tsai-chung ti Hsi-jung-mien [Fine Velvet Cotton Suitable for Plantation in China] (Shanghai, 1953), pp. 8-9; Mu Chen, "Cotton-Producing Areas in China," Ta Kung Pao, Peking, April 5, 1962, p. 2.

10. Ch'en Jen, "Multiplication and Popularization of Superior Cotton Varieties," JMJP, May 28, 1963, p. 5.

11. Jen-min Shou-ts'e [People's Handbook], Peking, 1962, p. 274.

12. The New York Times, October 26, 1969, p. 21; The Green Revolution, Proceedings Before the Subcommittee on the National Security Policy and Scientific Developments of the Committee on Foreign Affairs, U.S. House of Representatives, Ninety-First

Congress, First Session (Washington, D. C.: December 5, 1969), p. 37.

13. The New York Times, May 16, 1971, p. 17.

14. Shen Hsueh-nien, op. cit., pp. 3-4, 18-28; Tseng Kwang-hui, op. cit., pp. 84-86.

15. Liu Ting-an, op. cit., pp. 22-23, 27.

16. Feng Chien-wei, "What Are the Explanations for the Golden Queen Incident?" Hsin-hua Pan-yueh-k'an [New China Semimonthly], Peking, No. 4, 1958, pp. 73-74.

17. Hupeh Provincial Bureau of Agriculture, "Introduction of Ch'ingsen No. 5 to Hupeh Province Is a Success," Chung-kuo Nung-pao [Chinese Agriculture Bulletin], Peking, No. 12, 1958, pp. 7-8; Chao Ch'un-wu, "Who Says That Ch'ingsen No. 5 Is Not Suitable for Plantation in Hunan?" Chung-kuo Nung-pao [Chinese Agriculture Bulletin], Peking, No. 12, 1958, pp. 9, 12.

18. Sun Chia-tseng, "Let Good Strains Permanently Preserve Their Youth," K'o-hsueh Ta-chung [Popular Science], Peking, No. 4, 1964, pp. 121-22.

19. "Proposals on Several Important Technical Measures for Increasing Cotton Output Next Year," JMJP, August 26, 1963, p. 2.

20. JMJP, November 11, 1961, p. 2; November 25, 1961, p. 1; December 3, 1961, p. 2; January 27, 1962, p. 1; March 15, 1962, p. 2; June 3, 1962, p. 1.

21. JMJP, November 12, 1960, p. 7.

22. Ts'ai Hsu and Chang Shu-ch'in, "Functions of the Farm Household Seeds in the Current Agricultural Production," Kuang-ming Jih-pao [Kuang-ming Daily], Peking, July 30, 1962, p. 1.

23. P'u Mu-hua, "Resources of Crop Varieties of Our Country," JMJP, December 11, 1962, p. 5.

24. Kuang-ming Jih-pao [Kuang-ming Daily], Peking, January 3, 1962, p. 1.

25. K'o-hsueh T'ung-pao [Scientia], Peking, No. 1, 1962, p. 1.

26. Training Class in Michurin's Methods of Seed Selection and Multiplication, Ministry of Agriculture, Nung-yeh K'o-hsueh Chuan-t'i Pao-kao chi Ts'an-k'ao Tzu-liao Chi [A Collection of Reports and Reference Materials on the Special Problems of Agricultural Science] (Peking, 1953), pp. 268-301.

27. Liang Cheng-lan, "China's Achievements in Michurin Genetics During the Past Decade," Sheng-wu-hsueh T'ung-pao [Biological Bulletin], Peking, No. 10, 1959, pp. 462-67.

28. Kuang-ming Jih-pao [Kuang-ming Daily], Peking, June 14, 1961.

29. C. C. Li, "Genetics and Animal and Plant Breeding," Sciences in Communist China, Publication No. 68 of the American Association for the Advancement of Science (Washington, D. C., 1961), pp. 297-321.

30. Tsu Te-ming, "Development and Accomplishments of Michurin's Genetics in China in the Past Ten Years," Nung-yeh Hsueh-pao [Acta Agriculture Sinica], Peking, Vol. X, No. 5 (1959), pp. 330-43.

31. Kuang-ming Jih-pao [Kuang-ming Daily], Peking, June 14, 1961.

32. The New York Times, April 6, 1962, p. 12.

33. Kuang-ming Jih-pao [Kuang-ming Daily], Peking, April 8, 1961.

34. Kuang-ming Jih-pao [Kuang-ming Daily], Peking, May 5, 1961.

35. Fang Chung-hsi, "Positive Influence of Discussions on Genetics During the Past Year or So," Kuang-ming Jih-pao [Kuang-ming Daily], Peking, May 3, 1962, p. 2.

10

The idea of planting crops at a proper density in order to obtain maximum yields is not new in China. In a book entitled Lu-shih Ch'nu-ch'iu (Lu's Annals), compiled by Lu Pu-wei, a prime minister in the Ch'in Dynasty (255-207 B.C.), the technique of close planting and its requirements and limitations were thoroughly discussed. For centuries, Chinese farmers have used such factors as the kinds of crops, land fertility, and local conditions for determining the density of seedlings that would result in higher yields. In general, close planting was adopted in China only to a limited extent before the Communist take-over.[1]

At the advice of F. C. Lutsenko, a Soviet agronomist, close planting was encouraged at the beginning of the Communist regime. An experiment was conducted by the Ministry of Agriculture in 1951 at the Shuangch'iao State Farm in the Municipality of Peking, where more than 4,000 cotton seedlings were planted to each mou. The yield was reported to have doubled that of the preceding year, although no actual amount was revealed. A similar experiment for wheat was conducted in 1951 at the same state farm, where plots sown with rows 6.5 inches apart produced 80 percent more wheat than those sown 18 inches apart. Cadres in charge of agriculture in various provinces were later sent to Peking to study the technique of close planting.[2] At the same time, close planting of rice was practiced at the Po Hai area in North China with a reported yield of more than 1,000 chin per mou, as compared with the average yield of rice in Mainland China in 1951, which was 300 chin per mou.[3]

Despite the reported success of these experiments, close planting was opposed by many scientists attending the January 1951 North China Conference on Agricultural Techniques. As a compromise, the conference recommended increasing the amount of seed sown in each row but widening the distance between the rows. Many farmers also doubted the wisdom of close planting, mainly because they could not afford the seeding and transplanting machines used by the state farms.

It was claimed that in 1955 some 150 million mou of wheat farms, or 37 percent of the land sown to wheat, adopted close planting, and that in most of the remaining wheat-growing areas traditional densities were modified to bring them nearer to close planting. The increase of the country's wheat production from 18.1 million metric tons in 1952 to 24.8 million metric tons in 1956 was partly attributed to the wide adoption of close planting throughout the country.[4]

Actually, however, during the First Five-Year Plan period, close planting was continued with only moderate enthusiasm. It was during the Leap Forward campaign that this practice of cultivation was again emphasized. In 1958, from 20 to 30 chin of wheat seeds were sown to one mou in many areas, and the resulting harvest was reported to be from 400 to 600 chin per mou, compared with yields of 200 to 300 chin per mou at the normal density of planting of 6 to 15 chin per mou. For rice, the target was from 35,000 to 4,000 clusters and from 350,000 to 400,000 seedlings per mou.[5]

Apparently because of the failure to increase agricultural production by the indiscriminate practice of close planting, a series of articles on the problem was published in the leading newspapers and scientific journals in 1959-61. Although some writers still placed an emphasis on close planting as a means of raising yields of the principal crops, many scientists warned that it should be practiced only to a certain degree according to certain circumstances.

In the case of wheat, a survey of 183 experimental plots of high-yielding winter wheat in the Municipality of Peking and the provinces of Hopei and Honan, conducted in 1958 by the Research Institute of Plant Breeding and Cultivation, indicated that close planting beyond a certain limit had resulted in a decrease in yield because of a serious interference with normal growth of the plants. It was suggested that close planting should be practiced according to the conditions of planting, fertilization, irrigation, light, temperature, moisture, seed variety, and other factors, and that the proper degree of close planting varies to a certain extent because of differences in these factors.[6]

Another experiment conducted in 1958 by the Kiangsu Provincial Branch of the Chinese Academy of Agricultural Science in Nanking indicated that, at the density of more than 500,000 wheat seedlings per mou, the normal development of both individual and plant community as a whole were upset, mainly because of progressive shading of the leaves. Under such circumstances, the fundamental basis for higher yield was lost. It was suggested that a density ranging from 250,000 to 350,000 seedlings per mou would seem to be more practicable.[7]

A similar conclusion was drawn from an experiment on wheat conducted in 1959-60 by a special tean of the Research Institute of Phytophysiology of the Chinese Academy of Sciences in collaboration with the Agricultural Research Institute of the Hsinhsiang Special District in Honan Province. The results indicated that, after the density of planting had been increased to a certain point, the "economic coefficient" of yield would tend to decline.[8]

In the case of rice, experience with close planting has been essentially the same as that with wheat. According to a survey of 335 farms in Kiangsu Province conducted in 1958, there were some cases where yield was higher than normal when 400,000 to 600,000 seedlings were planted to one mou. But when the number of seedlings per mou exceeded 600,000, the average number of grains in each ear tended to decrease.[9]

In a series of eleven experiments on the density of planting of corn conducted in northern Kiangsu in 1958, the following results were reported by the participants:

1. The optimum density of planting varied with "agrotechnic levels." Under the conventional agrotechnic level, higher yield for the variety with a stalk of 200 centimeters or more in height could be reaped by a density of 3,000 plants per mou in spring sowing. Under a higher agrotechnic level, it was preferable to run as many as 4,000 plants per mou in both spring and summer sowing to obtain the best results. It was indicated that, within the range between 2,000 and 8,000 plants per mou, the closer the density, the higher the yield per stalk.

2. There was close relationship between the grain yield per unit area of land and agrotechnic level. The average grain yield per mou treated under higher agrotechnic level exceeded that under conventional agrotechnic level by 50 to 63 percent. Under higher agrotechnic level the reduction of grain yield as a result of too close spacing was more slack than that under conventional agrotechnic level.

3. The addition of manure at a heavier density in proportion to the planting also gave a slacker reduction than planting spaced too closely without a corresponding increase of manure.

4. The heavier density of planting increased the total number of ears per mou, but the rate of increase was not as great as that of the increased plants. For instance, if the number of plants per mou increased by 4 times, e.g., from 2,000 to 8,000, the number of ears per mou increased by only 2.26 to 2.62 times. Furthermore, under too closely spaced conditions the number of kernels per ear and the weight per 1,000 grains were significantly decreased and a lower yield per unit area of land was obtained.

5. By increasing the density of planting, it was apparent that the height of plant and ear was neither increased nor decreased but the stem became markedly slender, thus resulting in a higher percentage of stalk breaking. The increased planting density also tended to delay the prevailing stages of tassel emergence and ear silking. For instance, in the case of 8,000 plants per mou, the prevailing stages of tassel emergence and ear silking were delayed by 2 days and 3 to 6 days, respectively, as compared with the case of 2,000 plants per mou. With regard to root development, with increased density of planting the number of permanent roots of a single plant was reduced and their distribution was shallower. In the case of 8,000 plants per mou, the depth of permanent roots and the distribution of a single plant's roots were reduced by 36.18 percent and 34 percent, respectively, as compared with the case of 2,000 plants per mou. Furthermore, under closely spaced conditions the accumulation of plant food materials was reduced and the development of underground parts was thereby inhibited. This inhibition, in turn, affected the accumulation of organic matter.

6. The differences of temperature and relative humidity between plants with different planting densities were remarkable only under such conditions as the entire shading of leaves between rows and great difference of temperature between day and night. With increased planting density, relative humidity increased, while light intensity decreased.

7. The closer the stands were, the greater the absolute value of the green leaf area. Consequently, the power of photosynthesis also was increased. However, the process of net assimilation was checked as the green leaf area and the power of photosynthesis increased. For this reason, the biological yield was not always raised by increasing the density of planting. Furthermore, under too closely spaced conditions the green leaf area would seriously decrease as soon as its maximum was reached because of the rapid increase in the lower part of yellow leaves that could hardly keep constant for a certain period.[10]

Among the most heated debates on the question of close planting was the one between Yin Hung-chang, Deputy Director of the Research Institute of Plant Physiology of the Chinese Academy of Sciences, and Wu Cho-nien, Assistant Head of the Department of Agricultural Science of the South China College of Agriculture. Yin conducted an experiment in Sunkiang in 1959 with single-cropping late rice of lao lai ch'ing strain, transplanted on various plots that previously were used for growing "hung hua ts'ao" (red-flower grass). Yin conducted another experiment in Sunkiang in 1959 with the same variety of rice but on the plot where barley had grown previously (see Table 19).

The first experiment indicated that, despite the great difference in the number of seedlings transplanted, the ultimate effective ears on different plots were "quite near to one another" in number. When the density (number of seedlings per mou) was increased twelve times, the number of effective ears showed less than a one-fold increase and the number of grains per ear decreased by almost one-half. The second experiment showed that, after the number of ears in a mou had increased to a certain extent, the number of grains per ear decreased, the percentage of empty grains increased, and the weight of each 1,000 grains fell off. Within a certain limit, the increase in the number of ears exceeded the decrease in the number of grains and in the weight of grains, and therefore the yield still rose along with the increase in density. Having reached a certain limit, the increase in the number of ears was offset by the decrease in the number of grains and the weight of grains, and therefore the yield no longer increased. After the density had exceeded this limit, the increase in the number of ears was not enough to offset the decrease in the number of grains and the weight of grains, and as a result the yield fell off.

In Yin Hung-chang's opinion, a plant group is a system quite capable of self-adjustment. In the plots with thin planting, there are more tillers and the density increased by itself. In the plots with close planting, there are fewer tillers, that is, a natural thinning out is brought about by the death of some of the tillers. Eventually, these two kinds of plots are "near to each other" as regards density. Therefore, relying on close planting as a major means of increasing agricultural production is improper: rational close planting can obtain the highest yield at the minimum cost under given conditions of soil, climate, fertilization, irrigation, and labor force.[11]

Wu Cho-nien disagreed with Yin Hung-chang about the latter's theory that a plant group is a system quite capable of self-adjustment and that thin planting and close planting will eventually result in approximately the same density through the increase and decrease of tillering.

TABLE 19

Results of Yin Hung-chang's Experiments with
Transplants of Lao Lai ch'ing Rice

	Transplants of Lao Lai Ch'ing on Plots Previously Used for Red-Flower Grass		
Plot	Number of Basic Seedlings Per Mou	Number of Effective Ears Per Mou	Number of Grains Per Ear
1	30,000	194,000	99.0
2	90,000	243,000	84.4
3	150,000	246,000	74.4
4	210,000	248,000	71.1
5	270,000	266,000	66.7
6	360,000	342,000	56.1

	Transplants of Lao Lai Ch'ing on Plots Previously Used for Barley					
	Number of Basic Seedlings (tens of thousands per mou)					
	15	25	30	35	40	5(
Number of effective ears (tens of thousands per mou)	19.1	21.8	27.0	29.6	31.0	39.(
Number of grains per ear	73.2	69.8	58.6	56.6	52.5	43."
Percentage of empty grains	12.0	17.0	15.8	23.1	21.4	25."
Weight of 1,000 grains (grams)	27.6	27.6	27.0	26.6	26.7	26."
Total number of grains (tens of thousands mou)	1,398.0	1,522.0	1,582.0	1,675.0	1,628.0	1,697.(
Number of full grains (tens of thousands per mou)	1,230.0	1,263.0	1,332.0	1,288.0	1,280.0	1,257.(
Computed yield (chin per mou)	679.0	697.0	719.0	685.0	683.0	659.(
Verified yield (chin per mou)	829.0	831.0	798.0	784.0	779.0	719.(

Using Yin's data (see Table 19), Wu maintained that in the first experiment, although the increase in the number of ears from 194,000 to 342,000 per mou did not keep pace with the increase in the number of seedlings from 30,000 to 360,000 per mou "because of cultivation technique," nevertheless the increase of the ears was caused by the increase of the seedlings and was anything but a gift given by the self-adjustment of the plants; Wu stated that close planting definitely had stepped up the yield.[12]

In the 1960's, the word "rational" was emphasized in discussing the problems of close planting. In claiming accomplishments in this field, Vice-Premier T'an Chen-lin stated: "Rational close planting has been widely popularized. Too close planting and too sparse planting are both on the wane, and the laws of rational close planting are being grasped by more and more people."[13]

Apparently, there has been hesitation about close planting, which was generally promoted during the Leap Forward campaign with some disastrous consequences. "There are people who do not show interest and do not welcome it," said the Kuang-ming Daily.[14] But in principle close planting is still being encouraged. The People's Daily, "Close planting is an important component of the Eight-Character Agricultural Charter, but we must remember that 'rational close planting' is what Chairman Mao has said. If we act accordingly, we can increase output and support socialist construction and world revolution."[15]

NOTES

1. Wan Kuo-ting, "The Theory and Methods of Equal Spacing, Close Planting and Maintenance of Seedlings in China 2,200 Years Ago," Nung-yeh Hsueh-pao [Acta Agriculturae Sinica], Peking, Vol. VII, No. 3 (1956), pp. 269-74.

2. Liu Chung-hsuan, "Close Planting Catches On," China Reconstructs, Peking, Vol. V, No. 10 (1956), pp. 22-24.

3. Jen-min Shou-ts'e [People's Handbook] (Peking, 1952), p. 354; State Statistical Bureau, Ten Great Years, English edition (Peking, 1960), p. 121.

4. Liu Chung-hsuan, op. cit., pp. 22-24.

5. "What Are the Key Factors in the Realization of a Continued Leap Forward in Agriculture This Year?" Ch'iu Shih [Seeking the Facts], Handchow, No. 3, March 15, 1960, pp. 1-13.

6. Research Institute of Plant Breeding and Cultivation, Chinese Academy of Agricultural Science, "The Extent of Rational Close Planting of Winter Wheat as Judged from Seedling Growth," Nung-yeh Hsueh-pao [Acta Agriculturae Sinica], Peking, Vol. X, No. 2 (1959), pp. 86-101.

7. Kiangsu Branch of the Chinese Academy of Agricultural Science, Nanking, "Studies on the Rational Sowing Density of Wheat Plants," Nung-yeh Hsueh-pao [Acta Agriculturae Sinica], Peking, Vol. X, No. 5 (1959), pp. 431-46.

8. Yu Shu-wen and Chou Chia-huai, "The Phenomena of Group Concept Development of Wheat Under Different Conditions of Close Planting," in Shang-hai-shih K'o-hsueh Chi-shu Lun-wen Hsuan-chi: Nung-yeh [Collection of Selected Scientific and Technological Essays of the Municipality of Shanghai: Agriculture] (Shanghai, 1960), pp. 35-49.

9. Research Institute of Phytophysiology and the Peking Research Office of Phytophysiology, both of the Chinese Academy of Sciences, "Functions of Phytophysiology in Summing Up the Experience in the Production Increase of Rice," K'o-hsueh T'ung-pao [Scientia], Peking, No. 6, 1959, pp. 177-78.

10. Fan Fu-jen, Mo Hui-tung; and Ch'in T'ai-ch'en, "A Study on the Close Planting of Corn," Nung-yeh Hsueh-pao [Acta Agriculturae Sinica], Peking, Vol. XI, No. 2 (May 1960), pp. 109-36.

11. Yin Hung-chang, "Group Concept in Agricultural Production," JMJP, June 13, 1960, p. 7; Yin Hung-chang, "More on Group Concept in Agricultural Production and Reply to Comrade Wu Cho-nien," JMJP, June 3, 1961, p. 7.

12. Wu Cho-nien, "A Discussion About the Article, 'Group Concept in Agricultural Production,'" JMJP, March 1, 1961, p. 7.

13. T'an Chen-lin, "Strive for the Fulfillment, Ahead of Schedule, of the National Program for Agricultural Development," JMJP, April 7, 1960, p. 1.

14. Ch'eng I-te, "Respect Experience and Stick to Traditions," Kuang-ming Jih-pao [Kuang-ming Daily], Peking, February 26, 1965, p. 4.

15. Joint Investigation Group of the Loyang Area Revolutionary Committee and Military Subregional Command, and the Yenshih Hsien

Revolutionary Committee and Militia Department, "A Lesson on Close
Planting, In Which Proletarian Politics Is Brought to the Fore," JMJP,
March 28, 1969, p. 3.

Losses of agricultural products as a result of pests, diseases, and weeds are difficult to measure. In the United States, a country where plant protection is highly developed, in 1951-60 insects were estimated to cause a loss of 4 to 12 percent in the potential yield of the main grains, diseases a loss of 7 to 14 percent, and weeds a loss of 10 to 17 percent.[1]

Although detailed data are not available on the quantities of crops damaged by insects and diseases in Mainland China, it is evident that the losses have been considerable. J. Lossing Buck has estimated that insects and diseases have damaged as much as 10 to 20 percent of grain crops.[2] In 1962, in the areas seriously affected, the loss of grains was about 10 percent of the total production; that of cotton, 20 percent; and that of fruits, 30 percent, according to an estimate made by the Bureau of Plant Protection of the Ministry of Agriculture.[3]

The seriousness of the damage was also indicated in a plan mapped out by the same bureau in 1958 for the thorough control of plant diseases and insect pests on a total of 182.3 million mou (30.38 million acres) of crop land in 18 provinces and municipalities; the area involved included 55 million mou of land for rice, 24 million mou for wheat, 63 million mou for miscellaneous grains (including underground insects), 37 million mou for cotton, and 3.3 million mou for fruits and other economic crops. The Bureau of Plant Protection estimated that the plan, if implemented, would save some 2,500 million chin (1.25 million metric tons) of grains and 1.8 million tan (90,000 metric tons) of cotton.[4] However, the results of the implementation of the plan were not revealed.

The National Program for Agricultural Development called for the general elimination, in the twelve years beginning in 1956, of the insect pests and plant diseases that are most harmful to crops, including locusts, rice borers, army worms, corn borers, cotton aphids, red spiders, pink boll worms, wheat juice-sucking worms (<u>Sitodiplosis mosellana</u> Gehin), wheat smut, wheat nematodes, and black rot on sweet potatoes. It also called for local plans for plant protection to include programs for the eradication other serious insect pests and plant diseases, the strengthening of quarantine systems, the production and improvement of pesticides and related apparatus, and the assurance of their safe and effective use (Article 15 of the Program).

Also included in the program was the elimination of "flour evils" (rats, sparrows, flies, and mosquitoes) in the twelve years beginning in 1956, for reasons of public health as well as agricultural production. When the program was revised in 1960, sparrows were replaced by bedbugs, in recognition of the sparrows' usefulness in destroying insects (Article 27 of the Program).

In his report to the Second Session of the Second National People's Congress on April 6, 1960, Vice-Premier T'an Chen-lin claimed that the damage caused by aphids and red spiders had been eliminated in the principal cotton-growing areas and that virtually no withered or red leaves could be seen on the cotton plants. Locusts and army worms were basically under control, and damage caused by wheat smut and rice borers had been generally reduced to less than 2 percent. According to T'an Chen-lin, "in many places, blocks of tens and hundreds of thousands of <u>mou</u> of farmland have been freed from diseases and insect pests."[5]

In another account, Vice-Minister of Agriculture Yang Hsien-tung stated that in 1962 the total area under control with pesticides was close to 400 million <u>mou</u> (67 million acres). According to Yang Hsien-tung, in ten provinces including Honan, Hopei, Shantung, Hupeh, and Kiangsu, more than 4,000 million <u>chin</u> (2.67 million tons) of grain and more than 1 million <u>chin</u> (666.50 tons) of cotton were additionally harvested because of the control of plant diseases and insect pests.[6]

INSECT PESTS AND CROP DISEASES

Following are the highlights of the accomplishments in the control of principal insect pests and crop diseases since 1949, according to Communist accounts.

Locusts

For centuries, locusts have been a great menace to China's
agricultural production. The earliest outbreak recorded in the Chinese
history was in 707 B.C., and since then more than 800 outbreaks have
taken place. In the past 1,000 years, a major locust pest usually broke
out once every two or three years, or twice every five years. The
frequency is believed to be closely related to the floods once every
three years and droughts once every two years on the great plains
along the lower reaches of the Yellow River, the Huai River, and the
Hai River. The outbreak of East Asian locusts (<u>Locusta migratoria</u>
<u>manilensis</u> Meyen) has been concentrated at the coastal areas, the
lakeside areas, the inland waterlogged areas, and the flooded areas
along these three rivers.

During the Economic Recovery Period (1949-52), more than
120 million persons, mainly peasants, participated in several locust
control campaigns. When a major outbreak of locust pest took place
in 1951, the methods of surrounding, whipping, and burning were
generally used in one of the most difficult fights against locusts, a
fight that was successful despite an acute shortage of insecticides and
equipment.[7] In 1951, for the first time in China aircraft were used
to apply pesticides for the control of locusts in some areas.[8]

Since 1952, locust control stations have been set up in many
areas to conduct reconnaisance work in finding the locust eggs, unfledged locusts, and full-grown locusts. Meanwhile, soil, climatic,
and vegetation conditions in many localities frequently affected by
locust pests have been improved by building water conservation projects
and converting the land into paddy fields, salt fields, or afforestation
sites.[9] By the use of insecticides and the transformation of breeding
grounds, the area affected by locusts had been curtailed by more than
60 percent by the end of 1962, according to Chin Shan-pao, Vice-
President of the Chinese Academy of Agricultural Science.[10]

However, the menace of locusts to crops remains serious. As
admitted in 1963 by Vice-Minister of Agriculture Yang Hsien-tung,
although the density of locusts had been reduced, the area over which
locust infestation occurred had not yet decreased. The waste in the
control work was immense, largely because in recent years many
areas weakened their locust control organizations and therefore the
facts concerning locusts were not mastered. At the same time, many
areas had not properly mobilized the masses for locust control. In
addition, too much reliance was placed on airplanes for spraying

insecticides and airplanes were used for the control even where they
should not be used.[11] In 1963, about 70 percent of the dusting of
insecticides for locust control was done by airplanes.[12]

Rice Borers

Rice borers in China are of two principal types: Schoenobius
incertellus Walker and Chilo simplex Butler. Both are generally
distributed along and south of the Yangtze River. Two or three
generations are produced each year in the Yangtze Basin, from three
to five generations south of the river, and as many as seven generations
on Hainan Island. The degree of their damage to rice crops depends
largely on climatic conditions, planting systems, and the varieties of
the rice plants used in a particular area. As a result of the improvement of planting systems in the rice-producing regions and the increasing application of chemical insecticides, the loss caused by rice
borers in China was reported to have been brought down to less than
2 percent by 1958. Before 1954, tobacco was the principal material
used for the control of rice-stem borers. Later, the use of "666"
was promoted gradually with good results. In recent years, experiments have proved that "1605" is even more effective for the control
of borers. Chloropicrin and methyl bromide are used successfully
to fumigate the insect pests in warehouses.[13]

However, rice borers apparently remain a menace to rice
production. While claiming that peasants of Kiangsu, Chekiang, Anhwei,
Hupeh, and other rice-producing provinces had successfully wiped out
rice borers on millions of mou of paddy fields, a People's Daily
editorial stated that one-sided emphasis was being given to control
instead of prevention, to chemical instead of agricultural techniques,
and to crash operations instead of consistent measures. According
to the editorial, this approach produced only a temporary effect and
the rice borer pests often multiplied again after being partly eliminated.
The result was fluctuation in rice output. The paper urged the communes to prevent as well as control rice borers, with emphasis on
prevention; to adopt both foreign and indigenous methods; to combine
the efforts of the leadership, the specialists, and the masses; and to
carry out measures against rice borers in an overall manner so as to
insure maximum efficiency and safety.[14]

Rice Blight

Rice blight (Piricularia oryzae Bri. et Cavara) has affected
practically all rice-growing areas in China, particularly those in the
north. Three major measures have been taken to control this disease:
(1) popularization of disease-resistant varieties of rice, such as
"853" and "412," which have been generally used in the T'ai Lake
area; (2) proper use of fertilizers, especially nitrogenous fertilizers;
and (3) application of pesticides, particularly ceresan, mersolite,
and slaked lime. In addition, studies have been made on the virus of
the disease, the ecology of rice, the occurance of leaf blight, and the
influence of climatic conditions.[15]

Wheat Aphids

These wheat juice-sucking worms (Sitodiplosis mosellana
Gehin) are generally distributed on the low-lying and wet plains along
the Wei River in Shensi, the Yi and Lo rivers in Honan, the Huai
River in Anhwei, the Chialing River in northern Szechuan, and the
Yangtze River and Han River. Generally, there is one generation
each year but, because the hatching of the unfledged worms depends
on the temperature and humidity of the soil, the dormant period may
last as long as several years if the environmental conditions are not
favorable for the aphids' growth. It is also known that the larvae
leave the soil when the wheat plants draw joints and that the adult
insects are in full flush when the wheat plants draw ears. In recent
years, "666" and other insecticides have been applied on the wheat
field as a means to retard the growth of the unfledged insects in the
soil. This measure is reported to have produced remarkable results.
Insecticides also are applied on the plants when the adult insects are
in full flush. In many areas, such insect-resistant varieties of wheat
as Nanta 2419 and Hsinung 6028 have been selected for cultivation.
The inner and outer glumes of the ears of these two varieties are
closely woven, and therefore the wheat aphids have no place to lay
their eggs.[16]

Wheat Rust

Wheat rust is among the most serious plant diseases in China,
and there has been an outbreak of wheat rust virtually every year. In

past years when there was a major outbreak of the disease, wheat
yield in North China and Northeast China often was cut by 30 to 40
percent. It has gradually been ascertained that the outbreak of rust
of wheat leaves occurs principally on the plateaus of Kansu and
Chinghai. The wheat rust virus thrives on young wheat plants in this
area during the summer and in autumn is spread by air currents to
the areas along the Wei River and North China, where it attacks the
autumn crops. In spring, the disease first breaks out in the Kuanchung
area in Shensi, the southern part of Shansi, and the southeastern
part of Honan, and then spreads to other areas. During the winter,
the virus that causes the outbreak of rust of wheat stalks thrives
principally on the young wheat plants in Fukien, Kwangtung, Yunnan,
and other provinces in South China and later spreads to Kiangsu,
Anhwei, and as far as North China and Northeast China.[17] More than
ten rust-resistant varieties of wheat have been selected from the
spring wheat regions in Northeast China and Northwest China for
popularization in other areas. Native agricultural drugs as well as
chemical pesticides have been used to control the disease with considerable success.[18]

Cotton Pink Boll Worms

With the exception of the Sinkiang-Uighur Autonomous Region,
western Kansu, and certain hsien in the northern parts of Shansi, all
cotton-producing areas in China have been invaded by pink bollworms
(Pectinophora gossypiella Saunders). The number of generations
each year varies among different regions from two to five, depending
on climatic conditions. A notice issued jointly by the Ministry of
Agriculture and the Ministry of Commerce on September 19, 1960,
stated that, since the Leap Forward campaign, damage caused by
bollworms had been basically eliminated in most cotton-growing areas
in Northeast China and areas north of the Yellow River, and that
damage suffered by cotton-growing areas in the Yangtze Valley had
been greatly alleviated. However, the notice added that on the whole
the work of eradication was "still not balanced well enough."

The ministries urged the cotton-growing communes and state
farms to pay special attention to the eradication of bollworms in
cotton that is being dried or temporarily stored. Communes and
state farms that use their own seeds were asked to have the seeds
well smoked to eradicate the pests. The ministries also directed
that, where feasible, the method of eradicating bollworms by natural
freezing, which had been popularized in Northeast China, be tested

in other areas. Various localities were urged to adopt the pest-
preventing types of warehouses used in Hupeh, Kiangsi, and other
provinces, to use lime of cement to build protective walls, and to
spray "666" powder on the walls.[19]

Cotton Aphids

The degree of damage caused by cotton aphids (Aphis gossypii
Glover) in China varies among regions according to climatic conditions,
and such damage is usually heavier in the north than south of the
Yangtze River. In the early years of the Communist regime, tobacco
water, cottonseed oil soap, and other vegetable insecticides were used
for the control of cotton aphids. Their effectiveness was low and not
durable. In 1952, the use of 0.5 percent "666" powder, "1605," and
"E-1059" were put to use. These chemical insecticides were reported
to have produced good results in controlling other cotton insects as
well as aphids.[20]

Late Blight of Potatoes

The outbreak of this disease (Phytophthora infestans [Mont.]
De Bary) in China was very serious in 1950, 1952, 1953, and 1954
because of the heavy precipitation and high humidity in the potato-
growing areas. In North China, Northeast China, and Northwest China,
where potatoes generally are sown in the spring and harvested in the
autumn, serious damage by this disease often occurs after the heavy
precipitation in June and July. In East China and Southwest China,
where there are two crops of potatoes each year, the first crop often
suffers heavy damage caused by the blight as a result of the high
humidity in the spring.[21] As part of a study on the potato-growing
areas in northern Shansi, conducted jointly by several agricultural
research institutions in 1958, a method of controlling the late blight
by eradicating the central diseased plants and applying copper sulfate
solution, ceresan, lime, and other insecticides was experimented
successfully.[22]

Army Worms

Army worms (Cirphis unipuncta Haworth) may be found in
virtually all parts of China. They travel in great armies, damaging
grains, grasses, and other crops. In Northeast China, there are two
or three generation each year; in North China, three or four generations;

and in East China, as many as eight generations. Reportedly, the use of DDT, "666," and other insecticides for killing the worms has been successful.[23]

PESTICIDES AND EQUIPMENT

Before the Communist takeover, China had only three factories manufacturing chemical pesticides. These factories were located in Shanghai, Peiping, and Shenyang and operated by the Ministry of Agriculture and Forestry of the National government.[24] Since 1949, the number of pesticide plants has increased steadily. Among the large newly constructed plants are those in Shanghai, Tientsin, and Changtien (Shantung Province).[25]

Copper sulfate was the only chemical pesticide produced in China prior to World War II, and its total production in 1949 was 64 tons, according to a Communist account. It was claimed that in 1957, the last year of the First Five-Year Plan, the output of chemical pesticides reached 64,700 tons, and that in 1958, 65,000 tons of "666" (benzene hexachloride, or BHC) and 4,700 tons of DDT were produced. The first pesticide produced on a large scale was "666," and its production increased about 110 times between 1952 and 1958. Trichlorfon (Dipterex) was produced on an experimental basis in 1957. Other pesticides produced domestically in considerable amounts in 1957 included dementon (E-1059), "1605," and chlordane.

It was also claimed that in 1963 China produced more than 60 kinds of chemical pesticides (insecticides, fungicides, and herbicides), as against 20 kinds in 1957 and 30 kinds in 1959. Special attention was paid to developing the production of organic phosphorous compounds because these are highly effective and can be used in a variety of ways against many kinds of pests.[26]

Because of the increasing demand for such chemicals as mercury, copper, and benzene in other industries, there has been an acute shortage of these materials for manufacturing chemical pesticides. Attempts have been made to use tin, arsenic, and other organics as substitutes.[27]

The quality of chemical pesticides produced in Communist China apparently is not satisfactory. Some pesticides are not processed in accordance with the specifications, and there is no strict inspection of the products. Instructions for the use of such highly poisonous pesticides as "1605" and demeton are not adequate.[28]

In the opinion of Yang Shih-hsien, President of Nankai University in Tientsin, although more and more pesticides are being produced in many provinces, what exists in China today is infinitesimal compared with the need and the quality of products lags far behind international standards. He suggested that knowledge of pesticides should be propagated among farmers and that special teams should be organized to handle highly poisonous and expensive pesticides in order to decreased fatal accidents and avoid wasting of the pesticides.[29] Although figures for accidents caused by poisonous pesticides have never been published, the matter is apparently quite serious as evidenced b: the inquires and discussions printed in the newspapers.[30]

In accordance with the "walking on two legs" policy, more than 500 varieties of plants and minerals have been used to make "native pesticides" for the control of plant diseases and insect pests, in addition to chemical pesticides. In 1958, 240 factories produced native pesticides and some 17 million tons of such chemicals used. For example, extracts from tomato (Lycopersicum esculentum [Linn.] Mill) leaves have been used to cure the rust disease of wheat, and the skin of the pomegranate (Punica granatum Linn.) fruit has been used to cure the rot disease of cabbages. Both are reported to have accomplished good results. In some areas, rice blast, rice borers, wheat rust, wheat mildew, wheat smut, cotton bollworms, cotton aphids, and red spiders are reported to have been brought under control partly through the use of the native pesticides.[31]

As a step to strengthen the plant protection program during the Leap Forward campaign, the Scientific Research Office for Native Pesticides was created in 1958 by ten related government agencies and research institutions. The office in turn appointed a special committee to prepare a book on native materials selected by Chinese scientists and peasants for the control of plants diseases and insect pests. The book, entitled Chung-kuo T'u-nung-yao Chih (Manual of Chinese Native Pesticides), was published in 1959 by the Science Press, Peking, and covered 522 items (403 plants and 119 minerals and other materials) that are considered effective for plant protection.

Native pesticides are said to have several advantages over chemical pesticides. China has abundant resources of plants and other materials for making native pesticides. The method of production is simple and the cost is lower. Furthermore, many of the native pesticides can be applied widely and safely to a great variety of crops. On the other hand, the available supply of some materials for making the native pesticides is seasonal and limited to certain

localities. Another disadvantage is that more labor is needed in the
production and application of native pesticides than that of chemical
pesticides. Regardless of these advantages and disadvantages, the
fact is that much more native pesticide than chemical pesticide has
been used in Communist China in the control of plant diseases and
insect pests. In 1958, 80 percent of pesticides used were of native
varieties, while only 20 percent were made of chemicals. It is likely
that the same situation will remain for some time to come, mainly
because of the shortage of chemicals.[32]

Many modern and native types of equipment for applying pesticides are reported to have been invented or improved. In 1966, more
than 20 types of spraying and dusting equipment were in production,[33]
most of them semimechanical. But the sprayers, dusters, and other
appliances produced generally are of low quality and efficiency, and
they are prone to break down.[34] Moreover, most peasants have very
little knowledge of how to use, maintain, and repair pesticide equipment.

In 1951, Communist China for the first time used aircraft to
apply pesticides for the control of locusts in Huanghua, Hopei Province.[35] It was claimed that the area of aerial control of locusts
increased from 13.7 percent of the locust-infested areas in 1958 to
more than 54 percent in 1960. But the use of airplanes for applying
pesticides has proved too expensive for the government. Vice-
Minister of Agriculture Yang Hsien-tung has suggested that such use
of airplanes should be confined to large tracts of wasteland or marshy
land where the population is sparse. Except in heavily stricken areas,
the local governments were urged to shoulder the expenses for the
use of airplanes in controlling plant diseases and insects.[36]

PROGNOSTIC AND WARNING SERVICES

During the earlier years of the Communist regime, prognostic
and warning measures were taken in various areas against locusts,
wheat aphids, potato late blight, rice borers, cotton aphids, and other
major plant insects and diseases. But the progress was piecemeal
and the methods adopted were mostly unscientific. It was not until
December 1955 that a nationwide "Program of Prognostic and Warning
Services Against Crop Insects and Diseases" was adopted. In February
and March 1956, a special training class on prognostic and warning
services was held in Peking under the auspices of the Ministry of
Agriculture, and 184 trainees were later assigned to various provinces. At the same time, a prognostic and warning section was set

up in the Plant Protection Bureau of the Ministry and a special study
team on this problem was organized by the Chinese Academy of
Sciences, the Peking University of Agriculture, the North China Agricultural Science Research Institute, and the Preparatory Committee
for the Chinese Academy of Agricultural Science. It was claimed that
by June 30, 1956, a total of 145 prognostic and warning stations and
862 crop disease and insect information posts had been established
by the agricultural experimental stations and the state farms, and
that by the same date 19 prognostic and warning service research
offices had been set up by various provincial governments.

At the end of 1958, the number of prognostic and warning
stations was reported to have increased to 678, and that of crop
disease and insect information posts to 12,000. By 1958, more than
700,000 peasants had been trained to serve as a major labor force
for these stations and posts.[37]

PLANT QUARANTINE

Since 1949, the Ministry of Agriculture has issued a number of
quarantine regulations and lists of objects shipped within the country
and from abroad that are subject to the regulations. By the end of
1958, more than 60 quarantine offices had been established for the
inspection of agricultural products and for research on methods of
inspecting and sterilizing plants.

On January 1, 1958, the "Experimental Provisions for Domestic
Plant Quarantine" were put into effect. These provisions were prepared by the Ministry of Agriculture in collaboration with five other
relevant ministries, those of forestry, food, railroads, communications,
and posts and telecommunications. The provisions included a list of
more than 30 plant diseases and insects commonly found in China.
The list was prepared on the basis of several lengthy discussions
among Chinese and Soviet scientists. Seeds, seedlings, tubers, and
other parts of principal crops shipped within the country were subject
to inspection for these diseases and insects.[38]

Communist China has reached agreements on plant quarantine
with most of the countries east of the Iron Curtain. In August 1956,
the Eighth International Conference on Plant Quarantine and Plant
Protection was held in Peking and was attended by delegates from the
U.S.S.R., Poland, East Germany, Czechoslovakia, Hungary, Bulgaria,
Albania, Romania, North Korea, Mongolia, North Vietnam, and Communist China. A 492-page volume containing nine reports submitted

by the Chinese delegation and Chinese translations of 41 reports by other delegations was published in 1957 by the Finance and Economics Press, Peking, under the title of Ti-pa-chieh Kuo-chi Chih-wu Chien-i chi Chih-wu Pao-hu Hui-i Wen-chien Hsüan-chi [Selected Documents of the Eighth International Conference on Plant Protection].

One of the major problems of quarantine work in China today is the lack of coordination. Several government agencies, including the ministries of agriculture, forestry, land reclamation, foreign affairs, and foreign trade, all have a share in the plant quarantine operations. This inevitably causes duplication, overlapping and confusion. Also, many aspects of the quarantine regulations and the lists of plants subject to quarantine are out-of-date and have not been revised or amended in accordance with current scientific and economic developments. Finally, the technique and facilities of plant sterilization and inspection are still below the desired standards.[39]

ENVIRONMENTAL AND
BIOLOGICAL CONTROL

Plant protection measures taken by the Chinese Communists in addition to the application of pesticides and the operation of prognostic, warning, and quarantine services include the selection of plant varieties that are resistant to diseases and insect pests, the adoption of agricultural techniques that tend to retard the growth of germs and insects, and the use of "natural enemies" of bacteria and insects to protect crops.

By using varieties that are resistant to diseases and insect pests, considerable pesticide and manpower can be saved. It has been reported that, as a result of the popularization of the Cooperation Nos. 1-5 and Kansu No. 96 varieties of wheat, both of which are highly resistant to stalk rust, this wheat disease has been basically brought under control in Northeast China. Of course, the breeding of varieties resistant to diseases and insect pests is not without difficulties because a single variety cannot always combine resisting power and high yield. Also, a variety that can resist one kind of disease or insect pest often is unable to resist another kind of disease or insect pest. Moreover, some varieties can retain their resisting power over a long period of time, as in the case of the Nanta 2419 variety of wheat, whose resisting power to rust on leaves does not degenerate for 20 to 30 years. However, the resisting power of some varieties degenerates rapidly. The reason for the degeneration of resisting power is that the bacteria and destructive insects themselves change continuously. Therefore, it is necessary to conduct intensive research on the variation of diseases and insect pests and to continually breed new varieties with stronger resisting power.

Considerable pesticide and manpower also can be saved by the adoption of certain agricultural techniques to make environmental conditions favorable to the growth of crops but unfavorable to the existence and development of bacteria, destructive insects, and weeds. For example, in some localities in Anhwei and Hunan where double-crop rice is grown, the adoption of winter plowing and winter flooding to kill the borers hidden in the rice stubble has made it possible to alleviate the damage done by rice-stem borers at the early stage. Similarly, rational crop rotation can be utilized to control cotton wilt. To a certain extent, the utilization of proper cultivation methods to reduce soil temperature can alleviate the degeneration of potatoes. The proper control of water and fertilizer supply can alleviate rice blast. Sowing in straight rows and at the right time in ridge culture, coupled with the taking of preventive measures against insects, can guard against cabbage rot. However, certain localities cannot adopt such measures because of the local arrangement of manpower and other difficulties.[40]

There are many kinds of natural enemies of the bacteria and destructive insects. Some of these natural enemies can control the outbreak of diseases and insect pests over a protracted period and are not expensive to breed. In 1958-59, for example, trichogramma evanescens (bees with red eyes) were used in Kwangtung to control the sugar cane borers with good results. In Chekiang, Hupeh, and Szechuan, scarlet ladybugs (Rodolia rufopilosa Muls.) were bred on a large scale over large areas for the destruction of some beetles. Hupeh and other provinces in Central China also made successful use of small golden-green bees (Dibrachys cavus Walk.) to control the pink cotton bollworms in cotton depots. This tiny wasp-like insect is a born enemy of the cotton pest. It hunts dormant pink boll-worm cocoons, stings the nymphs to death, and deposits its eggs on the dead worms, which serve as food for its larvae. In 1955, two types of ladybugs (Rodolia cardinalis Muls. and Cryptolaemus montrouzieri Muls.) were introduced from Russia for the control of certain beetles in Canton and Tienpai Hsien in Kwangtung, with remarkable success.[41] In the summer of 1963, the Ministry of Agriculture launched a campaign for the protection of frogs, which are considered to play an important role in exterminating harmful insects in the fields.[42]

But control by biological methods also has its shortcomings. It is not as simple and convenient as chemical control, and it is less broad in the scope of application. Biological control also is affected to a greater extent by the environment, and it produces results at a slower rate.[43]

CONTROL OF HARMFUL
ANIMALS AND WEEDS

Rodents are the principal animals harmful to crops. In some localities in Northeast China and Northwest China, there are an average of about four moles to each mou (one-sixth of an acre) of land. The number has reached as many as thirty moles to a mou in a few areas. Each mole consumes about 20 to 30 chin (27 to 40 pounds) of grain per year. With four or five moles to each mou of land, the loss of grain amounts to from 30 to 50 percent. The use of poisonous bait containing ANTU (alphanapthylthiourea) and zinc phosphide has been popularized for the control of rodents. Special efforts have been made to control rodents in spring and autumn, when their activities of consuming and storing grains are heaviest. In the spring and autumn of 1958, for instance, a total of 17 million field rats were exterminated in Kwangtung, and grain damage by rodents was basically controlled in 42 hsien of that province.[44] In 1964 and 1965, more than 2 million hectares of farmland and grassland in Chinghai were freed of rats.[45] Considerable attention also has been given to research on moles and other types of rodents, especially those in northern Shensi, Chinghai, and other parts of North China.

In the mountainous area of northern Kwantung, where mountain hogs have done considerable harm to agricultural production over a large area of farmland, since early 1970 "three-way alliance" hunting teams of militiamen, hunters, and cadres have been organized to control harmful animals.[46]

The menace of weeds to agricultural production is usually serious in areas that are sparsely populated, such as many localities in Heilungkiang Province. In the Mishan area of Kirin Province, sanling weed and darnel (Lolium temulentum) are found in the paddy fields. Before 1949, some previously cultivated land was left uncultivated because of these weeds and the peasants were forced to migrate elsewhere. In recent years, wide use has been made of herbicides manufactured abroad, such as "2,4-D," "2,4,5-T" and IPC, and studies have been conducted on their effectiveness. An experiment conducted in the Mishan area indicates that it takes only three or four chin (4 or 5.3 pounds) of "2,4-D" on each hectare to exterminate the sanling weed within a few days. The cost amounts to no more than one yuan (about

U.S. $0.40) per <u>mou</u>, which is much lower than the cost for weed
removal by manual labor.[47]

More recently, an effective chemical herbicide for paddy fields
was reported to have been developed by the Peking Academy of Agriculture in collaboration with the Shenyang Chemical Engineering
Research Institute and the Research Institute of Botany of the Chinese
Academy of Sciences. Composed mainly of chemicals generally known
as DCPA (Dacthal), the weed killer, when applied on barnyard grass,
has no harmful effect on the rice. The proper dosage is 3 kilograms
per hectare. This weed killer causes dehydration of the barnyard
grass but does not affect paddy rice because of its strong ability to
preserve moisture. A test in Peking's suburb's in 1963 showed that
the blades of weed began to turn dark 5 or 6 hours after the application
of the chemical and died completely within 4 or 5 days. Experimentation of this weed killer on small seed plots for nursing young shoots
have been successful thus far. Use of the chemical on large tracts
of paddy fields has yet to be studied.[48]

A series of articles in the <u>People's Daily</u> in 1960 indicated that
weed control work in China had not gone quite according to plan,
because of weather, improper use of labor, and lack of enthusiasm on
the part of the peasants.[49]

THE PROSPECTS

In the 1950's and 1960's Communist China made considerable
progress in plant protection, mainly by utilizing local manpower and
resources. However, diseases and insects have taken an enormous
toll of growing crops and stored agricultural products, as press
reports have indicated. Aside from financial and technical difficulties,
mismanagement has resulted in the ineffectiveness of many programs.
Substantial quantities of food and other farm products could be saved
with technical and managerial improvement.

The use of modern pesticides in Mainland China has thus far
been restricted to state farms and large communes. It will take some
time before most communes can be supplied with funds and technical
knowledge required for the utilization of modern chemicals and
equipment. For this reason, Communist China will have to continue
the combined use of chemical and less sophisticated methods (mechanical, physical, biological, and cultural) for some time to come.

186   AGRICULTURE IN COMMUNIST CHINA

NOTES

1. Agricultural Research Service, U.S. Department of Agriculture, Losses in Agriculture, Agricultural Handbook No. 291, (Washington, D. C.: GPO, 1965), pp. 5, 41, 56.

2. J. Lossing Buck, Land Utilization in China (Nanking: University of Nanking, 1937), p. 4.

3. Shen Ch'i-i, "The Role of Plant Protection in Insuring the Increase of Agricultural Production," Hung Ch'i [Red Flag], Peking, No. 22, 1962, pp. 33-41.

4. Bureau of Plant Protection, Ministry of Agriculture, People's Republic of China, "Stir Up the High Tide for Thorough Control of Plant Diseases and Insect Pests," Chung-kuo Nung-pao Tseng-k'an [Supplements to Chinese Agriculture Bulletin], Peking, No. 3, 1958, pp. 1, 4.

5. T'an Chen-lin, "Strive for the Fulfillment, Ahead of Schedule, of the National Program for Agricultural Development," JMJP, April 7, 1960, p. 1.

6. Yang Hsien-tung, "Strive for Greater Success on the Plant Protection Front," Chung-kuo Nung-pao [Chinese Agriculture Bulletin], Peking, No. 6, 1963, pp. 1-4.

7. Kao Min-chen, "Great Achievements in China's Plant Protection Work in the Past Decade," Chung-kuo Nung-pao [Chinese Agriculture Bulletin], Peking, No. 15, 1959, pp. 24-26.

8. Jen-min Shou-ts'e [People's Handbook] (Peking, 1952), pp. 375-77.

9. Bureau of Plant Protection, Ministry of Agriculture, People's Republic of China, Ti-pa-chieh Kuo-chi Chih-wu Chien-i chi Chih-wu Pao-hu Hui-i Wen-chien Hsuan-chi [Selected Documents of the Eighth International Conference on Plant Quarantine and Plant Protection] (Peking, 1957), pp. 37, 41-42; Shen Ch-i-i, op. cit., pp. 33-41.

10. NCNA, Peking, December 8, 1962.

11. Yang Hsien-tung, op. cit., pp. 1-4.

12. NCNA-English, Peking, July 16, 1963.

13. Research Institute of Plant Protection, Chinese Academy of Agricultural Science, "Accomplishments of Plant Protection in China During the Past Decade," Nung-yeh K'o-hsueh T'ung-hsun [Agricultural Science Bulletin], Peking, No. 18, 1959, pp. 629-32; Shen Ch'i-i, op. cit., pp. 33-41.

14. "War Against Rice Borers Must Be Won This Year," editorial, JMJP, May 10, 1964, p. 1.

15. Bureau of Plant Protection, Ministry of Agriculture, People's Republic of China, Ti-pa-chieh Kuo-chi Chih-wu . . . , op. cit., pp. 48, 474-475.

16. Ibid., pp. 43-44; Tai Sung-en, "Fully Develop the Role of Crops of Good Breed to Increase Production," Hung Ch'i [Red Flag], Peking, No. 2, 1963, pp. 25-34.

17. Shen Ch'i-i, op. cit., pp. 33-41.

18. Research Institute of Plant Protection, Chinese Academy of Agricultural Science, op. cit., pp. 629-32.

19. NCNA, Peking, September 23, 1960.

20. Bureau of Plant Protection, Ministry of Agriculture, People's Republic of China, Ti-pa-chieh Kuo-chi Chih-wu . . . , op. cit., pp. 45-46.

21. Ibid., pp. 47-48.

22. Research Institute of Plant Protection, Chinese Academy of Agricultural Science, op. cit., pp. 629-32.

23. Bureau of Plant Protection, Ministry of Agriculture, People's Republic of China, Ti-pa-chieh Kuo-chi Chih-wu . . . , op. cit., pp. 44-45.

24. Shen Tsung-han, Agricultural Resources of China (Ithaca, N.Y.: Cornell University Press, 1951), p. 52.

25. NCNA-English, Peking, March 8, 1961.

26. Wang Nen-wu, "Characteristics and Application of Dipterex," Nung-yeh K'o-hsueh T'ung-hsun [Agricultural Science Bulletin], Peking, No. 4, 1958, pp. 222-24; Pesticide Research Office, Research Institute of Plant Protection, Chinese Academy of Agricultural Science, "Development of Insecticides in China in the Past Decade and Their Increasing Uses in Insect Control," K'un-ch'ung Chih-shih [Knowledge of Insects], Peking, No. 8, 1959, pp. 248-49; Kao Kuang-chien, "Chemical Industry Serves Agriculture," Peking Review, No. 29, 1963, pp. 25-28.

27. Chinese Academy of Sciences, "Organic Tin and Organic Chemistry," K'o-hsueh T'ung-pao [Scientia], Peking, No. 19, 1959, pp. 653-54.

28. Shen Ch'i-i, op. cit., pp. 33-41.

29. Yang Shih-hsien, "A Chat About the Pesticide Problem," JMJP, December 4, 1962, p. 5.

30. Yao Sun-ch'ien, "Attention Must Be Given to Safety When Using Poisonous Pesticides," JMJP, June 9, 1962, p. 2.

31. Research Institute of Plant Protection, Chinese Academy of Agricultural Science, op. cit., pp. 629-32.

32. P'ei Li-sheng, "Ten Big Advantages in Popularizing Native Pesticides," K'un-ch'ung Chih-shih [Knowledge of Insects], Peking, No. 2, 1959, pp. 49-55.

33. NCNA-English, Peking, February 26, 1966.

34. Shen Ch'i-i, op. cit., pp. 33-41.

35. Jen-min Shou-ts'e [People's Handbook] (Peking, 1952), pp. 375-77.

36. Yang Hsien-tung, op. cit., pp. 1-4.

37. Kao Min-chen, op. cit., pp. 24-26.

38. Plant Quarantine Laboratory, Ministry of Agriculture, People's Republic of China, Tui-nei Chih-wu Chien-i Tui-hsiang T'u-shuo [Illustrated Explanations on the Objects for Domestic Plant Quarantine] (Peking, 1956), p. 3; "Experimental Provisions for Domestic Plant Quarantine," Nung-yeh K'o-hsueh T'ung-hsun [Agricultural Science Bulletin], No. 1, 1958, pp. 17-20.

39. Chen Shan-min, "Certain Problems in the Plant Protection Work," JMJP, December 4, 1962, p. 5.

40. Shen Ch'i-i, op. cit., pp. 33-41.

41. Chao Shan-huan, "China's Accomplishments in the Control of Insects Harmful to Agriculture in the Past Ten Years," K'un-ch'ung Chih-shih [Knowledge of Insects], No. 8, 1959, pp. 241-43.

42. Yang Hsien-tung, "Protecting Frogs," JMJP, September 12, 1963, p. 2; Cheng Tso-hsin, "Frogs' Functions in Protecting Agriculture," JMJP, September 12, 1963, p. 2.

43. Shen Ch'i-i, op. cit., pp. 33-41.

44. Kao Min-chen, op. cit., pp. 24-26.

45. NCNA-English, Sining, January 4, 1966.

46. NCNA, Canton, August 22, 1970.

47. Shen Ch'i-i, op. cit., pp. 33-41.

48. NCNA, Peking, June 27, 1963.

49. JMJP, July 15, 1960, p. 7; July 23, 1960, p. 7; July 27, 1960, p. 7.

12

Farm operations in China are accomplished largely by human labor, with very little or no assistance from animals and machinery. Work thus done is slow and tedious. Frequently, crops either become overripe or are damaged by unfavorable weather conditions before they can be harvested. Despite its large population, China actually suffers from a shortage of farm labor during busy seasons, and the employment of extra hands at harvesting time is virtually impossible. There is an urgent need for the improvement of agricultural implements.

Because of the low purchasing power and low educational level of the farmers, the introduction of new and improved implements is difficult without extensive government assistance. For decades prior to the Communist takeover, the national and provincial authorities as well as private institutions (including the University of Nanking, Ling Nan University, Southeastern University) attempted to introduce and popularize agricultural implements and machinery from abroad. But the influence of the imported implements and machinery was limited. The establishment of the National Agricultural Engineering Corporation in 1943 by the Ministry of Agriculture and Forestry together with the Farmers' Bank represented the first attempt on the part of the government to place the manufacture of farm implements and machinery on a national and organized scale. The program called for the establishment in the principal agricultural centers of plants to manufacture implements and for a plan of education and demonstration. However, the accomplishments were sporadic and small-scale.[1]

The general policy at the outset of the Communist regime was to improve farm implements and to move gradually toward mechanization. During the Economic Recovery Period (1949-52), efforts were

made to increase supplies of old-fashioned implements and to popularize
some new implements through demonstrations. In the First Five-
Year Plan period (1953-57), many innovations of farm implements
were developed and some 5,110,000 improved and modern farm
implements for plowing, tilling, raking, pressing, sowing, harvesting,
and threshing were made available to farmers.[2] During the Leap
Forward period, an ambitious campaign was launched to speed up
both agricultural mechanization and tool innovation in accordance
with the "walking on two legs" policy, but the campaign was not very
successful. In recent years, the policy has been simultaneous development of mechanization and semimechanization with the main stress on
the latter.

IMPROVEMENT OF OLD-TYPE IMPLEMENTS

Article 7 of the National Program for Agricultural Development
provided:

> Energetic efforts should be made to extend the use of
> improved and new types of farm tools suited to local con-
> ditions on the basis of the needs of production and by
> trial and remodeling to adapt them to the conditions of
> the particular region. Attention should always be paid to
> the maintenance and repair of farm tools. Technical
> guidance in the use of the new types of farm tools should
> be strengthened.

Perhaps the most important item under the program for the
improvement and innovation of old-fashioned agricultural implements
was the plan for the popularization of some 6 million double-wheel/
double-share plows and double-wheel/single-share plows throughout
the country within three to five years beginning in 1956. Both types
were animal-drawn and regarded as suitable for cultivating sandy
or light clay soils, and single-share type also was regarded as suitable for reclaiming wasteland.[3] But this plan was almost a complete
failure. The plows were mainly copies of plows used in the broad,
flat wheat lands of the Soviet Union and were unsuited to China's
terraced and small plots. Many farmers complained that the plows
were too heavy, that their farm animals were too few and too weak
to pull the plows, and that they had no means of repairing the plows
even if they had been able to use them successfully. In South China,
farmers complained that the rice paddies were too small and too
muddy for the plows. Consequently, the plan was revised to include
only 3.5 million plows, and finally only 100,000 to 150,000 were

distributed to farmers.[4] It was reported that in 1957 only 72,000 double-wheel/double-share plows were distributed to farmers while 800,000 were left idle and that many of those distributed were later returned or destroyed by farmers.[5]

At the beginning of the Leap Forward campaign in 1958, a further effort was made to popularize the double-wheel/double-share plows in areas other than the rice fields of South China.[6] It also was reported that a modified type, which eliminated the drawbacks of the original type, had been designed by the Chekiang Agricultural Research Institute in Hangchow and was personally tried by Mao Tse-tung during his visit to the institute in January 1958.[7]

Since rice is the most important crop in China and transplanting of seedlings is the most labor-consuming operation in rice growing, Communist China has given considerable attention to the improvement of rice transplanters of all types--those operated by hand, those operated by animals, and mechanized transplanters--although manual types remain the most widely used. The first improved model was introduced in 1956. It was an oxen-drawn transplanter developed jointly by seven agricultural research institutes, and it was reported to be able to do the work of 30 persons.[8] During the Leap Forward campaign, the use of locally constructed transplanters of wood and bamboo was extensively publicized.

In the 1960's the Kwangsi-Chuang Autonomous Region led in the use of rice transplanters. In 1968, the region had more than 30,000 transplanters, mostly of the Kwangsi-65 hand-propelled type, working over 53,000 hectares of paddy fields.[9]

Many farm tools and implements in addition to plows and rice transplanters were reported to have been developed or innovated by the masses during the Leap Forward Period, for use in manure accumulation, transport, irrigation and drainage, tilling, processing of farm products, and other purposes.[10] But many of these tools and implements were lost, wasted, or destroyed, mainly because of mismanagement and the overemphasis on mechanization. As reported by the People's Daily, "They were left scattered in the open air in the field where rains and winds ruined them."[11] It was not until the latter part of 1960 that responsibilities toward farm tools and implements were clearly defined for the commune and its components (the production brigade, the production team, and the individual commune member). After the country had suffered two consecutive years of bad harvest in 1959-60, the policy of "taking agriculture as the foundation of the national economy" was adopted. A movement was

started in August 1960 to send all available hands to the fields, and
all available land was devoted to grain production. In order that
these people would not go to the fields empty-handed, the importance
of medium-sized and small tools and implements was again emphasized.[12]

Under the new directives, such medium-sized implements as
plows, harrows, weeding discs, water wheels, carts, fertilizer dispen-
sers, and threshers should be under the care of the commune or the
care of the production brigade or production team using them. A
shed should be built to store them. A commune member "known for
his high consciousness and his zeal for common property" should be
appointed guard, and he should also inspect these implements and
see that they are repaired in good time. Individual commune members
are responsible for the care and use of small implements (such as
spades, hoes, picks, sickles).[13] In all cases, a pressing duty should
be "the education of the masses toward love of the common property."[14]

It was further admitted that care of the existing implements
would not alone be sufficient to provide for the millions who had been
urged to take part in agricultural production. There was an urgent
need for the manufacture of new implements as well as the repair
of old ones. Survey reports from a number of communes revealed
almost uniformly that the shortage of farm implements was very
seriously felt.[15]

But manufacturing and repair were impeded by an acute shortage
of steel and other necessary materials. Although it was reported
that in 1962 the state allocated and made arrangements for the delivery
of some 2 million cubic meters of lumber and "corresponding quantities
of rolled steel, copper, and hemp to various localities for the repair,
maintenance, and manufacturing of farm implements, may hsien
(counties) had to obtain much of the material locally, to use various
kinds of substitutes, and to collect scrap iron, pieces of wood, split
bamboo, nails, and screws. The process of casting, instead of forging,
had to be adopted for making implements and spare parts because the
"native" iron cannot be forged; the use of cheap native iron and steel
has resulted in the breakdown and deterioration of millions of implements produced or repaired in innumerable improvised small factories.[16] In the 1960's, the supply and maintenance of small and
medium-sized farm implements as a whole seemed to have improved
somewhat, but the problems of high costs, high depreciation rates,
shortage of necessary materials, and poor management remained
unsolved in many areas.

MECHANIZATION OF FARMING

Although the Chinese Communists realize that agriculture in China can only be mechanized gradually in view of limited industrial capacity and raw materials, nationwide farm mechanization is one of the great benefits that the Communist regime promised to bring to the peasants from the outset. Mechanization was first emphasized during the land reform in 1951-52 and again during the cooperativization of agriculture in 1955-56. But prior to the Leap Forward campaign Communist China's plan for agricultural mechanization was by no means very ambitious. Thus, in a report delivered on July 31, 1955, at a meeting of the secretaries of the provincial, municipal, and district committees of the Chinese Communist Party, Mao Tse-tung stated: "All through the First and Second Five-Year Plans, the number of big farm machines will certainly increase, but not to any great extent. During the Third Five-Year Plan, more big farm machinery will be employed year by year." He estimated that it would take four or five five-year plans, or from twenty to twenty-five years, to complete agricultural mechanization in China.[17]

The provision for agricultural mechanization in Article 7 of the National Program for Agricultural Development likewise seemed moderate as it stated:

> Keeping pace with the development of industrialization of
> the country, mechanization of agriculture should be
> carried out energetically step by step. Within the short-
> est possible time beginning in 1956, the engineering and
> agricultural departments should draw up, on the basis of
> extensive experiments and research, a program for
> agricultural mechanization suited to the conditions in
> China, so as to make good preparations to extend the
> mechanization of agriculture. Then machinery suited
> for use in various places should be improved as circum-
> stances require and its use extended energetically.

In any case, agricultural mechanization did not make spectacular progress during the Economic Recovery Period and the First Five-Year Plan period, although it was reported that the number of tractors increased from 401 in 1949 to 24,629 in 1957 and that the number of other agricultural machines also increased considerably.[18] It was not until the launching of the Leap Forward campaign in 1958 that an ambitious program of agricultural mechanization was mapped out.

In order to expedite farm mechanization, the State Council set up the Ministry of Agricultural Machine-Building Industry in August 1959 (renamed the Eighth Ministry of Machine-Building Industry in December 1964) with the functions of administering the manufacture and popularization of tractors and other farm machines.[19] Meanwhile, China's first large tractor plant went into full production in November 1959 at Loyang, Honan Province. It was built with technical aid from the U.S.S.R. and was estimated to have an annual capacity of 15,000 54-horsepower tractors. Additional tractor plants have since been constructed in Tientsin, Nanchang, Changchun, Anshan, Shenyang, and a few other cities. A number of factories manufacturing other agricultural machines also have been established or expanded.

According to Ch'en Cheng-jen, Minister of Agricultural Machine-Building Industry, the general aim was to enable agriculture, forestry, animal husbandry, fishery, and side occupations to advance gradually toward overall mechanization and electrification within about ten years. However, owing to insufficient production of machinery, primary attention would be given to agriculture and animal husbandry during the first four years, striving first to mechanize a small part of agricultural and pastoral production and a fundamental portion of farmland irrigation. During this period, emphasis would be placed on the suburbs of the large cities, the commodity grain production centers, the major centers of other economic crops, and the principal pastoral areas. Ch'en Cheng-jen estimated that the supply of farm machinery would be adequate to permit completion of over half the task of mechanization in seven years and to complete it fully in ten years.[20]

But the progress of agricultural mechanization during and immediately after the Leap Forward campaign (1958-62) was considerably slower than had been expected. At the end of 1960, only 5 percent of the country's cultivated land was cultivated with machines (the target for that year was 6.9 percent), 15 percent with semimechanized methods, and 80 percent with improved small implements.[21] Toward the end of 1962, the area farmed by tractors still accounted for less than 10 percent of the cultivated land.[22]

Mechanization materialized primarily on the state farms and some large communes. In Heilungkiang Province, where many large state farms are located, 20 percent of the cultivated land was cultivated in 1960 by machines and more than 30 percent by modern animal-drawn implements.[23] Among other areas where the acreage of mechanized farming made up an important portion of the total area of cultivated land were Hopei and Shantung Provinces, the Sinkiang-

Uighur Autonomous Region, and the suburbs of Peking and Shanghai.

Although the number of tractors in operation was reported to have increased rather rapidly, from 401 in 1949 to 154,161 in 1965 (see Table 20), the increase was far from sufficient to meet the current needs. As the People's Daily pointed out, on the basis of one tractor for 1,500 mou (250 acres), more than one million tractors would be required for the mechanization of the estimated 1.6 billion mou (267 million acres) of farmland in China.[24]

Of the 45,330 tractors in operation in 1958, 957 were produced in China for the first time.[25] Production figures for more recent years are not available, but it was claimed that by the end of 1965 the country had developed thirteen types of tractors, including heavy (100-horsepower) and medium-sized caterpillar tractors for large-scale land reclamation and contouring, medium-sized wheeled tractors for haulage of timber as well as ordinary field work, light tractors (under six-horsepower) for garden-type cultivation, and tractors specifically designed for rice paddies.[26]

In addition to tractors, Communist China was reported to have developed a wide range of agricultural machinery and semimechanized implements for irrigation and drainage, sowing, harvesting, transplanting, fertilizing, controlling weeds, and processing agricultural products. For example, most of the new farm machines and semimechanized tools used in the 36 state farms in the Sanchiang Plain Reclamation Area in Heilungkiang Province in 1965 were made in China, including tractors from Loyang, combine harvesters from Kaifeng, tractor-drawn five-share plows from Anshan, cultivators from Tsitsihar, and sowing machines from Sian.[27]

Since the Leap Forward campaign, the agricultural machinery industry in Communist China has placed increasing emphasis on mechanized pumps. In 1962, the country had 26 large factories producing pumps and power units for pumps.[28] Some of the factories originally built to manufacture tractors were producing pumps as well as tractor parts, because pumps require much less steel, capital, and fuel than tractors and because mechanization of irrigation and drainage is considered more urgent than that of land cultivation.

Mechanized wheat cultivation has been introduced in most parts of the principal wheat-producing areas--Northeast China, the Yellow River basin, and the Huai River basin. The "East Wind" combine-harvester, which first appeared in 1964, reaps about 13.3 hectares of wheat per day. In Northeast China, complete sets of

TABLE 20

Number of Tractors in Communist China,
1949-65

Year	Number of 15-Horsepower Units
1949	401
1950	1,286
1951	1,410
1952	2,006
1953	2,719
1954	5,061
1955	8,094
1956	19,367
1957	24,629
1958	45,330
1959	59,000
1960	79,000
1961	99,000
1962	100,000
1963	115,017
1964	123,000
1965	154,161

Sources: For 1949-58, State Statistical Bureau, Ten Great Years, English edition (Peking, 1960), p. 135; for 1959, Ch'en Cheng-jen, "Speed Up the Technical Transformation of Agriculture," Hung Ch'i [Red Flag], Peking, No. 4, 1960, pp. 4-10; for 1960 and 1961, Chang Feng-shih, "Produce Suitable Agricultural Machinery to Support Agriculture," Kung-jen Jih-pao [Daily Worker], January 18, 1962, p. 1; for 1962, "Actively and Systematically Bring About the Technical Transformation of Our Country's Agriculture," editorial, JMJP, November 9, 1962, pp. 1-2; for 1963, News Release, China News Service, Canton, January 5, 1964; for 1964, Chou En-lai, "Report on the Work of the Government," presented at the First Session of the Third National People's Congress on December 21-22, 1964 (NCNA-English, Peking, December 30, 1964); for 1965, "Paving a Way to Agricultural Mechanization in China: A Visit to the Agricultural Mechanization Hall of the National Agricultural Exhibition," JMJP, April 13, 1965, p. 1.

farm tools for ridge culture and a corn seeder have been popularized.
For South China's paddy fields, several kinds of rice transplanters
and a rice harvester to be attached to the walking tractor have gone
into mass production. In many parts of the South where silt of lakes
and rivers is available, a wide variety of suction pumps and winches
for silt extraction have been in general use. Types of apparatus for
spraying liquid ammonia and for applying powder or granular fertilizers
have appeared in the countryside. There also is an increasing range
of machines for processing agricultural products, including machines
for rice husking, flour grinding, potato slicing, cotton ginning, and
oil pressing.[29]

Domestic production of tractors and other agricultural machines
has been handicapped by the shortage of raw materials, particularly
steel, electric power, coal, gasoline, and other fuels.[30] The few
centers of the steel industry have experimented with new products
suitable for agricultural machinery and more than 700 types of rolled
steel were reported to have been produced in 1962, but this amount
is not commensurate with the needs of the country.[31] Certain types
of steel products and essential parts of agricultural machinery cannot
be produced in China and therefore must be imported. The "East Is
Red" tractor, for example, consists of some 10,000 parts requiring
more than 450 kinds of steel and other metals. When the tractor was
first manufactured in 1959, most of these metals were imported.
Although the variety of metals produced domestically has increased,
in 1962 there were still more than 30 kinds of metals needed for
making farm machinery that China could not produce or could produce
only in small quantities. Furthermore, the quality of some of the
metals and parts produced in China was below the required standard.[32]

Other serious problems in addition to lagging production have
handicapped the mechanization of agriculture. Tractors were first
managed by the state-operated tractor stations, but many of them
were turned over to the communes during the Leap Forward campaign.
Despite the claimed advantages through collective strength and self-
reliance, management under the communes has been far from satisfactory. The depreciation rate and maintenance costs have been high,
partly because of "lack of the sense of political responsibility to take
good care of tractors on the part of drivers." In 1961, about 20 percent
of tractors and 20-30 percent of irrigation machines needed repair;
many tractors were without machine-drawn farm tools, and irrigation
and drainage machines were without pipes and pumps. Moreover,
operators and maintenance personnel for tractors and other farm
machines generally had undergone only a very short period of technical
training.[33]

Up to the late 1960's, very little attention was paid to producing attachment tools and spare parts or to maintenance and repairs. Hsiang Nan, Secretary of the Secretariat of the Chinese Young Communist League, blamed low tractor efficiency and high operational cost on the imbalance of investment in the four different segments of the industry. He pointed out that a 200-million yuan investment made on a tractor plant should be matched with additional investments of 200 million yuan on plants producing tractor-drawn tools, 200 million yuan on plants producing spare parts, and 300 million yuan on a network of maintenance and repair stations.34

The use of a great variety of agricultural machines has created additional problems. A visitor to the six production brigades in Shulu hsien, Hopei Province, found that as many as eight models of motors of different horsepower and consuming different fuels (natural gas, gasoline, and so on) were used for various machines. In the Ningpo district, Chekiang Province, more than forty types of internal combustion machines were used for irrigation and drainage. This situation made it difficult for the technicians to handle the machines because most of them had had only limited technical training. It also created the problem of getting an adequate supply of all kinds of fuels and accessories.35

Another technical problem is that in many areas farmland still does not meet the conditions for satisfactory mechanized farming. In Pingku hsien of the Municipality of Peking, for example, the local authorities instructed in 1962 that land of less than 10 mou (1.7 acres) in area or less than 150 meters (165 yards) in length should not be cultivated with caterpillar tractors, and that land of less than 5 mou (0.85 acre) in area or less than 100 meters (110 yards) in length should not be cultivated with wheeled tractors. Under these instructions there is very little land suitable for mechanical cultivation. Moreover, even after the agricultural collectivization, many parcels of land still have not been properly adjusted to make them suitable for mechanization. Within each piece of land, there are abandoned wells and ditches not yet flattened or boundary stones not yet removed. Also, on some pieces of land, irrigation canals are not well located and sometimes divided the land into a number of small fragments so that mechanization of farming can hardly be carried out. Finally, some roads, bridges, and tunnels between the farms are not sufficiently wide or strong for the passage of large farm machines, and sometimes such machines must take a long roundabout route to get from one place to another.36

Still another problem that has handicapped agricultural mechanization in Communist China is that, under the three-level ownership system, the production team, as the basic accounting unit of the commune, has no ability to buy large quantities of farm machinery and is not suitable for centralized operation of large machines.[37]

For years, the problem of how agricultural mechanization should be carried out has been heatedly debated between Mao Tse-tung and Liu Shao-ch'i, although the differences in their opinions were not revealed until the Cultural Revolution. The focus of the dispute was the question of "who should run agricultural mechanization." In Mao's opinion, the collective strength of peasants should be relied on as the mainstay of agricultural mechanization. The communes or the production brigades should have the full ownership of farm machines and power to operate them. It was Mao's belief that the communes or the production brigades can achieve agricultural mechanization with greater, faster, better, and more economical results. For this reason, cooperativization should precede agricultural mechanization. Liu Shao-ch'i, on the other hand, was of the opinion that the communes or the production brigades do not have sufficient experience or adequate funds to run agricultural mechanization, and that the state should first invest funds and train technical personnel. Later, agricultural mechanization may gradually be taken over by the communes.

In November 1962, T'an Chen-lin, Director of the State Council's Office of Agriculture and Forestry, in stating his "Opinions on Readjusting and Improving the Work of Tractor Stations," asserted that the communes "have no means to purchase, manage and run" tractors, which should be handed over to the state for operation. For several years thereafter, the communes no longer ran tractor stations. But during the Cultural Revolution the policy of the government on agricultural mechanization was severely criticized by the Maoists as a revisionist line of Liu Shao-ch'i. The operation of tractor stations was taken as one of the key points in dispute, and in many hsien tractor stations were again placed under the management of the communes.[38]

Despite the slow progress, even toward the end of 1960, the People's Daily still maintained that modernization of small agricultural implements would be solved in four years beginning in 1959, that of medium-sized implements in seven years, and complete agricultural mechanization in ten years.[39] It was not until the beginning of 1962, after three consecutive years of bad harvest, that the failure of agricultural mechanization was admitted. Chang Feng-shih, Vice-Minister of Agricultural Machine-Building Industry, revealed:

In the two years of 1960 and 1961, the agricultural machine-building industry has supplied agriculture with

40,000 standard tractors, 37,000 motor-powered plows,
37,000 motor-powered harrows, 3,300,000 horsepower of
agricultural irrigation equipment, 150,000 rubber-wheel
animal propelled carts, 11,500,000 rubber-wheel hand
carts, 800,000,000 small agricultural tools and many other
semi-mechanized agricultural tools. But these are far
from satisfying the agricultural needs. Furthermore, the
quality of certain products is not high. They are not properly coordinated, and their supply is not in time.[40]

DRAFT ANIMALS

Many medium-sized farm implements depend on draft animals
as a principal source of power for operation. Even in some areas
with a higher degree of mechanization, draft animals are needed
because of the particular types of farming and because of the limitation
of climatic and soil conditions. The cultivated land of Heilungkiang,
for example, is composed of black, yellowish black, and light salty
soil, which is sticky and with a comparatively low speed of evaporation. After a downpour, tractors are of no use, and certain kinds
of farming would be impossible without draft animals. Therefore, a
combined use of machines, horses, and oxen will remain essential to
agricultural production.[41]

The National Program for Agricultural Development called for
the mapping out of different plans for the cooperativization of animal
husbandry in accordance with local conditions, and for the development
of state livestock farms. Specifically, the program emphasized the
protection and breeding of domestic animals and fowl; special care
for female, young, and stud animals for breeding purposes; the
establishment of breeding stations; and the improvement of livestock
strains. For pastoral areas, the program called for the protection of
grassland, the improvement and cultivation of green pastures, the
opening up of water sources, the gradual establishment of feed and
fodder bases by livestock cooperatives, and the popularization of
ensilage.

The program also required that, wherever possible, diseases
most harmful to domestic animals--such as rinderpest, hog cholera,
Newcastle disease, contagious pleuro-pneumonia of cattle, foot and
mouth disease, pork measles (cysticerocis), lamb smallpox, and
sheep mange--be fundamentally eradicated with a period of seven to
twelve years. By 1962, veterinary stations were to be set up in all
hsien (counties), chu (districts), and hsiang (townships) in agricultural

and pastoral areas; cooperatives were to have personnel with basic training in the prevention and treatment of animal diseases; and peasant veterinarians were to be developed, organized, and guided in order to improve their technique in veterinary work (Article 3 of the Program).

The program also provided that, in the twelve years beginning in 1956, every agricultural producers' cooperative (or commune) should raise an adequate number of strong draft animals and that sufficient grass and fodder crops for the draft animals should be produced. The cooperatives (or communes) were urged to constantly improve the breeding and management of draft animals according to their conditions (Article 14 of the program).

The number of draft animals in Communist China increased from 59,775,000 in 1949 to 87,388,000 in 1955 but decreased steadily to 84,689,000 in 1958 (see Table 21). The net gain from 1949 to 1959 was 43 percent, or an average annual gain of 4.3 percent. No official figures of draft animals have been released since 1959, but according to Communist Chinese press the progress of draft animal production in Inner Mongolia, Sinkiang, Chinghai, Tibet, and other important livestock areas has been slow in recent years.

There were several causes for the slow growth. First, many animals weakened or died because of overwork, excessive heat or cold, and diseases. Draft animals were used in China traditionally for irrigation, for turning the primitive village mills, and for local transport. Their functions increased tremendously during the Leap Forward years, when the deep-plowing practice was introduced. However, it was not until the summer of 1960 that several provincial authorities issued orders for the strengthening of draft animals. In Heilungkiang, it was directed that animals should be granted some rest and that females during gestation should be exempted from work for one month.[42]

Another reason for the failure in propagation of draft animals was the absence of incentive, because of low wages, amont the herdsmen and those in charge of animals in the cooperatives or communes. Cases of deliberate neglect and secret slaughter have been reported in some areas. Under the communes, there were practically no systems of care, which did exist at the time of agricultural producers' cooperatives, and the men in charge of the animals were paid uniformly, regardless of whether the work was well or badly done. The need to reintroduce a regular system of management was emphasized at the end of 1960, and it was urged that production teams and persons in charge of animals be given a premium for work well-done.[43]

TABLE 21

Number of Draft Animals in Communist China,
1949 and 1952-59
(thousands)

Year	Cattle	Horses	Donkeys	Mules	Total
1949	43,936	4,874	9,494	1,471	59,775
1952	56,600	6,130	11,806	1,637	76,173
1953	60,083	6,512	12,215	1,645	80,455
1954	63,623	6,939	12,700	1,717	84,979
1955	65,951	7,312	12,402	1,723	87,388
1956	66,601	7,372	11,686	1,711	87,370
1957	65,860	7,510	10,900	1,840	86,110
1958	64,952	7,512	10,601	1,624	84,689
1959	n.a.	n.a.	n.a.	n.a.	85,400

Sources: For 1949 and 1958, Ts'ai Tsu-wei, "Accomplishments in Animal Husbandry in the Past Decade," Chung-kuo Hsu-mu-hsueh Tsa-chih [Chinese Animal Husbandry Journal], Peking, No. 10, 1959, pp. 289-93; for 1952-57, Yu N. Kapelinskiy et al., Development of the Economy and Foreign Economic Contacts of the People's Republic of China, (1959), translated from the Russian by the Joint Publications Research Service, JPRS No. 3234, (Washington, D. C., May 23, 1960), p. 311; for 1959, JMJP, January 26, 1960, p. 3.

Beginning in the spring of 1961, the care and mating of animals was given over to the production brigades or production teams and the payment to the persons in charge of animals was readjusted.[44]

The shortage of fodder has been another cause for the failure to improve the situation of draft animals. An improvement in the feeding of livestock and in the related problems of management is a prerequisite to any substantial livestock improvement program through breeding. However, draft animals in China have been fed primarily on roughage and have received only limited amounts of concentrates, although the Chinese Communist authorities have made efforts to improve the feeding of farm animals. It was reported that, by the end of 1958, the chemical composition of 1,032 kinds of feed from different parts of the country had been analyzed. Of these, 581 were green feeds, many of which grow wild and have a fairly high nutritive value. Studies also have been made on methods of expanding cultivation of certain high-quality feeds in various parts of the country.[45] But despite all these efforts the supply of fodder remained insufficient. The situation was particularly serious during the three consecutive years of natural calamities in 1959-61, which caused draft animals to be badly underfed.

The propagation of draft animals also was adversely affected by the shortage of technical personnel and necessary instruments. A directive on the promotion of mating of large animals, issued in February 1959 by the central government, indicated that there were 27 million head of female animals at the right age for propagation, of which 15 million were pregnant. Artificial insemination was encouraged in order to increase the number of large animals by 10 percent by the end of 1959, but trained technicians and necessary instruments were not sufficient.

The shortage of veterinarians remained very acute in the 1960's, and the strengthening of the veterinary centers throughout the country was urged.[46] In 1965, Communist China had about 10,000 veterinarians, most of them graduates of the seventeen universities with veterinary training facilities. In addition, there were 20-30,000 graduates from a number of professional veterinary schools that offered a three-year curriculum.[47]

The "walking on two legs" policy calls for the simultaneous development of native and modern veterinary methods. Traditional Chinese veterinarians have been practicing in villages for centuries using knowledge handed down from father to son, but they have not possessed any real scientific knowledge. In a directive on the

strengthening of veterinary work, issued by the State Council in
January 1956, modern and native veterinarians were urged to unite
and to exchange knowledge. Special efforts have since been made to
collect native prescriptions and native herbs and to study native
methods of diagnosis and treatment, particularly acupuncture. The
Western-trained veterinarians' task usually is that of diagnosis,
while most of the treatment work is left to the native veterinatians.[48]

In recent years, many provinces and autonomous regions have
selected students from among the poor and lower-middle-class peasants
and trained them as "barefoot" veterinarians. Working closely with
personnel of the veterinary stations, the "barefoot" veterinarians have
organized teams to carry out roving veterinary work in the rural
areas.

ELECTRIFICATION

A special mention should be made here of one aspect of agricultural mechanization, namely electrification, because it is regarded
by the Chinese Communists as one of the four major transformations
(szu hua) essential to the modernization of Chinese agriculture, the
others being mechanization, water conservation, and "chemicalization"
(meaning the widespread use of chemical fertilizers and chemical
pesticides).

Prior to the Communist takeover, the use of electricity in
China's rural areas was infinitesimal. The progress of rural electrification during the Economic Recovery and the First Five-Year Plan
periods was slow, mainly because of financial and technical difficulties.
By the end of 1957, the country's rural areas had only 544 hydroelectric
power stations with a total capacity of over 20,000 kilowatts (see table
22). In fact, no goals for rural electrification were provided in the
National Program for Agricultural Development, 1956-67, which
merely stated in Article 5: "In building water conservation projects
where power generation is possible, every effort should be made
to undertake the simultaneous construction of small and medium-sized
hydroelectric power stations; and by coordinating them with the
medium-sized and large power stations built by the State, the supply
of electricity to the countryside should be gradually increased."

It was not until the beginning of the Leap Forward campaign in
August 1958 that a plan for first-stage rural electrification was
adopted at a national conference held in Tientsin. Under this plan,
a mass campaign for rural electrification was to be launched in five

TABLE 22

Number of Hydroelectric Plants in Rural China
At the End of the Year, 1949-58

Year	Total Number of Plants	Total Capacity (in kilowatts)	Average Capacity Per Plant (in kilowatts)
1949	57	5,330	94
1950	68	6,248	92
1951	88	7,804	89
1952	98	8,137	83
1953	105	8,321	80
1954	114	8,445	74
1955	127	8,900	70
1956	240	11,860	49
1957	544*	20,324*	37*
1958	4,878	151,826	31

*Based on incomplete statistics.

Sources: For 1949-57, Shui-li Fa-tien [Hydroelectrics], No. 12, 1958, p. 54; for 1958, Chang Chung-wei et al., "Communization Is Beneficial to Rural Electrification," JMJP, January 26, 1960, p. 7.

selected hsien (counties) and 100 selected agricultural producers'
cooperatives in each province of autonomous region during the winter
and spring of 1958-59, and the first-stage rural electrification was to
be completed in all rural areas during the three years 1959-61.[49]

The conference also recommended that, by the end of 1961, the
total capacity of all electric power plants in the rural areas should
reach 15-18 million kilowatts, producing 37.5-45 billion kilowatt-hours
of electric power, so that the average annual consumption of electricity
per person could reach 50-80 kilowatt-hours.[50]

The Tientsin conference also recommended that, as a means of
popularizing rural electrification, emphasis be given to the construction
of small hydroelectric plants, each with a generating capacity of not
more than 50 kilowatts. It was believed that such plants would not
require specialized technique, equipment, or critical materials.[51]

China's prospective water power resources provided another
principal reason for emphasizing hydroelectric plants; these resources
were first estimated by the National Resources Commission of the
National government at 137 million kilowatts. The Communist
Government revised this figure several times: 140 million kilowatts
in 1950, 150 million kilowatts in 1953, 540 million kilowatts in 1955,
and 580 million kilowatts in 1958. However, these reassessments
were made without considering such unfavorable conditions as the
uneven distribution of precipitation in Mainland China, which causes
the waste of water in the high water season and the decrease of power
generation in the low water season; the heavy investments needed for
the construction of reservoirs, dams, generators, and transmission
lines; and the difficulty of simultaneously maintaining supplies of
water for irrigation and for power generation, especially in the North
and Northwest regions, which are subject to periodic droughts.[52]

Table 22 indicates that, although the number of hydroelectric
plants in rural China and their total capacity increased steadily from
1949 to 1958, the average capacity per plant declined as a result of
the construction of small plants. At the end of 1958, there were
4,878 plants in the country's rural areas with a total capacity of
151,826 kilowatts, or an average capacity of 31 kilowatts. Of these
plants, 4,334 with a total capacity of 131,502 kilowatts, or an average
capacity of 30 kilowatts, were built in 1958. Like the numerous native
fertilizer plants and primitive blast furnaces for steel production
constructed during the Leap Forward campaign, many of these small
hydroelectric plants were ineffective. Some were constructed with
only one water turbine, mostly made of wood, and had a generating
capacity as small as three or four kilowatts each.

Despite the Tientsin conference, the development of rural electrification continued to be slow. In the first half of 1959, the total capacity of rural hydroelectric plants was increased by only slightly more than 30,000 kilowatts. The shortage of technical personnel and equipment was reported to be the major cause of the slow progress.[53] Probably, the ineffectiveness of the small plants constructed in 1958 also hindered progress in this area. The development was further handicapped by the high cost of construction. Moreover, there was a lack of overall planning and of the accurate data needed for planning; Surveys of hydraulic resources only been conducted in some isolated regions.

As droughts spread to many provinces and autonomous regions in 1959, the operations of most of the hydroelectric power stations were badly affected. Losing all hope for the implementation of preliminary rural electrification planned for 1959-61, the Communist government had to adopt a new plan that called for "the realization of rural electrification to a considerable degree in a period of about ten years beginning in 1959."[54]

In addition to the small plants, a number of larger hydroelectric plants have been constructed in connection with projects for multiple purposes--flood control, and electric and water supply for industrial, domestic, and agricultural uses. In general, these plants are consider- ably more efficient and economical than the small hydroelectric plants.[55] One of them is the Hsin-an River Hydroelectric Station, near Chienteh Hsien in Chekiang Province, designed and constructed with Soviet assistance. Construction began in 1957, and the station went into operation in April 1960 when its first generator unit was installed. Since then, the station has been supplying electric power to Shanghai, Nanking, Hangchow, and other cities and to pumping stations irrigating vast stretches of farmland in the Yangtze Delta. It also serves to safeguard 300,000 mou of land along the lower reaches of the Hsin-an River from the menace of flood. The station was designed to have nine hydroturbine generator units with a total capacity of 652,500 kilowatts. The fourth generator, with a capacity of 72,500 kilowatts, was installed in 1963.[56]

Only a small number of thermal electric power plants have been constructed in the rural areas. Their total number at the end of 1958 was 2,112. One of the major problems here is that most of the equipment and tools used are more complicated and must be imported, whereas those for hydroelectric plants can be partly manufactured in China. Another difficulty is the shortage of coal, caused by the great demand in other industries and by the inadequacy of transportation facilities.[57]

In addition to the hydroelectric and thermal electric plants, another major source of electric supply in rural China is provided by the transformer substations of large electric power stations in urban and suburban areas. However, power transmission lines still are poorly developed, partly because of the shortage of metals and cement. Before the Leap Forward period, electric power networks of 35-, 10-, 6.6-, and 3.3-kilovolt transmission lines were the most common ones, but even these networks were rather scarce.[58] By the end of 1965, 126,000 kilometers of power transmission lines had been installed, as compared with 18,500 kilometers in 1957.[59] However, most of these power transmission lines are no more than local hookups serving small areas, rather than integrated hydro-thermal power transmission systems.

One of the principal networks of high tension transmission lines was installed in 1966 on the vast plain around Poyang Lake, an important area for producing rice, cotton, and oil-bearing crops in East China. The grid links up the hydroelectric power stations in the area and the thermal power plants of nearby cities and towns. In a district of Nanchang hsien, 75.5 kilometers of high tension transmission lines and 1,857 kilowatts of electric motors were installed to provide 6,600 hectares of farmland with electric pumping. The project was financed mainly by the eight communes of the district and undertaken by locally trained electricians, mechanics, and other technicians with state aid in certain equipment, building materials, and technical personnel. Local carpenters and masons were enlisted for construction work, and stones and rocks were substituted for cement to cut down costs.[60]

For several years prior to the Cultural Revolution, the general policy of rural electrification was reliance on transmission lines as the primary source of electrical supply, supplemented by small hydroelectric stations.[61] The emphasis on transmission lines was due not only to the severe droughts in many parts of the country which affected the operations of hydroelectric power stations, but also to the industrial recession in the early 1960's, which resulted in under-utilization of the expanded generating capacity in the urban and suburban areas. As a part of the new policy of priority for agriculture, a program was set forth for the installation of transmission lines from the industrial and mining centers with surplus generating capacity to the surrounding rural areas.[62]

Subsequently, the policy was reversed, mainly because of the contradictions between the demands of factories and mines and the needs power supply of agricultural users. In accordance with Mao Tse-tung's instructions on self-reliance and along the same lines

as the development of small chemical fertilizer plants and small farm
machinery plants, increasing numbers of small hydroelectric stations
again have been constructed or remodeled. These stations use largely
local manpower and financial resources, with very little investment
by the central authorities. This seems to indicate that industrial
production was affected by the establishment of electric irrigation and
drainage networks at the expense of urban power grids.

Rural consumption of electricity in Communist China in 1965
was reported to be 25 times that in 1957, increasing from 100 million
to 2,500 million kilowatt-hours. In 1965, electricity was available in
most of the villages in about 1,300 of China's 2,126 hsien (counties)
and benefited some 80 million farmers. The rapid increase was
attributed to "the collective effort of the communes, energetically
supported by the state"; in 1964, state investment in rural electrification
was reported to be more than half the total funds appropriated for
China's power industry as a whole.[63] However, it has been estimated
that, on the basis of 5 kilowatt-hours for each mou of cultivated land,
China would need at least 8,000 million kilowatt-hours each year for
its 1,600 million mou of cultivated land.[64]

Electric power is used in rural China primarily for the processing
of agricultural products, especially rice husking and flour grinding,
for the preparation of fertilizers and animal feed, and for illumination.
The use of the electricity for irrigation and drainage is increasing
but still is not widespread. At the end of 1961, the total land area
irrigated by electricity amounted to approximately 10 million mou (1.67
million acres), or about one percent of the reported total area irrigated
by all means. Most of the electrically irrigated farms were located
in areas producing rice, wheat, cotton, or vegetables.[65] In 1965,
electricity was used for irrigation and drainage on 84 million mou of
farm land, or about 16 percent of the reported total area irrigated by
all means.[66]

Electric power also has been used on an experimental basis
in the cultivation of land with a new type of plow operated by rope
traction. It is claimed that, compared with tractors, the "electric
plows" have the advantages of lower cost of manufacturing, less
steel required, higher efficiency of operation, especially on paddy
fields, and possibility of operation by human and animal power, by
wind, as well as by electricity.[67] But thus far no definite success has
been revealed, although the use of the "electric plow" was expanded
in Chekiang and a few other provinces the late 1960's.[68]

The use of tide, wind, marsh gas, and other sources of natural energy began to be gradually popularized in July 1958. Special attention has been given to the transformation of tidal energy into electricity for agricultural uses. It is maintained that, with a total coastal line of more than 11,000 kilometers (6,830 miles), China has the possibility of generating some 34 million kilowatts of tidal energy. As an experiment, several small tidal electric power stations have been built along the seacoast with capacities ranging from 15 to 250 kilowatts. Preliminary results indicate that, although the construction of tidal electric stations is less expensive than that of the ordinary hydroelectric plants, tidal energy is not dependable because of the wide fluctuations of the tide.[69]

Thus, rural electrification in Communist China, which started virtually from scratch, progressed slowly but steadily in the 1950's and 1960's. There is little doubt that electricity, as a less expensive form of power, will become increasingly important in both agricultural production and household uses in the rural areas. In view of the country's rich hydraulic resources and the constant shortage of coal, metals, and cement, the principal sources of electricity in rural China probably will continue to be small hydroelectric plants, supplemented by transformer substations of large electric power stations in urban and suburban areas. Therefore, more rapid development of China's rural electrification will depend largely on the improvement of small hydroelectric plants and the expansion of a number of large projects to serve the principal crop-producing areas, as well as on the development of an integrated hydro-thermal power transmission system on a nationwide scale.

THE PROSPECTS

In view of the slow progress of the tool innovation program, a series of a remedial measures were taken following the crop failure of 1959-61. The First National Conference for Scientific Discussion on Agricultural Machinery was held in Peking for three weeks in June and July 1962. Participants included Vice-Premier Teng Tzu-hui; Han Kuang, Vice-Chairman of the State Science and Technology Commission; Ch'en Cheng-jen and Chang Feng-shih, Minister and Vice-Minister of Agricultural Machinery, respectively; and other high government officials. This conference was followed by the establishment of the Chinese Academy of Agricultural Mechanization in Peking on July 16, 1962.[70] Research institutes of agricultural mechanization have also been set up in various provinces and autonomous regions.[71]

The problem of agricultural mechanization was again thoroughly discussed at the Eighth Plenary Session of the Tenth Central Committee of the Chinese Communist Party, held in September 1962. Participants in the meeting recognized that the "arduous and complicated" task of mechanization of agriculture would require a period of twenty to twenty-five years as originally planned, rather than ten years as revised during the Leap Forward period, and that semimechanized and improved farm tools would remain in a very important position for a long time to come.[72] Subsequently, the policy of "simultaneous development of mechanization and semimechanization, with the main stress on the latter," was been implemented. In Communist China, "semimechanization" generally refers to the use of machines and implements with improved working mechanizm that still must be operated mainly by human or animal power. Semimechanization includes many types of farm implements and tools of 20 horsepower or less for sowing, cultivation, plant protection, irrigation and drainage, harvesting and threshing, rural transportation, and processing of agricultural products.[73] Most of these semimechanized implements and tools are manufactured locally: in 1966, the total output value of local agricultural machinery plants accounted for more than two-thirds of that of the agricultural machine-building industry as a whole.[74]

In 1965, there were more than 25,000 handicraft factories and workshops employing a total of 810,000 persons and producing farm machines and implements to suit local needs, according to Teng Chieh, Vice-Minister of the Second Ministry of Light Industry.[75] Chia An-lan, an alternate member of the National Committee of the All-China Federation of Handicraft Cooperatives, revealed that in the first nine months of 1965 a total of more than 1.3 million semimechanized farm machines and tools were made by handicraft works and cooperatives in 19 provinces and municipalities. He pointed out many advantages of semimechanized farm implements and tools over large and more elaborate farm machines, including adaptability to different types of land, transportability due to small size, simplicity of construction, and lower cost.[76]

The current policy of agricultural mechanization was clearly reflected at the National Agricultural Exhibition held in Peking in 1966. The approximately 1,300 farm machines and implements on display were designed with local conditions taken into account; they were of all sizes, but the small ones formed the bulk.[77]

Meanwhile, in order to improve maintenance and repair facilities, a number of agricultural machinery accessories plants were constructed or reconstructed after 1960, including the Shihchiachuang (Hopei) Tractor Accessories plant, the Wusih Oil Pipes and Oil Pumps Plant, the Nanch'ang Tractor Accessories Plant, the Pengpu

(Anhwei) Tractor Accessories Plant, the K'aifeng Tractor and Electrical Machinery and Tools Factory, and the Luk'ou (Hunan) Internal Combustion Machine Accessories Factory. A large portion of capital construction investment in the agricultural machinery industry has been allotted for accessories plants.[78] By the end of 1965, agricultural machinery and tractor stations were reported to have been set up in seven of every ten hsien in Mainland China.[79] But in 1966 the supply of spare parts for farm machinery remained inadequate in many areas.[80]

Although the revised plan for agricultural mechanization is much less ambitious than the plan mapped out during the Leap Forward campaign, whether or not it can be carried out according the schedule remains to be seen. Two basic questions arise: (1) how many agricultural machines and implements can be produced and (2) how much mechanization agriculture will be able to absorb profitably. The shortage of technical personnel, and steel and other raw materials, and the somewhat improved but still inefficient management under the communes, undoubtedly will continue to give the Chinese Communists difficulties in regard to the production and maintenance of agricultural machinery and tools. In the meanwhile, it is generally believed that economic and social conditions in Communist China probably will remain immature for a nationwide agricultural mechanization for some time to come. As the People's Daily pointed out, "On the one hand, the level of our industrial production still cannot supply a sufficient amount of farm machinery for agricultural production; and on the other hand, it is necessary to raise the cultural and technical level of the peasants if farm machinery is to be put into extensive use in the rural areas."[81]

To what extent and in what manner Chinese agriculture should be mechanized is a matter that needs careful consideration. Simple small-scale mechanization of the type being developed in Japan, for example, may prove more economical than the employment of human labor and the maintenance of draft animals. Mechanization also may contribute to higher yields by permitting more timely operations when the soil is in the best condition for cultivation or the weather is favorable for harvesting. Furthermore, mechanization may free for other crops land that was formerly needed to provide livestock feed. For some operations, the greater efficiency of mechanization may outweigh other considerations. For example, deep plowing, which can help improve soil fertility and increase yields under certain conditions, is difficult without heavy equipment. Many modern pesticides cannot be applied effectively without improved types of sprayers and dusters, and most modern mechanized planters and fertilizer appliers do a much better job of seeding and fertilizing than traditional manual methods.

On the other hand, sufficient attention should be paid to evolving types of farm equipment specifically adapted to the country's conditions and needs. This includes the use of garden-type tractors, small harvesting and threshing machines, and motorized tricycles in rice-producing in the South and densely populated areas in the North, in order to meet local conditions of small field plots and highly intensified cultivation. Research on mechanization is required to provide guidance as to the most appropriate forms of mechanization and thus help to avoid repetition of the costly mistakes that Communist China has made, as in the case of double-wheel/double-share plows.

In view of Communist China's limited industrial capacity and other difficulties, the present policy of "simultaneous development of mechanization and semimechanization, with the main stress on the latter," for twenty or twenty-five years (1962-82 or 1962-87) seems both more feasible as well as more profitable that the overambitious plan mapped out during the Leap Forward campaign, which called for the complete mechanization within the ten years 1959-68.

NOTES

1. Government of the Republic of China, Chungking, Program and Estimated Requirements for Relief and Rehabilitation in China, presented to the United Nations Relief and Rehabilitation Administration, Washington, D. C., 1944, Annex F (Agriculture), pp. 75-81. (Mimeographed.)

2. Li Ching-yu, "Gradual Realization of Agricultural Mechanization Through Tool Innovation," Nung-yeh Chi-hsieh [Agricultural Machinery], Peking, No. 18, 1959, pp. 1-5.

3. Ni Ts'ai-wang, "How to Use Double-Wheel/Double-Share Plows and Double-Wheel/Single-Share Plows?" Sheng-wu-hsueh T'ung-pao [Biological Bulletin], Peking, September 1956, pp. 65-68.

4. "Why the Demand and Production of Double-Wheel/Double-Share Plows Have Stopped?" editorial, Chi-hua Ching-chi [Planned Economy], Peking, No. 9, 1956, pp. 1-4.

5. "Raise the Effectiveness of the Double-Wheel/Double-Share Plows," editorial, JMJP, April 16, 1958, p. 1; Hsin-hua Pan-yueh-k'an [New China Semimonthly], Peking, No. 9, 1958, pp. 86-88.

6. "Ten Years of Great Accomplishment and Experience in Farm Machinery Work in China," Nung-yeh Chi-hsieh [Agricultural Machinery], Peking, No. 18, 1959, pp. 10-14.

7. Nung-yeh K'o-hsueh T'ung-hsun [Agricultural Science Bulletin], Peking, No. 2, 1958, pp. 62-63.

8. China Reconstructs, Peking, No. 5, 1957, p. 9.

9. Liu Jui-lung, "The Revolutionary Significance of Rice Transplanters," K'o-hsueh Ta-chung [Popular Science], Peking, No. 4, 1960, pp. 133-35; NCNA-English, Peking, April 27, 1969.

10. Li Ching-yu, op. cit., pp. 1-5.

11. "Grasp Firmly the Repair and Manufacturing of Agricultural Machinery and Implements," editorial, JMJP, November 15, 1960, p. 1.

12. JMJP, December 26, 1960, p. 3.

13. JMJP, November 18, 1960, p. 3.

14. JMJP, December 2, 1960, p. 2.

15. JMJP, November 16, 1960, p. 1; November 18, 1960, p. 3.

16. JMJP, December 29, 1960, p. 2.

17. "On the Question of Agricultural Cooperativization," Jen-min Shou-ts'e [People's Handbook] (Peking, 1956), pp. 80-86.

18. State Statistical Bureau, Ten Great Years, English edition (Peking, 1960), p. 135.

19. Hsin-hua Pan-yueh-k'an [New China Semimonthly], Peking, No. 17, 1959, p. 24.

20. Ch'en Cheng-jen, "Speed Up Technical Transformation of Agriculture," Hung Ch'i [Red Flag], Peking, No. 4, 1960, pp. 4-10.

21. JMJP, April 11, 1960, p. 3; October 28, 1960, p. 4.

22. "Actively and Systematically Bring About the Technical Transformation of Our Country's Agriculture," editorial, JMJP, November 9, 1962, pp. 1-2.

23. JMJP, October 27, 1960, p. 1.

24. "Actively and Systematically Bring About the Technical Transformation of Our Country's Agriculture," op. cit., pp. 1-2.

25. State Statistical Bureau, op. cit., p. 98.

26. NCNA-English, Peking, January 31, 1966.

27. China News Service, Canton, news release No. 4146, August 9, 1965.

28. JMJP, April 28, 1962, p. 1.

29. NCNA, Peking, February 5, 1966.

30. Teng Chieh, "Bring the Role of Handicrafts Into Full Play and Serve Agricultural Production Better," JMJP, January 4, 1966, p. 5.

31. Hsu Pao-yuan, "How Are the More Than 700 Types of Rolled Steel Connected With Agriculture?" Shih-shih Shou-ts'e [Current Events Handbook], Peking, No. 17, 1962, pp.

32. JMJP, January 7, 1962, p. 1.

33. Chao Hsueh, "Current Problems in Agricultural Mechanization," Ta Kung Pao, Peking, May 15, 1961, p. 3.

34. Hsiang Nan, "Certain Problems of Agricultural Mechanization," JMJP, December 22, 1962, p. 5.

35. JMJP, December 18, 1962, p. 2.

36. JMJP, December 8, 1962, p. 2.

37. Teng Chieh, op. cit., p. 5.

38. "It Is Fine to Have Tractors Back to Chairman Mao's Revolutionary Line--A Report of Investigation of the Re-collectivization of the Operation of Tractors in Lankao Hsien," Nung-yeh Chi-hsieh Chi-shu [Technique of Agricultural Machinery], Peking, No. 10, 1968, pp. 4-7.

39. JMJP, November 5, 1960, p. 7.

40. Chang Feng-shih, "Produce Suitable Agricultural Machinery to Support Agriculture," Kung-jen Jih-pao [The Daily Worker], Peking, January 18, 1962, p. 1.

41. Yang I-ch'eng, "Positively Develop Draft Animals and Accelerate Agricultural Production," JMJP, May 9, 1961, p. 7.

42. JMJP, July 28, 1960, p. 2; March 27, 1961, p. 2.

43. "Protect Safe Wintering of Draft Animals," editorial, JMJP, December 23, 1960, p. 1.

44. JMJP, April 12, 1961, p. 3.

45. Hsu Chi, "Accomplishments of Animal Husbandry in the Past Decade," Chung-kuo Hsu-mu-hsueh Tsa-chih [Chinese Animal Husbandry Magazine], (Peking), No. 10, 1959, pp. 289-94.

46. JMJP, November 17, 1962, p. 2; "Properly Manage Livestock Breeding and Veterinary Stations," editorial, JMJP, February 17, 1963, p. 1.

47. G., Meisinger, "Training of Veterinarians in the Chinese People's Republic," Monatshefte fuer Veterinaer-Medizin [Monthly Bulletin of Veterinary Medicine], Jena, No. 1, 1966, translation by Joint Publications Research Service, JPRS 34,331 (Washington, D. C., March 1, 1966), pp. 7-11.

48. "Celebrating the Tenth Birthday of Our Great Nation," editorial, Chung-kuo Shou-i-hsueh Tsa-chih [Chinese Veterinary Science Magazine], No. 9, 1959, pp. 253, 261.

49. Hsin-hua Pan-yueh-k'an [New China Semimonthly], Peking, No. 17, 1958, p. 97.

50. "A Bugle Is Blown for the March Toward Rural Electrification," editorial, Shui-li Fa-tien [Hydroelectrics], Peking, No. 17, 1958, pp. 3-5.

51. Ho Chi-feng, "Summary of Report to the National Conference on Rural Electrification," Shui-li Fa-tien [Hydroelectrics], Peking, No. 17, 1958, pp. 6-7.

52. Robert Carin, Power Industry in Communist China (Hong Kong: Union Research Institute, 1969), pp. 36-40.

53. Chang Chung-wei et al., "Communization Is Beneficial to Rural Electrification," JMJP, January 26, 1960, p. 7.

54. Liu Lan-p'o, "The Road to the Realization of Rural Electrification," Hung Ch'i [Red Flag], Peking, No. 13, 1960, pp. 8-15.

55. Shui-li Fa-tien [Hydroelectrics], Peking, No. 12, 1958, p. 54.

56. Hsu Hsia-shih, "The Hsin-an River Hydroelectric Station," Ti-li Chih-shih [Geographical Knowledge], Peking, No. 6, 1957, pp. 257-59; "1963 Successes of China's Economy," Peking Review, No. 40, 1963, pp. 17-21; JMJP, September 23, 1963, p. 2.

57. B. Bannikov, "Rural Electrification in the Chinese People's Republic," Tekhnika v Sek'skom Khozvaystve, Moscow, No. 2, 1960, translation by Joint Publications Research Service, JPRS 4529 (Washington, D. C., April 12, 1961) of an article in pp. 88-92.

58. Ibid.

59. "The Practice of Operating the Electricity Service in Rural Areas on a Part-Work and Part-Farming Basis," editorial, JMJP, September 7, 1965, p. 1.

60. NCNA-English, Nanchang, June 4, 1966.

61. Chung Hsin, "New Development of Rural Electrification in China," Press Release, Chung-kuo Hsin-wen [China News Service], Canton, February 9, 1965.

62. Tso Hu, "Several Problems of Agricultural Electrification," Ching-chi Yen-chiu [Economic Research], Peking, No. 3, 1963, pp. 9-16.

63. JMJP, December 25, 1965, p. 1; NCNA's special report on the occasion of the sixteenth anniversary of the founding of the Chinese People's Republic, Peking, September 16, 1965.

64. Liu Jih-hsiun, "A Discussion of Several Problems Concerningtthe Modernization of Our Country's Agriculture," JMJP, June 20, 1963, p. 5.

65. JMJP, May 11, 1961, p. 3; December 23, 1961, p. 1.

66. NCNA, Peking, September 16, 1965; Peking Review, No. 41, October 8, 1965, p. 29.

67. "Energetically Popularize Rope Traction Machines," editorial, Nung-yeh Chi-hsieh [Agricultural Machinery], Peking, No. 7, 1958, p. 1; "A Rapid Way Toward the Mechanization and Electrification of Cultivation," editorial, JMJP, editorial, September 12, 1958, p. 1; Nung-yeh K'o-hsueh T'ung-hsun [Agricultural Science Bulletin], Peking, No. 10, 1958, pp. 518-20.

68. Ching-chi Tao-pao [Economic Reporter], Hong Kong, March 6, 1967, p. 16.

69. Chang Han-ying, "Report to the National Conference on the Transformation of Tidal Energy Into Electricity, Shanghai, October 1958," Shui-li Shui-tien Chien-she [Water Conservation and Hydroelectric Construction], Peking, No. 2, 1958, pp. 3-5.

70. Nung-yeh Chi-hsieh Chi-shu [Technique of Agricultural Machinery], Peking, No. 5, 1962, pp. 2-3.

71. NCNA-English, Peking, February 7, 1966.

72. "Actively and Systematically Bring About the Technical Transformation of Our Country's Agriculture," editorial JMJP, November 9, 1962, pp. 1-2.

73. "What Are Semimechanized Farm Machines and Tools?" JMJP, November 9, 1964, p. 2.

74. NCNA, Peking, October 17, 1966.

75. Teng Chieh, op. cit., p. 5.

76. Chia An-lan, "Produce and Popularize Semimechanized Farm Tools on the Basis of Reality," JMJP, January 4, 1966, p. 5.

77. Liu Pang, "Paving a Way to Agricultural Mechanization in China--A Visit to the Agricultural Mechanization Hall of the National Agricultural Exhibition," JMJP, April 13, 1966, p. 2.

78. JMJP, August 1, 1963, p. 2; Kuang-ming Jih-pao [Kuang-ming Daily], Peking, September 2, 1963, p. 4.

79. NCNA-English, Peking, December 28, 1965.

80. "Do Not Underestimate the Problem of Parts," JMJP, April 12, 1966, p. 2.

81. "The Spirit of Self-Reliance Must Be Upheld in the Movement of Farm Implement Innovation," editorial, JMJP, October 15, 1964, p. 1.

13

Kuan, or field management, is the last and also the least discussed of the eight major aspects of Mao Tse-tung's "agricultural charter." It generally refers to the meticulous management of farmland from the time of sowing or transplanting to the time of harvest, including the coordination and timely application of horticultural techniques used by Chinese farmers for many generations to promote factors and conditions favorable to agricultural production. The purpose of field management, according to the Research Institute of Crop Breeding and Cultivation, is "to adjust the physiological activities of crops during various stages of their growth so that a maximum yield of the crops may be obtained."[1]

Provisions on field management in the National Program for Agricultural Development were very general and not very clear. Article 11 stated the following:

All agricultural producers' cooperatives should undertake intensive and meticulous farming and should in a rational way improve their methods of cultivation, fertilization, irrigation, crop rotation, inter-cropping, multiple-cropping, and close planting. Efforts should also be made to ensure that field work, such as sowing, weeding, and thinning, will be done in right time, that field management will be strengthened, and that harvesting as well as threshing will be carried out promptly with care in order to ensure high yields and bumper harvests.

More specifically, field management requires concern with the following matters during the growing period of crops: (1) conditions essential for the germination of seeds, including the supply of moisture and air and the elimination of soil crust; (2) suitable moisture, air, nutrients, and soil temperature; (3) weed control; (4) elimination or lessening of unfavorable meteorological conditions, such as frost, drought, and waterlogging; (5) inter-tillage, i.e., cultivation of land between the rows of crops; (6) thinning of seedlings to space them reasonably evenly, especially for cotton, jute, corn, kaoliang, and millet; (7) ridging of ground to protect plants against cold, water-logging, ineffective off-shoots, growth of weeds, and insect pests and diseases; and (8) pinching off of leaves to control the growth of upper part of plants and to concentrate nutrients on their lower part, especially for rapeseed, tobacco, cotton, and sweet potatoes and other vegetables.[2]

One of the most frequently quoted examples of field management is the "three-yellow and three-black" technique of controlling the growth of the single-crop late-ripening variety of paddy rice, devised by Ch'en Yung-k'ang (see Chapter 3). Ch'en, a farmer of Kiangsu Province, gained nationwide fame as a model peasant because he achieved one of the country's highest yields of paddy rice. According to his observations, the color of shoots of the late rice crop changes three times from yellow to black (or dark green) and three times from black to yellow during the whole period of growth. The schedule of the changes in color helped Ch'en to determine when and how to use additional manure and to water or drain the fields in order to promote a high yield. In other words, the management of rice fields should be based on observations of the subtle changes of leaf color in order to obtain high yields.

Another example of good field management is the use of the shape of seedlings at different stages (pig-ear, donkey-ear, and horse-ear) by a Honan peasant, Liu Ying-hsing, as the basis for fertilizing and watering the wheat crop. When the leaves of wheat seedlings are in the shape of pigs' ears, dark green in color, and hanging down, it is an indication of overgrowth and the fields should be watered sparsely. When the leaves are in the shape of donkeys' ears, bluish-green in color, and with tops slightly bent over, it is an indication of normal growth and the fields should be fertilized with additional nitrogen, phosphate, and potassium in proper pro-portion and should be watered. When the leaves are in the shape of horses' ears, light green in color, and standing straight, it is an indication of fertilizer deficiency and the fields should immediately be fertilized with large quantities of nitrogen and should be proportion-ately watered at the same time.[3]

In urging good field management of winter wheat in 1961, the People's Daily stated:

> The promising growth of the wheat seedlings had caused some people to slacken efforts in field management in the belief that a bumper harvest is already certain. This is wrong. Good seedlings are only the foundation for increased output. Wheat requires a relatively long period to grow and mature. During the long winter and spring months, the wheat has to face frequent and varied natural calamities, and needs sufficient nutrients and tender care.

> Measures for field management of wheat depend on local conditions. To hasten the growth of wheat, give it water if it needs water and give it additional fertilizer if it needs fertilizer. On the other hand, land which is too fertile should be so controlled so as to retard the growth of wheat during the early stage. Dig drainage ditches if there is too much rain and water. All these tasks must be properly carried out during the growth of the wheat seedlings.

> Meanwhile, preparations should be made for late-stage wheatfield management next spring. The winter months are especially important for making preparations to fight wheat diseases and pests and for carrying out the installation and repair of irrigation projects. What is more important, the fertilizer needed by wheat during the coming spring when it begins to turn green and grow rapidly should be gathered in the winter, since fertilizer gathered then, after a period of fermentation, can be used immediately after the melting of the snow and ice in spring. If we miss the winter season and rely on spring for gathering fertilizer, there will not be enough time for the fertilizer to ferment.[4]

In the case of cotton, the People's Daily, in another editorial, stated the following: Field management should be strengthened to insure the healthy growth of cotton seedlings. Tilling and weeding should be carried out expeditiously during the early period of cotton cultivation because of the quick evaporation and the fast growth of weeds around the cotton seedlings. Even a day's delay

can mean the difference. The most suitable time to apply
additional fertilizer to cotton fields is in June or around
the first half of July, the early and intermediate periods
of cotton growth. Control of insect pests in cotton fields
should be carried out in a timely manner. Missing this
opportunity might bring about a need for several times
more manpower and material to do the job later and
possibly without much effect.[5]

In claiming the achievements of field management, Vice-Premier
T'an Chen-lin stated: "The people's communes are now everywhere
making big efforts to cultivate large high-yielding tracts and to exercise meticulous care in farming, just as in gardening. The peasants
say that the farms now look like vegetable gardens with deep plowing,
close planting, good seed strains, proper manuring, proper irrigation,
careful cultivation and intensive farming, and elimination of weeds,
insect pests and plant diseases."[6]

However, the fact is that in the 1950's and 1960's field management was neglected because of labor dislocation and the increasing
emphasis on the modernization of agriculture, although the communes
were repeatedly asked to give 30 percent of their efforts to sowing
and 70 percent to field management.

NOTES

1. Research Institute of Crop Breeding and Cultivation, Chinese
Academy of Agricultural Science, "Field Management," Hsin-hua
Pan-yueh-k'an [New China Semimonthly], Peking, No. 12, 1959,
pp. 129-30.

2. Chu Chien-nung, T'u-ti Fei-li Ching-chi Yuan-li [Economic
Principles of Land Fertility], Shanghai, 1964, pp. 298-99, 328-33.

3. Ibid., pp. 298-99.

4. "Grasp the Important Link in Increasing Wheat Production,"
editorial, JMJP, December 27, 1961, p. 1.

5. "Momentous Juncture in the Raising of the Cotton Output,"
editorial, JMJP, June 10, 1963, p. 1.

6. T'an Chen-lin, "Strive for the Fulfillment, Ahead of Schedule,
of the National Program for Agricultural Development," JMJP, April
9, 1960, p. 1.

14

THE PROSPECTS
FOR RAISING
THE YIELD
PER UNIT
OF LAND

China is reaching the limit of the area that can be cultivated economically and is extending into very marginal land. The so-called "uncultivated arable land" is mostly of poor quality and can be brought into production only after heavy investment. Reclamation of such land is often a costly and lengthy process. Therefore, the more effective means to improve agricultural production would be to increase the productivity of the land already cultivated. For this reason, most measures prescribed in the National Program for Agricultural Development were geared to raising the yield per unit of land.

Although many accomplishments have been claimed in all of the eight aspects of the "agricultural charter" that Mao Tse-tung considers the concentration areas of the program, the preceding chapters clearly indicate that none of these measures has progressed as successfully as expected. Moreover, in adopting various new techniques and inputs, the Communist government has not paid sufficient attention to the principle of complementarity and the need to introduce new approaches in an integrated rather than piecemeal fashion. For example, outside the paddy rice area in China, only a limited portion of the lands for grain crops can at present make economical use of chemical fertilizers without irrigation. Also, the use of new varieties of crops in many cases requires heavier application of fertilizers, adequate irrigation, timely control of plant diseases and insect pests, and a broad range of improved farming practices. The full impact of these measures can be obtained only when they are combined in a suitable "package."

As a whole, Mao Tse-tung's eight major aspects of the technical transformation of agriculture progressed at only a moderate pace

during the First Five-Year Plan period, and progress was slowed
down by the Leap Forward campaign and the crop failures of 1959-61.
The recovery since then has been slow but steady. It is likely that
progress in the 1970's will accelerate somewhat as a result of the
adoption of remedial measures in recent years and the improvement
of general economic conditions.

The preceding chapters indicate quite clearly that the Communist government did not fare well in its efforts both to expand the area under cultivation and to raise yields per unit of the existing cultivated land. The country's total area of cultivated land is reported to have increased only slightly from 1,468,220,000 mou (244,704,000 acres) in 1949 to 1,616,800,000 mou (269,467,000 acres) in 1958, or from 10.20 percent to 11.23 percent of the total land area. Data for the more recent years are not available, but any increase in cultivated land during the first two decades of the Communist regime probably would not have amounted to much because of the limited acreage of additional land suitable for cultivation, the tremendous cost involved in reclamation work, the abandonment of some land that became unfit for cultivation, and the acquisition of farmland for construction projects in suburban areas.

The National Program for Agricultural Development called for the average annual yields of grains to reach 400, 500, or 800 chin per mou and for that of ginned cotton to reach 40, 60, 80, or 100 chin per mou, depending on local conditions, within the twelve years beginning in 1956. To what extent have these targets been fulfilled? In his report to the Second Session of the Second National People's Congress on April 6, 1960, Vice-Premier T'an Chen-lin stated that by the end of 1959 only 28 percent of the grain-growing hsien and 20 percent of the cotton-growing hsien had fulfilled or surpassed their respective targets.[1]

Despite the fact that, after four years of implementation of the program, 72 percent of the grain-growing hsien and 80 percent of the cotton-growing hsien had not reached the targets, the Second National

People's Congress, at its Second Session on April 10, 1960, adopted a
resolution calling upon the people to exert concerted efforts in the
struggle for realizing the program two or three years ahead of
schedule.[2] This was based on claims that agricultural production in
1958 and 1959 registered a "big leap forward," with increases of 35
and 46 percent, respectively, in grain production and increases of 28
and 47 percent, respectively, in cotton production over those in 1957,
and on the assumption that a continuation of the efforts to bring the
advantages of the three red banners (the general line, the leap forward
and the communes) into full play would further accelerate the implementation of the program. These optimistic illusions continued until
the end of 1960, when the disastrous crop failure in that year and in
1959 was revealed.

    No data are available to indicate the extent to which the targets
for grain and cotton yields have been fulfilled since 1959. In view
of the unsatisfactory progress in carrying out the technical programs
and the fact that these goals were, as a whole, unrealistically high,
it is very doubtful that they could have been attained according to
schedule. This was evidenced by an editorial in the People's Daily
on January 27, 1966, which stated that after ten years of implementation of the National Program for Agricultural Development, "a
number of production teams, communes, chu, hsien, and administrative
districts have either prefulfilled or overfulfilled the targets of grain
yields as prescribed in the program." However, the paper admitted
that "for the nation as a whole, a great deal of hard work remained
to be done before this program can be fulfilled."[3]

    The Communist government has blamed natural calamities and
the withdrawal of Soviet assistance as the only factors responsible
for the failure to attain the goals for expanding cultivated acreage and
raising yields per unit of land. But it is apparent that in part the
failure should also be attributed to the unsuccessful attempt to improve
agricultural techniques, as well as to the peasants' indifference,
discontentment, and lack of incentive to work under the commune
system. Analyses given in the preceding chapters clearly indicate
that, although progress has been made with varying degrees in certain
aspects of the technical transformation of agriculture, the accomplishments in general have been far behind the targets or the actual need,
even if we accept the Chinese Communists' claims. For example,
the 1959 output of 1,333,000 tons of chemical fertilizers represented
only 19-27 percent of the goal for 1962 which was set between 5 and
7 million tons, or 9 percent of the target of 15 million tons set for
1967, the final year of the Program. The 154,000 tractors that were
reported to be available in 1965 constituted only 15.4 percent of at

least one million tractors that were needed for the land suitable for
mechanical cultivation. The seriousness of floods and droughts in
recent years indicated that the Chinese Communists were not likely
to meet the provision in the National Program for Agricultural Development that "ordinary floods and droughts should be eliminated in the
main within twelve years."

What is even more significant is that, qualitatively, the measures
taken by the Chinese Communists have been far below the minimum
standards that are required to improve agricultural production. More
than one billion mou of cultivated land were said to be under irrigation
in 1958. Although this figure was ahead of the target of 900 million
mou for 1967, irrigation could actually be carried out "in a normal
manner" on less that one-third of this land. A considerable number
of irrigation projects either had not developed their usefulness in
time or had only low resistance to droughts, as admitted by Ho Chi-
feng, Vice-Minister of Agriculture. Like the steel produced with
primitive blast furnaces in thousands of backyards at the beginning
of the Leap Forward campaign, most of the chemical fertilizers
produced by numerous small plants built in the communes during
1958 and 1959 were of low grade. The same situation existed in the
production of chemical pesticides. Also, most of the hydroelectric
power plants, especially those built during the Leap Forward period,
were ineffective.

Thus, technological innovation in Chinese agriculture appears
to have helped agricultural production to a very small degree in the
1950's and 1960's. It is true that many new techniques and new inputs
have been introduced to the country since the Communist takeover.
But to date the progress of the technical transformation of agriculture
is relatively small as compared with the vast backlog of traditional
Chinese agriculture. Moreover, many of the new techniques and
inputs have been misused, as many examples given in the preceding
chapters indicate. As a result, the technical level of Chinese agriculture remains very low.

There were several major causes for the failure to fulfill the
targets for the technical transformation of agriculture. First, facts
and figures cited in this study give abundant evidence that the failure
was caused partly by improper planning and execution of programs.
Many projects that require a steady long-term policy have suffered
from sudden changes, uncertainties, and reversals of directives. A
typical example was the adoption of the "smaller acreage, higher yield,
and greater harvest" system in 1958 and the sudden shift to the "large
acreage and greater harvest" system in 1959, which resulted in a loss

of grain production. The digging of innumerable canals under the so-called "canalization" program in 1959 and 1960 without a scientific blueprint has not improved the irrigation situation but has caused salification alkalization of land in many areas. The arbitrary changes of multiple cropping systems in some areas without consideration of local conditions and the peremptory order for deep plowing and close planting on all farmland have deteriorated the productivity of the soil. Also, the indiscriminate popularization of high-yield varieties of crops regardless of local conditions and the discarding of low-yield but indispensable varieties at the same time have aggravated the shortage of seeds.

Another cause for the failure in the technical transformation of Chinese agriculture is the shortage of trained personnel. Despite numerous claims about accomplishments in agricultural research, education, and extension, the number and quality of trained agricultural workers at all levels are far behind the need. Many blunders have been made by members of the Central Committee of the Chinese Communist Party, who issue directives and instructions, and by the cadres in charge of agriculture in the communes, who execute slavishly orders from above. Both groups have the will but neither the knowledge nor the intelligence required, and their efforts in seeking new methods of increasing agricultural production often do more harm than good. Many programs have been pushed without sufficient consideration of local natural conditions, cropping patterns, cultivation practices, and other important factors of agricultural production. In many cases, efforts to replace traditional farming methods with a more scientific approach to agriculture run into resistance. Farmer opposition to the new inputs and technology is partly rooted in ignorance but also partly due to a better appreciation of the local unsuitability of some new techniques than is recognized by the administrative officials pushing the programs. Commune members often insist that modern inputs and techniques that have worked well elsewhere would not automatically suit local conditions in their areas.

Moreover, many of the limited number of agriculturists have been misused. Through all the years since 1949, agricultural scientists and other "high-grade intellectuals" have been alternately oppressed and caressed. They have been classified according to their attitudes toward communism rather than by their achievements.

During the Leap Forward campaign, the belief was inculcated that science, particularly Western science, was superstition and nothing more than a worshiping of foreigners. "Agricultural geniuses," such as Ch'en Yung-k'ang, were discovered among peasants. Some

Chinese scientists ventured rather timidly to suggest that indiscriminate deep plowing, close planting, and so on would not do the job.
But their suggestions were totally ignored.

The departure of Soviet experts beginning in the early 1960's
has affected a number of important agricultural construction plans.
In recent years, increasing numbers of projects have been designed
and constructed by Chinese engineers with Chinese-produced equipment and materials; an example is the first-stage installation of the
Wu Ching Chemical Plant in Shanghai, completed in 1963. However,
the absence of Russian aid, has created a serious handicap.

Another difficulty in carrying out the program of technical
transformation of Chinese agriculture is the deficiency of funds for
capital construction investment and the purchase of the means of
production. In its efforts to industrialize the country, the Communist
regime has placed high priority on the development of heavy industry.
The distribution of basic construction investment among various major
sectors of the national economy in the First Five-Year Plan period
was as follows: for heavy industry, 49 percent; for light industry, 7
percent; for agriculture, 8.2 percent; for transportation and communications, 18.7 percent; and for other sectors (including trade,
banking, storage, culture, education, public health, and public utilities),
17.1 percent. Thus, the investment for heavy industry was six times
as much as that for agriculture; of the total investment for industry,
87.4 percent was allocated to heavy industry, and 12.6 percent to light
industry.[4]

When the recommendations on the Second Five-Year Plan
(1958-62) were adopted at the Eighth Plenary Session of the Chinese
Communist Party in September 1956, heavy industry again received
top priority. In comparison with the First Five-Year Plan, the total
amount of basic investment during the second five years was expected
to double, with the share for industry (heavy and light) increasing
from 56.0 percent to about 60 percent, and that for agriculture from
8.2 percent to 10 percent.[5]

Although exact data are not available, there are indications that
the shortage of funds for capital construction investment for agriculture has continued despite the adoption in 1960 of the policy of
"developing agriculture as the foundation of the national economy."

Equally acute is the shortage of funds that the communes need
for buying fertilizer, seeds, pesticides, tools, and other necessities
for agricultural production. For years, the Communist government

has advocated that such funds should come mainly from the communes' own efforts while the support of the state should be considered as a secondary means. Moreover, in extending loans to the communes, the banks have been told to rely mainly on the funds that are available from the repayment of expired loans. In recent years, although funds for agricultural loans were provided by state appropriations in the national budget, the amount of loans recalled on expiry was greater than the amount of new loans granted.[6]

Another difficulty in the technical transformation of agriculture in Communist China is the shortage of certain necessary materials and equipment, including rolled steel, copper, cement, and lumber. The production of chemical fertilizers has been handicapped by the weak deposits of phosphate and potash, and that of chemical pesticides has been impeded by the shortage of such materials as mercury, copper and benzene. The sharply declining supply of Russian equipment and materials, together with the departure of Soviet experts, has affected a number of important agricultural construction plans.

Despite the shortages, much of the material and equipment was misused and mismanaged. Until recent years, there were no repair networks, nor were there sufficient spare parts for farm machines. Many tractors were without machine-drawn farm tools, and irrigation and drainage machines were without pipes and pumps. Moreover, operators and maintenance personnel for tractors and other farm machines generally had received only a very short period of technical training. Many plows and other small farm implements were reported to have been lost, wasted, or destroyed, partly because of the over-emphasis on mechanization. Mismanagement also has caused the spoilage of seeds by heat, insects, or damp granaries, and has like-wise reduced the effectiveness of fertilizers.

Still another problem is that in many areas economic and social conditions are not mature for technical transformation. At the end of 1962, land in many localities had not been properly adjusted to make it suitable for mechanization. Within each piece of land, there were abandoned wells and ditches not yet flattened or boundary stones not yet removed. On some pieces of land, irrigation canals were not well located, sometimes dividing the land into a number of small fragments so that mechanization of farming was virtually impossible. There is also the problem of making efficient use of farm machinery, chemical fertilizers, and chemical pesticides; this requires a kind of technical knowledge that is not yet common in the communes.

Since the crop failures of 1959-61, several important measures have been taken to expedite the technical transformation of agriculture. First, the disastrous agricultural failure and the absence of Russian experts, which was caused by the deterioration of Sino-Soviet relations, have necessitated conciliation with China's own experts. In the communique of the Tenth Plenary Session of the Eighth Central Committee of the Chinese Communist Party, released on September 28, 1962, the government was urged to strengthen scientific and technological research, particularly in agriculture; to vigorously train personnel; and to promote cooperation with the intellectuals so that they may fully play their role as they should.[7] Shortly thereafter, in October 1962, a conference was called in Peking to study measures for strengthening research work in agricultural science and for training more young agricultural scientists and technicians.[8]

In the 1960's, a number of national conferences, each taking up a major problem of agricultural techniques, have been held. These culminated in the National Conference on Agricultural Science and Technology, held in Peking under the joint sponsorship of the Central Committee of the Chinese Communist Party and the State Council. The importance of this conference was indicated not only by its length, from February 8 to March 31, 1963, but also by the "unprecedentedly large" attendance of more than 1,200 agricultural scientists, leading members of the relevant departments and organizations of the Central Government, and cadres and officers of the various regional offices and associations of agriculture. In the course of the conference, the delegates were received by Mao Tse-tung and Chou En-lai.

The conference drew up a plan for the development of agricultural science and technology for the next few years. It called for the following measures:

1. Extensive investigations of the natural resources in agriculture, forestry, animal husbandry, fisheries, and side occupations, including the condition of their use and the exploration of new resources;

2. Application of China's rich traditions of intensive farming as well as modern scientific and technological measures for a higher productivity of existing cultivated land, forestry, animal husbandry, fisheries, and side occupations;

3. Comprehensive studies of the problems of utilization of the 9.6 million square kilometers of land in the country, including the

expansion of the cultivated acreage, the use of mountainous land, grassland, and water bodies, the harnessing of deserts, and the prevention, improvement, and rational use of alkaline soil;

4. Strengthening of theoretical research into fundamental agricultural science, the establishment of those branches of agricultural science now lacking, and the development of the weak branches;

5. Application of the latest theories, simultaneously with the study of Chinese agricultural legacies; and

6. Strengthening of the study of agricultural economics.

This plan actually included very few new ideas, but the government's attitude toward their implementation had changed. A People's Daily editorial commented that this conference marked an important starting point for the further development of agricultural science and technology in China and that at the same time it definitely would have a far-reaching influence on the development of the country's agricultural production. However, the editorial issued a word of warning, stating that agricultural research is not a simple and easy task as it must be tried out repeatedly in different areas. This statement apparently referred to the cadres' hasty way of conducting scientific research in wasteful attempts to obtain immediate results.

The People's Daily editorial also recognized that, because of the backwardness in science and the dense population in China's rural acres, the dissemination of modern scientific and technical knowledge in the countryside is extremely important and difficult. It urged government agencies and mass associations concerned with agriculture forestry, commerce, education, culture, and public health to assume their responsibilities in the dissemination of scientific and technical knowledge. It also suggested that the dissemination of agricultural science and technology should be extended to the cadres as well as to the peasants "because it would be difficult for one to display good leadership over modern agricultural production without having any knowledge of agricultural science and technology."[9] This clearly was an admission that the cadres' ignorance is a serious bottleneck to the present efforts to improve agricultural production in Communist China.

In another editorial reviewing the ten-year implementation of the National Program for Agricultural Development, the People's Daily stated: "although China should make strenuous efforts to increase agricultural production, it is of utmost importance that actual condition

be taken into consideration in giving production assignments and
setting yield goals, and the people be allowed some leeway for
adjustment. Under no circumstances should one seek blindly for
high targets and work out measures for increasing output in a rigid
way."[10]

Although numerous incredible claims about harvests of principal
crops were made during the Cultural Revolution, the National Program
for Agricultural Development was buried in discreet oblivion in 1967,
its target year. The reason was simple: most of the goals prescribed
in the Program had not been fulfilled. These goals were still the
ultimate objective, but there was no longer a timetable. Moreover,
indications were that Communist Chinese leaders did not expect to
make up in the 1970's for the slower than anticipated performance of
agricultural production in the 1960's. The rates of growth called for
under the new policy were moderate by past standards.

Another important measure taken in recent years in an effort
to expedite the technical transformation of agriculture was the adjustment of heavy industry to serve agriculture. After the crop failure
of 1959-61, the government repeatedly ordered that above all industry
must satisfy the needs for technical innovation of agriculture. In
1962, according to Ta Kung Pao, heavy industry's aid to agriculture
improved not only in quantity but also in variety and quality.

However, despite the increased industrial aid to agriculture,
according to Ta Kung Pao:

> The supply of production materials is far below the need of
> the big collective rural market. The country needs one
> million tractors for the land suitable for mechanical culti-
> vation instead of the 100,000 tractors available at present;
> tens of million horsepower of machines for irrigation and
> drainage, as compared to the present several million
> horsepower; and more than 100 chin of chemical fertiliz-
> ers for each mou of cultivated land each year, rather
> than the present three or four chin.[11]

Data on industrial aid to agriculture are sketchy, but it is
clear that the program involves many serious economic problems.
First, it is an extra burden added to the already heavy tasks of industry. Steel, copper, cement, timber, and benzene, for example, are
badly needed in many fields, including agriculture. In addition, there
is the question of the extent to which industry can change its objectives
and structure without suffering financial loss and reducing production

efficiency. This leads to another question: Even with the readjust-
ment of heavy industry, how much machinery, equipment and materials
for agriculture can be produced?[12]

The modification of policy and attitude toward the technical
transformation of agriculture was definitely more sound and more
convincing than the big words during the Leap Forward campaign.
Since the 1959-61 crop failure, Communist China has appeared to be
in a continuous process of learning, mainly by trial and error, the
types of techniques and inputs suited to its own circumstances and
stage of agricultural development. It would seem that, if such efforts
continue, yields of grains and other principal crops could be raised
considerably within the next few decades, both because of the country's present low technical levels and because of the availability of
new production techniques and inputs that modern agricultural science
has provided. Yields in other countries in similar situations have
on occasion increased substantially within a short time period: in
Taiwan, for example, rice yields rose by two-thirds between 1948-52
and 1963-67, and in Mexico wheat yields nearly trebled during the
same time period.[13] Other countries that had food crop deficits a
decade or so ago but now are in a self-sufficiency or surplus situation
despite rapid population growth include India, Pakistan, Kenya, the
Philippines, Thailand, and Turkey.

But realization of such progress will require large-scale
investment of manpower, funds, and other resources; organization
or reorientation of a great number of activities; and coordination of
the national, provincial, and local efforts. Raising a country's agricultural productivity is not only a technical problem; it is no less a
social and economic problem, and also a problem of organization.
In some countries, the underlying economic and social factors have
made it possible and profitable for farmers to make use of new
knowledge and techniques, but in other countries the same factors
have hindered the adoption of new approaches. The principal block in
Communist China is not the lack of technical knowledge but the problem of transmitting that knowledge to millions of uneducated and
often illiterate farmers; perhaps still more important is the creation
of an environment in which farmers will have the incentive and also
the means to put improved methods of farming into practice. In any
event, even if there should be more favorable weather and economic
conditions, as well as a continued relaxation of the organization
framework of communes, no substantial increase of agricultural
production in Mainland China should be expected until the capital
inputs have been increased to a reasonably large scale and until the
planning and execution of the program for technical transformation
of agriculture have been sufficiently improved.

NOTES

1. T'an Chen-lin, "Strive for the Fulfillment, Ahead of Schedule, of the National Program for Agricultural Development," JMJP, April 9, 1960, p. 1.

2. JMJP, April 11, 1960, p. 1.

3. "Make Strenuous Efforts and Take Steady Steps," editorial, JMJP, January 27, 1966, p. 1.

4. Jen-min Shou-ts'e [People's Handbook] (Peking, 1956), pp. 17-18; Hsin-hua Pan-yueh-k'an [New China Semimonthly], Peking, No. 8, 1959, p. 48.

5. Jen-min Shou-ts'e [People's Handbook] (Peking, 1957), pp. 58-64.

6. Hu Li-chiao, "Manage Well Rural Finance and Aid Effectively Collective Economy," JMJP, July 11, 1963, p. 5.

7. JMJP, September 29, 1962, p. 1.

8. JMJP, October 11, 1962, p. 1.

9. "Raise the Agricultural Science to a New Level," editorial, JMJP, April 6, 1963, p. 1.

10. "Make Strenuous Efforts and Take Steady Steps," op. cit., p. 1.

11. Liu Jih-hsin, "Heavy Industry Should Make Agriculture Its Important Market," Ta Kung Pao, Peking, January 7, 1963, p. 3.

12. Leslie T. C. Kuo, "Industrial Aid to Agriculture in Communist China," International Development Review, Washington, D. C., Vol. IX, No. 2 (June 1967), pp. 6-10, 29.

13. Food and Agriculture Organization of the United Nations, The State of Food and Agriculture, 1968 (Rome, 1968), p. 78.

APPENDIX:
THE NATIONAL PROGRAM
FOR
AGRICULTURAL
DEVELOPMENT,
1956-67

The English translation used in this study was published
by the Foreign Language Press, Peking, in 1960. It should
be noted that the program was presented as though wholly
devised in 1956 and that the communes, which were established in 1958, were not envisioned in the program as
presented.

INTRODUCTION

This is a programme of endeavour to bring about a rapid increase of the agricultural productive forces, so as to reinforce socialist industrialization in our country and raise the living standards of
the peasants and the people as a whole during the period from the
First Five-Year Plan to the Third.

Socialist industry is the leading force of our national economy.
But the development of agriculture occupies a vital place in our
socialist construction. Agriculture supplies industry with grain and
raw materials. At the same time, the contryside, with its more than
500 million population, provides our industry with the biggest domestic
market in the world. In this sense, without our agriculture there could
be no industry in our country. It is utterly wrong to belittle the
importance of agricultural work.

There are two ways to develop agriculture. One is the capitalist
road whereby the fate of the peasants is in the hands of landlords,
rich peasants and speculating merchants and a handful of people get
rich while the vast majority are driven to destitution and constant
bankruptcy. The other is the socialist road by which the peasants
take their fate into their own hands under the leadership of the working
class, and all become rich and prosperous together. The struggle
over which of these two roads to take, is one that will exist for a long
time during the period of transition in our country. However, as a
result of the virtual completion of agricultural co-operation, the
overwhelming majority of China's peasants have left the first road
and are going along the second. The task ahead is to do our best to
consolidate the system of cooperation while continuing to combat the
spontaneous development of capitalism in the countryside.

Agricultural cooperation has opened up the broadest avenue for
developing China's agricultural productive forces. Without agricultural
cooperation, under the conditions of individual economy it would be
mere idle fancy to strive for an average annual grain yield, with some
exceptions, of 400, 500 and 800 catties per mou in the various major
areas of the country within twelve years or for the aim of enabling,
during the Second Five-Year Plan, the majority of the co-operatives
to reach or exceed the output and income of the local well-to-do middle
peasants working on their own. But with the coming of agricultural
cooperation, together with the great achievements in socialist industrialisation under the First Five-Year Plan, and given the persistent
efforts of all from now on, it is possible to attain the aims set out in
this Programme.

The agricultural economy has great potentialities because of the generally good natural conditions in China, the abundance of rural manpower, fine traditions of industry and thrift among the peasants and their rich experience in intensive and meticulous farming. These potentialities of agriculture must be fully brought out on the basis of co-operation by every sort of vigorous and rational measure and by energetically extending agricultural mechanisation that is suited to actual conditions step by step and in a prepared manner. It also necessary to combat conservatism in striving to attain the aims laid down in this Programme.

The raising of the level of agricultural production and the living standards of the peasants depends mainly on the hard work of the peasants themselves. However, the People's Government under the leadership of the working class and the Communist Party will of course do everything possible to help the peasants. The People's Government will from now on gradually give more and more of whatever assistance is necessary for carrying out the numerous measures to increase agricultural production as set out in this Programme. In fact, this means mutual support between the workers and peasants, the towns and the countryside.

The worker-peasant alliance led by the working class and the mutual support between the workers and peasants is the guarantee of the emancipation of the peasantry. The bourgeois rightist and feudal remnants have done their utmost to estrange relations between the workers and peasants and between the towns and countryside with the aim of restoring the landlord and capitalist systems. Such base attempts have failed and will continue to fail.

Education among the peasants should teach them to love their country, their co-operatives and their family as one. Without the People's Republic of China led by the Communist Party, the peasant masses would have continued to be ruled and exploited by the imperialists, landlords, rich peasants and speculating merchants, they could not possibly have had their own co-operatives and countless scenes of homelessness and death would have gone on being enacted. If one is to love one's own family, it is imperative to love the country and the co-operative. All forms of departmentalism and individualism which disregard the interests of the state and the collective interests of the co-operatives are wrong. In fact, they must end by jeopardising the interests of one's family.

Difficulties will still continue to emerge on the path of agricultural development. But man is the determining factor in doing things. To our liberated people, there are no difficulties that cannot be overcome. Fearlessness of difficulties is a great characteristic inherent in our working people.

This Programme is put forward for the whole nation. There are many different conditions in various localities and co-operatives. Therefore, on the basis of this Programme and in accordance with the specific conditions of each locality and co-operative, the leading" organs of the Party and Government and the co-operatives in the various provinces (including municipalities and autonomous regions), special administrative regions (including autonomous chou), counties (including autonomous counties), districts, townships (including nationality townships) should realistically draw up their concrete plans for the development of the work in each locality, item by item and stage by stage, by means of the mass line. At the same time, all the state's economic departments, departments of science, culture, education and public health and the civic and judicial departments should also reexamine and renew their own working plans in accordance with the Programme.

Among the various tasks provided in this Programme, those such as afforestation, industry and thrift in running households, elimination of rats, flies and mosquitoes, the wiping out of the diseases from which the people suffer most seriously, and the advocation of birth control also apply to city residents. Such tasks can only be effectively carried out with the co-ordinated efforts of the towns and the countryside.

PROGRAM

1. Consolidate the agricultural co-operation system. Agricultural co-operation in our country was virtually completed in 1957. The future task is to strive to consolidate all the agricultural producers' co-operatives during the Period of the Second Five-Year Plan, or a little longer.

The conditions for consolidating the co-operatives are: (1) To maintain the supremacy of the former poor peasants, hired farmhands and lower middle peasants (chiefly those who are now poor peasants, and the lower middle peasants among the new middle peasants) in the composition of the leadership of the co-operatives, and at the same time see to it that the upper middle peasants have appropriate representation. (2) To thoroughly carry out the policy of democratic management of the co-operatives. At fixed intervals the leading body

of the co-operative should publicly declare the financial income and
expenditure, and the functionaries should consult the masses on work
and take part in production. (3) To thoroughly carry out the policy
of running the co-operatives in the spirit of industry and thrift, and
to fight against idleness and oppose extravagance and waste. (4)
According to the economic conditions of the co-operatives and local
natural conditions, to take various measures to increase production,
gradually increase capital construction in agriculture, ensure adherence
to and fulfillment of state plans, continuously expand production, and
strive to enable the majority of the co-operatives to rise to or above
the level of production and income of the local well-to-do middle
peasants during the Second Five-Year Plan. (5) To handle the question
of distribution rationally, give all-around consideration to the interests
of the state, the co-operatives and the co-operative members; through
the growth of production and in years of normal harvest, to increase
the public accumulation funds of the co-operatives and the incomes
of the co-operative members year by year so that the income of the
collective economy of the co-operatives, plus the income from side-
occupations undertaken by the co-operative members' families, will
on an average per capita basis reach or surpass by around 1962 that of
the local well-to-do middle peasants. (6) To strengthen political and
ideological work, continuously raise the socialist consciousness of the
co-operative members, overcome the capitalist ideology and depart-
mental and individualist ways of thinking that run counter to the
interests of the state and the collective interests of the co-operatives;
in co-ordination with the rectification campaign among rural functionaries and the check-up in the co-operatives each year, systematically
sum up the year's work and conduct intensive socialist education
among the entire rural population. In multi-national areas, special
attention should be paid to fostering solidarity and mutual help among
the nationalities.

      The few elementary co-operatives that still remain should be
guided to switch over voluntarily to advanced co-operatives when the
conditions are ripe. The education of and leadership over the small
number of individual peasants who continue to work on their own
should be strengthened, to enable them voluntarily and gradually to
join the co-operatives. Those who will not join should be let alone.

      2. Strive energetically for increased grain and other crops.
In the twelve years starting from 1956, in areas north of the Yellow
River, the Tsinling Mountains, the Pailung River and the Yellow
River (in Chinghai), the average annual grain yield should be rised
from the 1955 figure of over 150 catties per mou to 400 catties; in
areas south of the Yellow River and north of the Huai River, the

yield should be raised from the 1955 figure of 208 catties to 500; in areas south of the Huai River, the Tsinling Mountains and the Pailung River, it should rise from the 1955 figure of 400 catties to 800 catties. In districts of sandy waste land of poor soil, in districts where there is waterlogging or drought all the year round, in mountainous districts at high altitude and with a cold climate, in districts with a very short period without frost, in sparsely populated districts and in districts where there is large-scale land reclamation, targets for increased production can be set with reference to specific conditions.

In the twelve years starting from 1956, the average annual yield of cotton (ginned) should be raised from the 1955 figure of 35 catties per mou (the average for the whole country) to 40, 60, 80 to 100 catties depending on local conditions.

While giving priority to increasing the output of grain, various places should develop a diversified agricultural economy, to ensure the attainment of the output figures set in the state plans for textile raw materials (cotton, bast fibre crops, silkworm cocoons), oil-bearing crops (soya beans, peanuts, rapeseed, sesame, tea-oil and tung-oil trees), sugar-bearing crops (sugar-cane and sugar-beet), tea, cured tobacco, fruits and medicinal herbs; and also take energetic measures to develop the cultivation of all other marketable industrial crops. In various provinces in South China where the conditions permit, attention should be paid to developing the cultivation of tropical and sub-tropical crops.

Agricultural co-operatives should encourage their members to grow vegetables and fodder crops on their own private plots. Co-operatives and state farms on the outskirts of cities and near indus-trial or mining districts should grow vegetables according to state plans so as to ensure a fully supply of vegetables to the cities and industrial or mining districts.

3. Develop livestock breeding. In animal husbandry co-operation, different plans of development should be mapped out in accordance with local conditions. State livestock farms should be extended according to plan.

Great efforts should be made to protect and breed cattle horses, donkeys, mules, camels, pigs, sheep, rabbits and other domestic animals and raise appropriate numbers of all types of poultry. Female, young and stud animals should be specially protected. Breeding stations should be set up, and the livestock strains improved.

In pastural areas, the pastures should be protected, and fodder grass grown and improved, and special attention should be paid to opening up sources of water. Livestock breeding co-operatives should gradually build up their own fields of fodder and grass, and silage should be popularised.

Within a period of from seven to twelve years, all possible areas should, in the main, have eliminated the most serious animal diseases such as rinderpest, hog cholera, Newcastle disease, contagious pleuropneumonia of cattle, foot and mouth disease, pork measles (cysticercosis), sheep pox, sheep mange, etc. By 1962, veterinary stations should have been set up in all townships in pastural areas. The co-operatives should have people who have had a basic training in the prevention and cure of animal diseases. The role of folk veterinarian should be developed fully, and they should be organised and guided to improve their technique and take part in the work of the prevention and cure of animal diseases.

4. Popularise measures to increase production and disseminate advanced experience--two fundamental conditions for increasing yields of farm crops. The chief measures to increase production are to: (1) Build water conservancy works; (2) Increase the supply of fertilisers; (3) Improve the old types of farm tools and extend the use of new types of farm tools; (4) Extend the use of good seed strains; (5) Expand the multiple-cropping areas; (6) Plant more high-yielding crops; (7) Carry out intensive and meticulous farming and improve farming methods; (8) Improve the soil; (9) Carry out water and soil conservation; (10) Protect and breed draught animals; (11) Wipe out insect pests and plant diseases; (12) Reclaim waste land and extend the cultivated area.

The chief steps in disseminating advanced experience are: (1) Provinces, municipalities and autonomous regions should collect local experiences in increasing yields and compile and publish books, so as to spread the knowledge; (2) Agricultural exhibitions should be held; (3) Conferences of model peasants should be called at regular intervals by the government at all levels, awarding and citing model peasants who have distinguished themselves in increasing production; (4) Mutual visits and comparisons should be arranged among the co-operatives to exchange experience in increasing production; (5) On the basis of summing up advanced experience, organisational work should be done to spread technical knowledge, and peasants and functionaries should be encouraged to study the advanced experience in management and technique of other cooperatives, other townships, counties and provinces (autonomous regions).

5. <u>Build water conservancy works, expand irrigation, prevent</u>
<u>and control flood and drought</u>. In the twelve years starting from 1956,
the development of water conservancy all over the country should be
directed chiefly to the building of small and medium-sized water conservancy projects and, wherever necessary and possible, also to the
building of large water conservancy projects.

In a planned way, as many small water conservancy projects as
possible (such as digging wells and ponds, building dykes, sinking
water storing wells, opening ditches, building embankments, reservoirs
and a network of ditches, raising land and terracing land to store and
drain water) should be built, and as many small rivers as possible
should be harnessed, both types of projects being undertaken by the
local governments and the agricultural co-operatives. Ordinary flood
and drought should be eliminated, in the main, within twelve years by
these measures that are to be co-ordinated with the building of medium-
sized and large water conservancy projects and the harnessing of
medium-sized and large rivers by the state.

In areas where waterlogging is serious, maximum efforts should
be made to construct projects to wipe out waterlogging, drain water
and transform low-lying land.

Paddy fields and irrigated land should be expanded in twelve
years from more than 390 million <u>mou</u> in 1955 to approximately 900
million <u>mou</u>. While taking into account the varied conditions in the
different localities, for the purpose of ensuring good harvests, the
capacity of the irrigation facilities to deal with drought should be
raised to between 30 and 50 days; and in places suitable for double-
crop paddy fields, to between 50 and 70 days. To make full use of all
available water resources, the departments concerned should work
energetically to survey underground water and provide the water
conservancy departments with the necessary data.

In building water conservancy projects where power-generation
is possible, every effort should be made to undertake the simultaneous
construction of small and medium-sized hydro-electric power stations;
and by co-ordinating them with the medium-sized and large power
stations built by the state, the supply of electricity to the countryside
should be gradually increased.

6. <u>Increase energetically the output of farm manure and chemical</u>
<u>fertilizer</u>. The agricultural co-operatives should undertake every
measure to rely as far as possible on their own efforts for the supply
of fertilizers. Particular attention should be paid to pig-breeding
(in some places sheep-breeding). With the exception of certain national

minority areas where pigs are not raised and of a small number of
households which do not raise pigs because of religious beliefs, each
household in the countryside should raise an average of one and a
half to two pigs by 1962 and an average of two and a half to three pigs
by 1967. Pigs should be kept in pigsties, sheep in sheepfolds, cattle
and horses in barns. Energetic efforts should also be put into growing
green manure crops according to local conditions and the fullest use
should be made of night-soil from the cities and countryside and
garbage and miscellaneous refuse which can be utilised as fertiliser.

Both the central and local authorities should work energetically
to develop the chemical fertiliser industry and strive to produce approximately five to seven million tons by 1962 and approximately
15 million tons by 1967. Bacterial fertilizer should be increased to
the fullest extent.

7. Improve old types of farm tools and extend the use of new
types. Energetic efforts should be made to extend the use of improved
and new types of farm tools suited to local conditions on the basis
of the needs of production and by trial and remodelling to adapt them
to the conditions of the particular region. Attention should always be
paid to the maintenance and repair of farm tools. Technical guidance
in the use of the new types of farm tools should be strengthened.

Keeping pace with the development of industrialisation of the
country, mechanisation of agriculture should be carried out energetically step by step. Within the shortest possible time starting from 1956,
the engineering and agricultural deparments should draw up, on the
basis of extensive experiments and research, a programme for agricultural mechanisation suited to the conditions in China, so as to
make good preparations to extend the mechanisation of agriculture.
Then machinery suited for use in various places should be manufactured
for supply to the peasants; such machinery should be improved as
circumstances require and its use extended energetically.

8. Put energetic efforts into propagating improved strains of
crop seeds suited to local conditions and extending their use. Before
1962, extend the use of all sorts of existing improved strains of farm
crops whose adaptability to local conditions has already been proved
by selected experiments. In the case of improved strains (cotton
for example) the use of which has in the main been popularised, steps
should be taken to strengthen the work of invigorating strains and
varying them. Major efforts should be made to cultivate new, improved
strains and attention paid to trying out improved strains from other
parts of the country and from abroad.

Agricultural co-operatives should set aside land specially for growing seed, strengthen the work of seed selecting among the masses and institute a system for propagating improved strains of seed and their alternate use. In areas where the harvest is unreliable, alternating between good and bad, attention should be paid to storing up good strains of seed. State farms under the central and local authorities should make themselves centres for propagating good strains of farm crops and take energetic steps to increase the available supplies and extend the use of improved strains of crops suited to local conditions. All provinces (including municipalities and autonomous regions), special administrative regions (including autonomous chou) and counties (including autonomous counties) should set up special seed agencies.

9. Extend the multiple-cropping area. In twelve years starting from 1956, the average multiple crop index (including green manure crops), depending on the varying conditions in different areas, is to be raised to the following levels: (a) areas south of the Wuling Mountains, about 230 percent; (b) areas north of the Wuling Mountains and south of the Yangtse River, about 200 percent; (c) areas north of the Yangtse River, and south of the Yellow River, the Tsinling Mountains and the Pailung River, about 160 percent; (d) areas north of the Yellow River, the Tsinling Mountains and the Pailung River and south of the Great Wall, about 120 percent; (e) in areas north of the Great Wall, in general, all cultivated land should be fully utilised and the area of unworked land reduced, and wherever possible energetic steps undertaken to expand the multiple-cropping areas.

10. Grow more high-yielding crops. All available water resources should be used to extend the area under rice. In the twelve years starting from 1956 the area under rice should be increased by 250 million mou. Such high-yielding crops as maize and tuber crops should be suitably developed according to the local needs and dietary habits of the people in the area.

11. Strive to improve methods of cultivation suited to local conditions. All agricultural co-operatives should undertake intensive and meticulous farming, improve their farming methods, and in a rational way apply fertiliser and irrigate their land, rotate crops, use inter-cropping, multiple cropping and close planting.

Field work should be done in good time. Sowing and weeding and thinning out in good time, improving field management, harvesting in good time and meticulously as well as careful threshing--all these things must be done to ensure good yields and good harvests.

12. Improve the soil. Agricultural co-operatives and state farms should actively improve and utilize saline and alkaline land, poor red soil and low-lying and sandy land and poor quality soil of other types. Attention should be paid to guarding against the land becoming saline and alkaline. Hilly land should be energetically terraced in a planned way. The utmost should be done to turn poor soil into rich, fertile land.

13. Extend water and soil conservation. In areas where water losses and soil erosion take place, the agricultural co-operatives should be relied upon and the masses mobilized on a wide scale, to undertake in a systematic and planned way water and soil conservation in co-ordination with their production work. In the twelve years starting from 1956, significant benefits from water and soil conservation must be reaped in all possible areas and water losses and soil erosion must be steadily reduced. In order to get quick results, the departments of agriculture, forestry, water conservancy, and animal husbandry, and scientific research institutions must co-operate closely and give vigorous support to this kind of work under the unified leadership of the local Party and government organisations.

14. Protect and breed draught animals. In from seven to twelve years starting from 1956, every agricultural co-operative should raise an adequate number of strong draught animals. For this, sufficient grass and fodder crops must be produced and high-yielding fodder crops grown. The co-operatives must constantly improve the breeding management of draught animals, according to their conditions. Co-operatives and government authorities should take proper measures to encourage the breeding of draught animals.

15. Prevent, combat and eliminate plant diseases and insect pests. In from seven to twelve years starting from 1956, wherever possible, the insect pests and plant diseases that do the most harm to crops should be wiped out in the main, such as locusts, rice borers, army-worms, maize borers, aphids, red spiders, pink boll-worms, Sitodiplosis mosellana Gehin, wheat smut, wheat nematode and black rot on sweet potato; at the same time the spread of other harmful insect pests, plant diseases and weeds should be prevented. All localities should include in their plans for destruction all other serious insect pests and plant diseases that can be wiped out. To this end, plant protection and quarantine should be strengthened.

The production of fungicides, insecticides and pest destroyers and their related apparatus should be developed in a planned way. The quality of such products and their supplies should be improved.

Technical directions for their use should also be improved and their
safety and effectiveness be ensured.

16. Reclaim waste land and extend the cultivated area. The
state should reclaim waste land in a planned way. In the twelve years
starting from 1956 the area cultivated by state farms should be increased from the 1955 figure of over 13 million mou to about 100
million mou. Wherever conditions permit, land reclamation should
be carried out by organising new settlers and encouraging co-operatives
to organise branch co-operatives or send out production brigades.
The reclamation of waste land should be linked with the plans for
water and soil conservation and livestock breeding, so as to prevent
water losses, soil erosion, and damage to forests and indispensable
grassland. Where forests have already been damaged, efforts should
be made to restore them.

Agricultural co-operatives should make full use of scattered
bits of idle land, such as ridges and corners of land plots, the edges
of ponds, land along the ditches, and disused threshing grounds. According to conditions such land may be distributed to production
brigades or co-operative members for private management.

In carrying out capital construction, the strictest economy in
using land must be exercised by factories, mines, commercial and
agricultural enterprises, departments of education, culture, public
health, water conservancy, communications and military affairs, and
mass organisations. They should refrain from using cultivated land,
or otherwise occupy as little cultivated land as possible.

17. Develop the economy of mountainous areas. Agriculture,
forestry, livestock breeding and production of various kinds of local
and special products should be developed in the mountainous areas
under the policy of promoting a diversified economy in a manner
appropriate to local conditions.

The production of grain in mountainous areas should be developed,
provided that this does not contradict the conservation of water and
soil. In areas which are still short of grain, efforts should be made
to achieve self-sufficiency or reduce the amount of grain that has to
be imported from other areas.

In remote mountainous areas, emphasis should be laid on
growing timber forests. In those that are less remote, the emphasis
should be on growing forests of special economic value and for
firewood and charcoal, on fruit growing and the development of local

and special products. In mountainous areas in the south, attention
should be paid to cultivating tea-oil and tung-oil trees, bamboo,
mulberries and tea plants. In mountainous areas in the north, attention
should be paid to growing walnuts, Mongolian oaks and wild pepper.

More medicinal herbs should be grown. Attention should be
paid to protecting those which grow wild and, wherever possible,
gradually bringing a certain amount under cultivation.

In the twelve years starting from 1956 all possible areas should
by and large eliminate the animals which cause most damage to
productive work in mountainous areas. Wild animals of economic
value should be protected and their breeding encouraged.

Special administrative regions, counties, townships and agricultural co-operatives in mountainous and semi-mountainous areas
should draw up production plans covering comparatively long periods.
They should make rational use of the land and bring about an all-round
development of production. All state departments concerned should
properly co-ordinate and strongly support such work by organising
communications and transport, supply and marketing, culture, education
public health work, and migration to these areas.

18. Develop forestry and clothe all possible bare land and
mountains with green. In the twelve years starting from 1956, where
natural conditions permit and where there is enough manpower to
undertake the task, bare waste land and mountains should be clothed
with green. Wherever possible trees should be planted in a planned
way near houses, villages, and along roads and rivers. To achieve
this, we must count on the agricultural co-operatives to plant trees
and adhere to the policy that trees planted by co-operatives belong to
them. The co-operatives themselves should collect the seeds and
grow saplings; there should be a division of labour with the due
responsibility for work done, and those who cultivate the trees should
ensure their growth. At the same time, co-operative members should
be encouraged to grow trees near their own houses. The trees they
cultivate should belong to them.

In addition to timber forests (including bamboo groves), the
utmost use should be made of all manpower and uncultivated land in
the cities and countryside to plant other trees of economic value such
as fruit trees, mulberries, Mongolian oak, tea plants, varnish trees
and oil-bearing trees.

Afforestation by the state should be vigorously promoted. State-
owned forestry stations should mainly undertake large tracts of timber

forests, while the creation of shelter belts for the conservation of water and soil, wind-breaks, sand-breaks and shelter belts along the sea coasts should also be undertaken in a planned way.

Departments of railways, communications and water conservancy, factories and mines, should plant and care for trees along railways, main roads, and large rivers, around large reservoirs, and mines, and enjoy the income derived from this source. Nearby agricultural co-operatives may also be entrusted with such afforestation work which should tally with the plans of government departments concerned; and the income derived from this source should accrue to the co-operatives.

Cultivated land should not be occupied for the purpose of afforestation.

Within twelve years state-owned forests should be put under proper management to the greatest extent possible. Small state-owned forests which the state finds inconvenient to manage itself should be entrusted to the care of the co-operatives. Forest resources should be protected and well cared for. Steps should be taken to prevent forest fires, prevent and deal with insect pests and plant diseases in forests; random felling and wasteful felling should be stopped. Timely steps should be taken to enable the re-growth of trees on the felling areas.

19. Raise the output of marine and freshwater products and develop their breeding. In marine fishing, on the basis of co-operative organisation the latent potentialities of existing gear should be fully tapped and the fishing techniques gradually improved. Attention should be paid to increasing public accumulation funds, replenishing and improving fishing equipment, and gradually increasing the number of motor trawlers and motorised junks. Safety measures for production should be strengthened so as to extend fishing to deep seas. All possible water resources should be used to develop fresh-water fish farming. The work of breeding good stocks of fish and preventing and dealing with fish diseases should be strengthened. Energetic steps should be taken to promote fish farming in shallow sea waters and the work to breed fish, shell-fish and aquatic grasses strengthened.

20. Run the state farms successfully. All state farms should unite with and help their neighbouring agricultural co-operatives and set good examples in farming technique as they are expected to do. They should develop a diversified economy, raise their efficiency in the use of manpower, continuously improve their production technique and labour management and raise their labour productivity. They

should exercise the strictest economy, apply the principle of running
the farms with industry and thrift, improve the wages system, and
both raise their output and cut down costs of production.

21. Improve research in agricultural science and technical
guidance. Wherever necessary and possible, organisations for research
in agricultural science or to provide technical guidance should be set
up or improved--such as academies of agricultural science, regional
and specialised research institutes of agricultural science, provincial
agricultural experimental stations, model country breeding farms and
agricultural advisory centres--so that research in agricultural science
may better serve the development of agriculture.

Scientific research in agriculture and technical guidance must
be closely linked with the practical work of the peasant masses.
Local peasants' experience in raising farm yields, particularly that
of the old peasants, must be summed up and the useful farming
experiences of other places must be studied. The staff of the county
agricultural advisory centres should choose key farms and agricultural
co-operatives as bases for their participation in farming.

To meet the needs of the growing co-operative economy, during
the twelve years starting from 1956, technical personnel of primary
and intermediate level should be trained for the agricultural co-
operatives from among peasants who have certain farming experience
and a certain level of general education.

22. Improve meteorological and hydrological work. In the main,
the networks of meteorological observatories and stations and hydrological survey stations should be completed in the twelve years starting from 1956. Weather forecasting, in particular forecasting of
hazardous weather, should be strengthened. Weather forecasting for
agriculture should be established. All areas should give attention to
meteorological broadcasts, so that precautions can be taken against
natural calamities such as floods, droughts, gales and frost.

23. Run agricultural co-operatives and households in the spirit
of industry and thrift. All agricultural co-operatives should apply
the principle of industry and thrift in their work. Industry means
giving full encouragement to members to work conscientiously and,
wherever possible and necessary, to make vigorous efforts to branch
out into new fields of production, develop a diversified economy and
exercise minute care in everything. Thrift means being strictly
economical, lowering the costs of production and taking a firm stand
against waste and extravagance. In all capital construction,

co-operatives should make the fullest use of the manpower and material and financial resources at their disposal.

Education should be carried out among the peasants to encourage them to run their households in the spirit of industry and thrift, make long-term plans and arrange their household expenditure in a planned way. Women's organisations in the countryside should regard it as one of their important tasks to spread education among the women in running households in the spirit of industry and thrift and doing a good job of housework. Attention should be given to popularising model examples of peasant household management in which every item is carefully counted, and thrift is exercised in every outlay, and saving and accumulation are increased. It is a wrong idea to make no long-term plans, to disregard household accumulation and to consume everything available at any time.

Expenditure on weddings, funerals and social occasions should be cut down in the countryside, and irrational past customs and habits changed.

24. Make fuller use of manpower, raise labour productivity and develop diversified economy in the agricultural co-operatives. Agricultural co-operatives must make fuller use of manpower in order to fully develop arable farming and side-occupations like forestry, livestock breeding and fishery, together with the rural handicrafts, and seek out fresh sources of production so as to increase the wealth of society and the income of the rural population. In the north, means should be found to undertake more forms of work during winter. Energetic efforts should be made at the same time to improve technical skills in production, improve labour organisation and management and steadily raise the labour productivity of the members of the co-operatives.

In the seven years starting from 1956, every able-bodied man in the countryside should be able to put in at least about 250 working days a year. The labour power of woman should be reasonably arranged and organised with consideration given to their particular characteristics. Within the seven years and depending on the different conditions in the various areas, every able-bodied woman in the countryside should, apart from time spent on household work, be able to give no less than 80 to 180 days a year, to agriculture or side-occupations (including household side-occupations). In addition, the co-operatives should make appropriate arrangements for all those in the countryside who can undertake only part-time work or who are fitted for light work, and encourage them to take an active part in whatever work they are fit for.

25. Build up grain reserves. In the twelve years from 1956, all agricultural co-operatives except those which engage mainly in mountain forestry or growing industrial crops and are short of grain, should make concrete plans in accordance with their own conditions to build up a surplus of grain against times of urgent need that, added to that of the members' families, is sufficient for three, six, twelve or eighteen months' consumption. Where harvests are habitually unreliable and communications inconvenient, special attention should be paid to making up for poor harvests in the years of rich harvest and to accumulating grain against famine.

In the twelve years from 1956, the state should build up enough grain stocks for one to two years' consumption, so as to meet urgent needs.

26. Improve housing conditions. As their production grows and their members' incomes increase, the agricultural co-operatives should encourage and assist the members to repair and build dwelling houses and thus improve their housing conditions, according to the need and possibilities. This should be done in a prepared, planned way, at different times and group by group, under the principle of voluntariness, mutual help, and economical use of money and land.

27. Wipe out the four pests. In the twelve years beginning from 1956, rats, bedbugs, flies and mosquitoes should be by and large wiped out wherever possible.

28. Strive to eliminate the most serious diseases among the people. In the twelve years beginning from 1956 the diseases from which the people suffer most seriously should be virtually wiped out wherever possible. These include schistosomiasis, smallpox, bubonic plague, malaria, kala-azar, hookworm, filariasis, tetanus neonatorum, and venereal diseases. Energetic measures should also be taken to prevent and cure other diseases such as measles, dysentery, typhoid fever, Japanese Type-B encephalitis, poliomyelitis, diphtheria, pulmonary tuberculosis, leprosy, trachoma, goitre, Kaschin-Beck's disease, and Keshan disease. There should be vigorous efforts to train medical personnel, including traditional Chinese doctors.

Energetic efforts should be made to unfold a regular, patriotic, mass movement for public health, so that every person and family acquire good habits of cleanliness and hygiene. The underlying spirit of paying attention to cleanliness and hygiene is to eliminate diseases, bring about a general invigoration, reform the outmoded habits and customs and transform the country.

29. Protect women and children. The principle of equal pay for equal work must be resolutely put into practice in relation to women's productive work. Whenever necessary and possible, agricultural co-operatives may set up temporary, simple creches suitable for the busy farming periods. In allocating work the physiological character of women members must be taken into consideration. Suitable regulations should be made concerning the participation of children in the countryside in auxiliary work during busy seasons, taking their age and physical strength into consideration.

Public health departments should train midwives for the rural areas, exert their utmost efforts to popularise modern methods of delivery, provide post-natal and infant care and cut down the incidence of maternal diseases and the infant mortality rate.

Other than in areas inhabited by national minority peoples, birth control should be publicised and popularised in all densely populated areas and family planning advocated, so that the family can avoid being overburdened and a better education can be given to the children and full chances of employment provided.

30. Carry out the "five guarantees"; care for the dependants of revolutionary martyrs and the disabled revolutionary ex-service men; support and respect parents. As regards those members--widows, widowers, orphans and the childless--who lack labour power and are without means of support, the co-operative should make overall plans and assign production brigades or teams to make proper arrangements in production for them so that they can take part in work they are physically able to do; and to give due consideration to their livelihood so that all will be guaranteed a regular supply of food, clothing and fuel, the young a chance of education and the aged a proper burial after death. In a word, they will be guaranteed a means of livelihood in their lifetime and a proper burial after death.

In accordance with the state regulations, the co-operatives should give favourable treatment to the dependants of revolutionary martyrs who lack labour power and to disabled revolutionary ex-service men who cannot make a living even after receiving the ex-service men's pensions. Their living standards should be no lower than that of the average for the co-operative.

Young and middle-aged men and women should be taught that they should support and respect their parents so that the aged who are incapable of working will receive reasonable care during their lives and enjoy mental ease.

31. Wipe out illiteracy, develop cultural and educational work in the rural areas. In the twelve years beginning from 1956, depending on the local conditions, illiteracy among young and middle-aged people must be virtually wiped out. Efforts should be made to set up spare-time schools step by step in the townships or co-operatives to further enhance the educational level of the functionaries in the primary rural units and the peasants. Diversified methods should be adopted in setting up rural schools. In order that primary education can gradually become universal, apart from schools established by the state, energetic steps must be taken to encourage people to set up schools collectively and the setting up of private schools should be allowed.

Following the development of agricultural production, the co-operatives should gradually improve and develop cultural and re-creational work as conditions permit and in accordance with the principle of industry and thrift in building the country, in running the co-operatives and in managing households.

32. Develop the radio diffusion network in the rural areas. In the seven or twelve years starting from 1956, depending on local circumstances, the radio diffusion network is to be extended to practically all rural areas. The majority of the producers' co-operatives in agriculture, forestry, fishery, livestock breeding, salt production and handicrafts should be enabled to receive the radio programmes.

33. Develop the rural telephone and postal network. In the seven or twelve years starting from 1956, depending on local conditions a telephone network should be set up in the townships and in a certain number of co-operatives. Radio telephone equipment is to be installed in some areas. Within the twelve years, a postal network should cover virtually all rural areas so that there are good postal and telegraphic services.

34. Develop rural communications and transport. Within the seven or twelve years starting from 1956, depending on local conditions, a network of local roads should be built throughout practically the entire country. Roads of various kinds suited to local means of transport should gradually be built by relying on the efforts of the masses, in accordance with growing local requirements for transport services between provinces (including municipalities or autonomous regions), between special administrative regions (including autonomous chou), between counties (including autonomous counties), between districts and between township (including

nationality townships). The following principles should govern road construction: realistic consideration of the actual conditions, suitability to local circumstances, use of local materials, economy and practicality in use, and no waste of land. At the same time, all roads must be well maintained. Special attention must be paid to road construction in the mountainous areas.

In places served by rivers, navigable channels, if possible, should be dredged and kept in good order to improve communications.

35. Adjust the rural network of commerce. In order to meet the new conditions arising after agricultural co-operation, the commercial departments and the supply and marketing co-operatives in the rural areas should complete the adjustment of the rural commercial network in the next few years. They should speed up the circulation of goods, strengthen the administration of primary markets, ensure that all rural areas get good service in the supply of goods and purchase of agricultural produce, combat the spontaneous development of capitalism and facilitate the development of rural production.

36. Promote rural credit co-operation. The rural credit co-operatives must be consolidated and energetic efforts made to extend rural credit and savings services, so as to help the agricultural co-operatives and peasants meet their needs for short-term capital turnover.

37. Raise the socialist initiative of the youth in the countryside. The young people in the rural areas should be educated to ardently love their motherland, their villages, and labour, and love their co-operatives as dearly as their homes. They must be encouraged to exert themselves in learning to read and write, studying agricultural science and farming techniques and learning from the production experience of the middle-aged and old peasants. The rural youth should become a shock force in production, construction and science and culture in the countryside.

Those with a primary or secondary school education in the cities, other than those who can enter higher schools or find local jobs, should enthusiastically respond to the state's call, go to the villages and mountainous areas and take part in agricultural production and in the great cause of socialist agricultural construction. Eighty-five percent of the population of our country are in the countryside and industry cannot develop by itself without the development of agriculture. To work in the rural areas is both an urgent necessity and a great honour.

39. <u>Remould the former landlords, rich peasants, counter-
revolutionaries and other bad elements and safeguard socialist order
in the countryside.</u> Former landlords and the rich peasants who have
given up exploitation and former counter-revolutionaries in the rural
areas may be admitted individually into the agricultural co-operatives
as members or candidate members in accordance with the "Model
Regulations for Advanced Agricultural Producers' Co-operatives"
and on consideration of their actual behaviour. Those who are not
qualified for admission may be referred to the co-operatives by the
township people's council and work under the co-operative's supervisio
The co-operatives must make greater efforts to educate and control
them according to individual cases; and must constantly enhance the
vigilance of the co-operative members and the peasants outside the
co-operatives against any subversive activities they may attempt.
Former landlords, rich peasants and counter-revolutionaries who have
already become members or candidate members of the co-operatives,
if they persistently misbehave despite repeated instructions, may be
demoted to candidate members or to the status of working under
supervision in the case of members, and to the status of working
under supervision in the case of candidate members. Those who
commit sabotage should be punished according to law.

Gambling is strictly prohibited and the activities of secret and
superstitious societies are banned. Thieves, swindlers, hooligans,
special agents and various bad elements seriously disrupting social
order should be punished according to law.

40. <u>Workers in the cities and peasants in the co-operatives
must support each other.</u> The workers should turn out more and better
industrial goods to meet the peasants' needs; the peasants should grow
more and better grain and industrial raw materials to meet the needs
of industry and the town dwellers. Workers in the cities and peasants
in the co-operatives should also arrange get-togethers, visit one
another, and exchange correspondence. Through ways like these,
they should strengthen their contacts, give each other encouragement
and swap experience so as to further the development of industry and
agriculture and the consolidation of the worker-peasant alliance led
by the working class.

INDEX

After serving for eleven years as a senior officer of the Food and Agriculture Organization (FAO) of the United Nations, Leslie T. C. Kuo was appointed Chief of the Oriental Project, National Agricultural Library, U.S. Department of Agriculture, in 1960. He did his undergraduate work in economics at Nankai University, Tientsin, China, and obtained his Master degrees (agricultural economics and regional and city planning) and Ph. D. (agricultural economics), all at Cornell University.

Dr. Kuo has written numerous articles for professional publications, including the Library Journal, the China Quarterly (London), the International Development Review (Washington, D.C.), Focus (American Geographical Society, New York), and publications by the American Association for the Advancement of Science, as well as reports and documents for FAO. He also has supervised the preparation of a series of bibliographies on Chinese, Japanese and Korean agriculture, published by the National Agricultural Library.